BL
5.93

THE TEACHING OF ECOLOGY

THE BRITISH ECOLOGICAL SOCIETY
SYMPOSIUM VOLUME NUMBER SEVEN

THE TEACHING OF ECOLOGY

A Symposium of
THE BRITISH ECOLOGICAL SOCIETY
Goldsmiths' College, University of London
13 April—16 April 1966

Edited by

J. M. LAMBERT

M.A., Ph.D., F.L.S.
Department of Botany
University of Southampton

BLACKWELL SCIENTIFIC PUBLICATIONS
OXFORD AND EDINBURGH

Printed in Great Britain in the City of Oxford at
THE ALDEN PRESS
and bound by
THE KEMP HALL BINDERY

CONTENTS

Section II
The Teaching of Ecology at School Level

Section III
Methods and Techniques in Ecological Teaching at Undergraduate Level

Section VI

Vocational Aspects

PREFACE

Ecology is a subject which seems to have given rise to more controversy as to its place in our educational system than any other branch of biology. On the one hand there are those who still regard it as a 'luxury' subject, with no real scientific content or educational value apart from indulging a taste for outdoor work; on the other there are those who consider it an essential component of all courses in biology and possibly in geography, and believe that the most rewarding method of approach to these subjects is through ecological phenomena. Moreover, given that some ecology is to be taught, there is disagreement as to the most appropriate time for its introduction; some favour its inclusion at the earliest possible stage, while others regard it as too complex and too time-demanding for work below undergraduate, or even postgraduate, level. Again, there are numerous different views, often approaching dogmas, as to what ecological subject-matter should be taught at a given level, how it should be presented, and what ultimate end is in view.

Whatever the difficulties, the fact remains that ecology is rapidly gaining ground as an integral part of modern education. Educational institutions at all levels are now often forced by pressure of opinion, by new examination syllabuses, and by the growing social need for trained ecologists, to include at least some ecological work in their teaching programme. To teach the subject competently, however, is not easy for even the most experienced ecologist; and for the teacher with no basic training in such thinking, the present trend can impose an almost intolerable burden unless some guidance is available as to the scope and nature of the subject.

With this in mind, the British Ecological Society decided to devote its 1966 Symposium to an open meeting on 'The Teaching of Ecology', to serve as a forum for discussion of the many problems involved. The fact that the Symposium was attended by some 400 teachers from all educational levels, as well as by others outside the teaching profession, is evidence of the general interest in the subject. The formal papers given at the meeting are presented in this volume, and provide a fund of current views and information on the topic. The contributions range from considerations of the basic problems, through the practical teaching of ecology in schools, colleges and universities, to discussions of the opportunities available to those who want to become professional ecologists at the end of their formal education.

As well as covering different subject-matter, the papers vary greatly in their approach. Some are more concerned with underlying philosophical concepts, some give first-hand details of courses in which the authors have been involved, some set out to suggest useful ecological exercises, and some are aimed at providing primary data on general facilities and opportunities for ecological work. However, the reader must not expect a 'cook-book' approach to the subject, a unified solution to the many problems, or even a clear directive to the kind of material which should be included in an ecology course. In fact, he may often be bewildered by the fact that the opinions of different contributors frequently conflict, and that a mode of thought or action adopted by one is often in direct antithesis to that recommended by another.

The very fact that this is so, however, is itself an indication of the vitality and potentialities of ecology today. Ecology is still essentially a 'young' subject in terms of established disciplines. Moreover, the development of ecological teaching is taking place at the same time as far-reaching changes in general educational theory, so that its 'growing-pains' are accentuated in the context of these changes. It would be unfortunate if teachers to whom the subject is new (as may well be the case in many schools) were deterred by a lack of specific instruction as to what is required in the teaching of ecology; for the range of possible subject-matter and approach is so immense that it offers unlimited opportunities for experiment with both material and mode of presentation. All that this volume can do is to offer suggestions for consideration by teachers in the light of their individual circumstances; and it will have have served its purpose even if it leads only to a recognition of the increasing part which ecology must play in the general field of education.

J.M.LAMBERT

Botany Department,
University of Southampton

ACKNOWLEDGMENTS

The British Ecological Society is extremely grateful to the authorities of Goldsmiths' College, University of London, for accommodating the Symposium; to the Registrar and other administrative staff at Goldsmiths' for the great assistance they gave in the practical arrangements; to Mr J.A.C.Gilson (Rank Organization Research Fellow at Goldsmiths') for arranging closed-circuit television for part of the Symposium; to the Chairmen of the various sessions, all of whom gave their time willingly and in some cases at considerable inconvenience to themselves; to the panel of the 'Brains Trust', who helped to provide a welcome light interlude between the more serious sessions; and to the various contributors themselves, several of whom were not members of the Society, for the time and trouble they spent in the preparation of their papers.

Finally, I should like to add my personal thanks to my colleagues on the Symposium Organizing Committee, without whose help the Symposium could never have been held: Professor J.L.Harper (Department of Agricultural Botany, University College of North Wales, Bangor), who made the original suggestion for a symposium on this topic; the late Mr P.F.Holmes (formerly of the Field Studies Council, Malham Tarn Field Centre), whose early membership of the committee was ended by his tragic death in December 1964; Mr C.A.Sinker (Field Studies Council, Preston Montford Field Centre), who agreed at short notice to take Mr Holmes's place, and who undertook all the publicity arrangements in connection with the Symposium; Dr J.T.Williams (Department of Biological Studies, Lanchester College of Technology, Coventry), who was responsible for the organization of the exhibits; and last, but not least, Mr T.K.Rees (Department of Biological Sciences, Goldsmiths' College), who, in dealing with all the local arrangements, carried the biggest burden of all, and whose tireless and efficient work was a major factor in the smooth running of the Symposium.

J.M.L.

SECTION I
INTRODUCTORY SECTION:
GENERAL PROBLEMS

BASIC PROBLEMS IN THE
TEACHING OF ECOLOGY

J.M.LAMBERT   G.T.GOODMAN
Botany Department,   Botany Department,
University of Southampton University College of Swansea

The term 'ecology' seems to have almost as many meanings as there are ecologists. From Haeckel's concept of it as dealing with 'nature's household' (Haeckel, 1866), its published definitions now range from the traditional 'study of the relationships between organisms and their environment' (*vide* e.g. Hughes & Walker, 1965) to the all-embracing 'study of the structure and function of nature' (Odum, 1963), which virtually identifies it with the whole of natural science. Indeed, it has been called 'scientific natural history' by Elton (1927), or, more provocatively, 'glorified nature study' by those who doubt its status as a serious discipline. Elsewhere it has been implicitly equated with field studies and with 'science out of doors'; or it has been restricted to the study of wildlife in so-called 'natural' habitats and thence confused with nature conservation; or it has been denied existence as a separate branch of learning and called 'a way of thought rather than a subject'. Some think of it as the easiest and most rewarding path of entry into the study of biology; while others regard it as too difficult and too complex to be tackled at all without considerable foreknowledge of other natural phenomena and experience of scientific method.

With such diversity of definitions and approaches, it is not surprising that ecology has been considered by many other scientists as one of the 'woolliest' and least valuable parts of a general scientific training. The very fact that ecology is often concerned with commonplace phenomena, that use can be made of comparatively simple apparatus, and that much of the terminology is that of common speech, means that good ecological work can frequently be done without the elaborate trappings and appurtenances often regarded as the hallmark of a modern scientist. This, which *should* be its strength, can also be its major source of weakness. For from this it is only a short step to regarding ecology as a 'soft option' in a given science course; from this to a deflection of the weaker students into ecological work; and from this to a general lowering of standards so that poor performance among ecologists becomes the rule rather than the exception.

For much of this criticism, therefore, it is possible that ecologists have only themselves to blame. A lack of well-defined and attainable objectives, the use of unnecessarily crude approximations, and imprecision in thought and terminology, could all be contributory causes to the suspicion with which ecology is still often viewed. More serious still is the fact that it is frequently the most ardent advocates of ecological teaching who cause most damage to the image of their subject. Enthusiasm for ecology is often engendered by enthusiasm for field work, and this in turn is often rooted in an emotional love of the countryside. But while an emotional foundation may be invaluable in stimulating interest, this in itself is hardly an adequate basis for advocating time and money spent in ecological work as against other claims. The practical scientist, the hard-headed administrator and the general educationalist may all be excused if they ask for justification in more concrete terms than the emotional satisfaction of what is probably a minority of individuals, particularly if their own interests lie elsewhere.

To avoid confusion at the outset, it is pertinent to start by briefly re-examining the concept of ecology itself. If we define it by subject-matter, rather than by where it is done, how it is approached or what techniques it uses, we immediately find a dichotomy between those who regard the living organism as the focal point, and those who think of the whole ecosystem as its nucleus. In the former case, it is the autecology of individual plants and animals, the structure and workings of living populations, and the interrelations of communities, which form the essence of the subject: the physical environment is used only as the setting in which these phenomena are studied. Conversely, with the ecosystem concept, the approach is usually more biogeochemical in nature, with the living part of the system regarded as only one of the many elements to be considered equally in the whole.

Under either definition—whether it is primarily conceived as the study of living organisms in relation to their environment or as a study of ecosystems—the theoretical importance of ecology is unlikely to be disputed; and it is probably true to say that some study of ecology is becoming increasingly accepted as an integral part of education. The very fact of its increasing popularity, however, brings a new set of dangers. The faster a subject becomes fashionable, the quicker it loses the freshness of approach which provides the initial impetus; and the more a subject becomes accepted as part of any system, the more the basic assumptions tend to be forgotten and unquestioned by those responsible for its prosecution. A meeting of ecologists may thus become a self-congratulatory and self-perpetuating body, in which, with a few noteworthy exceptions (*vide* Newbould, 1965), heretical views are far too rarely heard.

The present symposium offers a unique opportunity for a reappraisal of the situation. In the first place, it comes at a time when the swing towards ecology is sufficiently established for its protagonists to be able to relax enough to take stock; secondly, since the main topic is the actual teaching of ecology at various educational levels, a critical awareness of the difficulties as well as the advantages must inevitably rear its head; and thirdly, since the symposium is open to all-comers, it provides a meeting-point between experienced ecologists and those who still require basic information before they make a judgment. Clearly, a teacher worth his salt cannot be expected to adopt an idea or a mode of thought merely because he is told it is good; and clearly, there are arguments to be raised *against* the teaching of ecology as well as *for* it, and the answer may not be the same in every circumstance. The function of this introductory paper is therefore to try to expose a number of the problems, rather than to try to solve them or to pontificate over what should or should not be done.

The question of whether at least some ecology should be automatically included in a teaching syllabus largely depends upon our views as to the overall function of education. With limited time available to cover the multifarious subjects which *could* be taught with profit, the question immediately leads us into the age-old controversy between advocates of general studies and those recommending early specialization. The very fact that ecology must encompass the whole of the physical environment as well as the organisms themselves brings in its train the requirement that other complementary subjects should be taught, many of which lie well outside a traditional science course. For instance, the current insistence that, for university entrance, biology should normally be teamed with chemistry and physics is an inadequate preparation for much ecological work; a fully equipped ecologist needs not only these, but an insight into geology, pedology, climatology, physiography, cartography, history, archaeology and mathematics as well. It is arguable that where this is impracticable, as at school and often at undergraduate level, it might be better to omit ecology altogether than to give a partial training; but the same could be said of any subject requiring accessory teaching, and an alternative course is deliberately to specialize in those aspects of ecology for which service facilities are available rather than to abandon it altogether.

The root of the difficulty in providing adequately for ecological teaching in our present educational system probably lies in the semantic convenience of dividing educational subject-matter into named sections which are then

accorded roughly equivalent status for examination purposes. The traditional place of ecology as a subsection of biology rather than an entity
in itself thus makes it subordinate to other biological requirements at the
expense of its own necessities. However, the recent decision by some
universities to provide postgraduate courses centred on ecology may mark
the beginning of a general raising of its status. The fact that Edinburgh
now offers a first degree in ecology is a further move in the same direction,
and it is conceivable that the trend will eventually spread to schools in the
same way as the old 'general science' course of the middle school is now
usually replaced by separate science subjects.

Whereas a division into subjects of equivalent status at a given educational level suggests the concept of a reticulum of knowledge, an alternative approach is to treat them as a linear system. This is the basis of Bertalanffy's division of science into 'integrative levels of organization'
(Bertalanffy, 1950), a concept which has since been elaborated by other
writers (*vide* e.g. Rowe, 1961). The essence of this type of classification is
that the 'environment' of any one unit at the level under study is con-
stituted by those elements which join it at the next level of the hierarchy.
Such a system ranges from the organization of matter into atoms at one
end of the scale to the study of the whole universe at the other; and in it,
the place of ecology, covering the organization of individuals into
populations, of populations into ecosystems, and of ecosystems into
ecospheres, could be deemed to lie roughly between traditional biology
and geography.

Although a progressive system such as this may seem attractive theoretically, the difficulty then arises as to where the system should be entered
for the best educational results. From those who favour a synthetic
approach, there is pressure to begin with the so-called fundamental
subjects, though this, if carried to its logical conclusion, could lead to the
teaching of nuclear physics in the kindergarten and ecology might never
be reached at all. Conversely, those who are analytically inclined would
prefer to begin towards the top and explain the phenomena encountered
in terms of progressively less complex systems, so that astronomy,
geography and ecology would thus come early in the course.

Ideally, a full education should encompass a training in the techniques of
both analysis and synthesis; the pupil is then equipped to enter the system
at any level and move upwards or downwards at will. If this is the aim,
there is a great deal to be said for entering at a level at which the scale of
the phenomena approximates to that which can be perceived by the
unaided senses of the human observer himself, and at a degree of com-

plexity roughly equivalent to that of his own immediate environment. This is perhaps the strongest argument for entering natural science in the first instance through ecological phenomena, rather than via abstractions from more unfamiliar material. We have already emphasized that good ecological work can easily be done by using commonplace situations, simple equipment, and a minimum of specialized terms; and from this beginning, it is then possible to move downwards into the minutiae of molecules and atoms, and upwards into the vastness of astronomical phenomena.

We have so far been concerned with mainly theoretical arguments for and against the teaching of ecology in its most liberal sense. The real difficulties start to arise, however, when practical considerations become paramount. Assuming that *some* ecology is to be taught, such problems fall into three categories: (1) the problem of *what* should be taught at any given level; (2) the problem of *where* it is to be carried out; and (3) the problem of *how* it is to be presented.

The problem of what to teach must depend both on the facilities available and on the abilities of the individual teacher. Ecology has so many facets that it is probably meaningless to talk of underlying principles other than the very general one of seeking correlations in an essentially multivariate system. It is perfectly possible to introduce ecological ideas at a very early stage from the study of domestic pets, from the observation of laboratory animals, from the growth of weeds in the school garden, from the contents of the rainwater tub, and even from the behaviour of the child's own fellow-creatures. Later, the subject can broaden and deepen by encompassing additional phenomena, more elaborate techniques and more sophisticated concepts; and the range of possible subject-matter is so immense that the danger of repetitive teaching at successive levels need scarcely ever arise. Even the tyranny of the rigid timetable and the set syllabus can be circumvented to a greater or lesser degree by careful planning, and we have yet to hear of a determined teacher completely thwarted by such obstacles.

The question of what to teach leads naturally to the problem of where to teach it. Most of the difficulties here arise with the conscious or unconscious identification of the term 'environment' with 'natural habitat', involving in turn the popular misconception that practical work in ecology can be properly pursued only in outdoor areas relatively free from human interference. Admittedly such areas have advantages in that they offer more scope for identifying and assessing a variety of ecological factors as against a single dominating influence, and that long-term work is less likely to be disturbed; admittedly, too, the excitement of visiting and working in a naturally attractive site with adventurous conditions often relieves the teacher of much of the burden of providing an initial stimulus for the work. Against this, the cost in time, in travel, in general inconvenience, and in the possible sterilization of land potentially useful for other purposes, must also be considered. It is arguable, in fact, that too much lip-service has already been paid to the importance of adequate nature reserves as aids to ecological teaching, for in the right hands even the most unpromising man-made habitat can often provide valuable material for ecological studies; in fact, in an increasingly overpopulated country like Great Britain, there is something to be said on vocational grounds for training our future generations of ecologists on largely urban sites rather than on the remnants of a vanishing countryside.

It is the question of how to teach ecology which requires the greatest judgment and experience. Many of the problems are common to the whole of teaching, and do not concern ecology alone. For instance, there is the choice between the so-called 'method of discovery' and the approach through 'assertion and proof'; as Hutchinson (1964) points out, both are equally viable methods if properly conducted, though the ease with which the latter can degenerate into 'assertion and acceptance' makes it appear superficially as the less time-consuming method. This leads in turn to the balance to be kept between the imparting of information and training in critical thought; if the primary aim of the teacher is to provide a foundation of generally accepted fact, then the method of approach can legitimately be different from that of the teacher more concerned with providing experience in the generation and testing of hypotheses. The main point to be noted in the present context is that a complex subject like ecology can easily contain more hidden pitfalls than a more exact discipline like chemistry or physics; and unless a teacher is fully aware of these, he may do more harm than good. Some of the particular dangers to be faced in ecological teaching have been set out elsewhere (Lambert, 1964) and need not be repeated here; all that can be done in this introductory paper is to reiterate the warning, and then leave it to the judgment of the individual teacher.

The papers which follow include a variety of different philosophies concerning the most effective methods to be employed, together with descriptions of techniques which have been found successful (or possibly unsuccessful) in particular circumstances. What must be remembered, however, is that most of the authors of these papers have some claim to be regarded as ecologists, either through training or through experience, and the job of teaching ecology is comparatively easy for them. In educational establishments where it is possible to employ a number of specialist teachers, the presence of an ecologist on the staff is probably sufficient to ensure that the subject is taught with competence and insight; but where teachers have to cover a variety of subjects, as in many schools, it could be wasteful, or even dangerous, to force an ecological approach on those whose own training and predilections lie along other lines. For a graduate highly trained in genetics or cell biology, for instance, the best use of his knowledge and abilities could easily be in concentrating on these aspects in his teaching, even to the exclusion of all mention of ecology; the inspiration which he brings to his own particular interest could easily compensate for lack of breadth in the subject-matter he teaches.

The ultimate danger in teaching—whether of ecology or of any other subject—lies in a passive acceptance of the precepts and assertions which trade under the name of authority; and on this theme it is appropriate to conclude with a quotation from Williams (1960) in a paper concerned with the whole problem of communication in biological teaching:

'Perhaps I can teach you to teach something to somebody; but if you merely do and say what I tell you to do and say, you are a purely passive agent, and it is I who have done the teaching. All of us hope—and many of us have the opportunity—to instruct teachers or research workers more able than ourselves; yet if teaching involved only the giving of precise instructions this would be impossible, for I cannot communicate to your brain abilities which I do not myself possess.

'Of course I can teach you [a particular] approach. I can, as it were, set the wheels of your car in the right direction, and perhaps even provide you with some fuel to help you on your way; but I cannot drive the car for you. If you are deficient in any of the things needed to drive cars— arms, or legs, or even the ability to react to visual stimuli—no amount of telling you what drivers do will help you. . . . I cannot, in fact, teach you to drive unless the stuff of driving is already in you.'

REFERENCES

BERTALANFFY L. VON (1950) An outline of general system theory. *Brit. J. Phil. Sci.* **1**, 134–165.
ELTON C. (1927) *Animal Ecology.* Sidgwick & Jackson, London.
HAECKEL E. (1866) *Generelle Morphologie der Organismen.* Reimer, Berlin.
HUGHES R.D. & WALKER D. (1965) Education and training in ecology. *Vestes,* **8**, 1–5.
HUTCHINSON S.A. (1964) Purpose and method in biology teaching. II. The organization of training. *School Sci. Rev.* **157**, 534–541.

LAMBERT J.M. (1964) Ecology as a biological discipline. *School Sci. Rev.* **157,** 568–575.
NEWBOULD P.J. (1965) Communication to the Conference on Education (Second Conference on 'The Countryside in 1970') at Keele University, March 1965. *Proceedings of the Conferences,* The Nature Conservancy, 24–25.
ODUM E.P. (1963) *Ecology.* Holt, Rinehart & Winston, New York.
ROWE J.S. (1961) The level of integration concept and ecology. *Ecology,* **42,** 420–427.
WILLIAMS W.T. (1960) The problem of communication in biological teaching. *Symp. Soc. exp. Biol.* **14,** 243–249.

THE PRACTICAL INTEGRATION OF PLANT
AND ANIMAL ECOLOGY AT SCHOOL LEVEL

A.DARLINGTON

Malvern College

I. INTRODUCTION

The traditional approach to school biology as a descriptive exercise, in which organisms are considered morphologically without reference to their ecological needs, has been responsible for the popular conception of biology as an inexact science. This is as outmoded as the subdivision into the separate disciplines of botany and zoology. Even at an elementary stage, initial field observations are desirable, leading to hypotheses which can subsequently be tested in the laboratory; and the laboratory then acquires its rightful status as a testing ground and clearing house. At sixth-form level, the traditional emphasis of such features as the nervous system of the dogfish remains a necrological rather than a biological study unless correlation can be established between them, on the one hand, and the animal's environmental conditions on the other: the development of large olfactory lobes, for instance, in a vertebrate colonizing water opalescent with suspended matter.

Few forward-looking teachers would deny the wisdom of the new approach, despite practical difficulties. These are mainly difficulties of administration; and administration should be relegated to its proper position of servant, not master. It exists to serve our ends, and a new measure of flexibility in the organization of our work is imperative. Some of us fail to recognize as a myth the conception that, to be effective, field-work requires ready access to such specialized regions as a seashore, lake or wood. Fortunate indeed is the teacher whose school permits visits in class time to one of these. Conversely, the teacher in an urban school is peculiarly unlucky if his students cannot, at least, reach an old wall or tree trunk, lawn, area of bare soil or a rubbish dump. All are richly colonized by organisms visibly undergoing reproduction—so that they are evidently successfully established in their respective habitats—and ecological factors are operative.

The kind of situation chosen is less important than the establishment of a climate of opinion conducive to sustained application to investigations beyond the narrow limits of class time. An active natural history society is invaluable, permitting extension along project lines of work initiated in class.

II. EXAMPLES OF POSSIBLE SITUATIONS FOR STUDY

The four situations selected for discussion are all examples having particular validity in urban areas, although rural districts provide similar instances.

1. *Colonization of tree-trunk or wall*

A wide variety of organisms colonize such surfaces, including the pleurococcoid algae, bryophytes and vascular plants, woodlice such as *Porcellio* which can tolerate a relatively low humidity and, in damp places, tardigrades and the larvae of crane-flies and gnats. Of these, the most widely distributed are probably algae of the *Pleurococcus* type. It is practically certain that this so-called genus is no more than a *phrase de convenance*, since it involves a range of unicellular forms, each having its own environmental needs which have yet to be worked out. Furthermore, it is common to discover the hyphae of Ascomycete fungi intermingled with such growths, so that a degree of lichenization is present. Such lichenized algae present a striking contrast to non-lichenized forms, being rougher looking and subdivided by fissures into polygonal areas, whereas the purer colonies are smoother and greener. The basic fact that the growths exhibit an unevenness of distribution over a surface may be apparent to the eye of a young student; but if an investigation into the pattern of this is planned, the need arises for a quantitative assessment. Complete removal from the substrate is difficult, but comparisons are possible on the basis of simple colour differences. Thus, colonization can be considered as falling into three groups:

(i) Low density, the substrate clearly showing through a barely visible coating spread over it like a transparent, green veil.

(ii) Medium density, thicker than (i), but still too thin to obscure the nature and texture of the substrate.

(iii) High density, so thick that the substrate is totally concealed.

If a small quadrat-frame is passed over the surface, and the densities within each sample recorded, the observations can be plotted as a histogram and the histogram used as a basis for checking hypotheses proposed by the students to account for the pattern of distribution. They may consider the factors determining the colonization to include:

(a) Retention of surface moisture by the substrate. This can be tested by fixing strips of cobalt thiocyanate paper and comparing the colour changes.

(b) Run-off of precipitated water flowing over the surface. This can be tested by comparing volumetrically the water collected in cups fixed in places which appear significant from the histogram.

(c) Incident light. This can be tested by a series of readings using a photo-electric cell, preferably in variable conditions of illumination.

At an unsophisticated level, it is probably sufficient merely to separate the lichenized from the non-lichenized growths, and to plot the readings separately on different histograms. All this falls within the compass of ordinary class work; but students may consider that the work has its limitations and that a follow-up by the natural history society is desirable. As one example, we can consider taking further the effects of run-off. If deflectors are fixed so as to alter the course of the water-flow, changes in distribution can be examined over a period of time.

2. *Animals colonizing soil, or epiphytic growths*

Epiphytic growths of this kind, as well as areas of undisturbed soil, support animals which are clearly visible without magnification. Are the ones we see likely to be the only colonizers? And, if animals are present, what are the conditions in which they are living? Some of these the students may find out for themselves: the situations are demonstrably dark, damp and cold. Presumably, established colonizers are adapted to such conditions. Therefore, if we change the conditions—remove a sample of the soil or epiphytic material and illuminate, dry and warm it—animals possessing the 'right' behavioural mechanisms might be expected to move out of their surroundings. And if the sample is placed on a sieve in a large paper funnel (Tullgren funnel) and is illuminated and warmed from above by an electric lamp, they should pass through the orifice of the funnel neck into a receiver placed below. Such work lends itself to quantitative assessment; if a sample of known area is taken, the number of animals extracted by this particular method can be assessed on the basis of acreage (an acre being estimated as an area 70 yards square, and a soil-core pressed out by a coffee-tin 3.15 in. in diameter estimated as representing 1/888,000 of an acre). Several projects suggest themselves for work in class or the natural history society. What are the animals doing in the situations where we find them? Let us take them alive and keep them, observing their feeding habits and constructing food chains (preferably in quantitative terms). If some types of soil (vegetation) support a richer fauna than others, let us make a series of comparisons with surrounding conditions. And, is it not at least possible that, if the situations are wet, some of the animal colonizers will be so aquatic as to be unable to leave the material as it dries out? Let us, then, repeat the work by immersing the material in water in a large glass funnel (Baermann funnel) and illuminate and warm it as before, so that extractions by the two techniques can be compared. Do the results correlate with what is observed in the field— more macroscopic animals in some places than others, a richer accumulation of humus, etc.? And even though it may be difficult, in class, to observe more than the simple fact of leaf decomposition, we may be able to carry this further in the laboratory by making transparent 'model' leaves of cellophane (cellulose), fixing them to microscopic slides, and inserting them in pots of soil, so that the form of decomposition can be observed more precisely and recorded quantitatively over squared paper. Furthermore, we can develop a project with dead leaves themselves, enclosing them in nylon bags of variable mesh-size, so that some organisms are admitted while others are excluded, burying these in situations which we have found to be 'rich' or 'poor', and measuring the destruction over squared paper.

3. Colonizers of rubbish-tips

Rubbish-tips of various sizes are a commonplace feature of urban and rural areas alike. They generally become heavily colonized with time. They are probably of particular value to urban schools with limited alternatives, and observations made there frequently provide good material for extended projects, occasionally by the class, more often by the natural history society. Some of the colonizers are surprising. Cultivated plants from gardens are almost of regular occurrence, but, if a fire is maintained permanently, the colonizers may include the house cricket (*Gryllulus domesticus*), breeding throughout the year and moving from place to place with the season. Observations in the field may suggest to students the hypothesis that these movements correlate with variations in physical factors, including temperature. This is something which can be checked by collecting the animals, bringing them to the laboratory, and setting up a model tip with known differences in the temperature and, preferably, in the humidity and substrate as well. Known numbers of crickets can be allowed to distribute themselves in the surroundings and be recollected and counted and the values compared with counts made when collecting in the field. If care is taken to distinguish between male and female, adult and nymph, the value of the work is augmented.

4. Run-off from a gas-works

Even so unpromising a situation as a gas-works may provide opportunities for similar work. The water sprayed over the coke to cool it is frequently discharged through an open drain into a river. When this is the case, the water shows a marked graduation in temperature and gaseous content along its course, and colonizers are often numerous and fall into a pattern of distribution which can be checked in the laboratory against physico-chemical conditions measured in the field.

III. CONCLUSION

So often, school ecology tends to suffer from effort wasted and time mis-spent in making transects, quadrats and drawing up lists of names of doubtful accuracy, simply because 'this is what you do in ecology'—and these activities become ends in themselves without a defined objective in view. Nevertheless, such exercises can form a precise means of recording observations and, if they lead to hypotheses which can then be subjected to experimental test, they constitute an integral and significant part of school biology.

REFERENCES

CHAPMAN, V. J. (1962) *The Algae*. Macmillan.

MACFADYEN A. (1959) Notes on methods for the extraction of soil arthropods. In *Soil Zoology* (ed. D.K.McE. Kevan), pp. 315–332. Butterworth.

PICKARD J.G. (1957) A survey of certain micro-organisms colonizing the polluted outflow from a gas-works. *Coturnix*, 7. Bishop's Stortford College Natural History Society.

RAISTRICK A. & GILBERT O.L. (1963) Malham Tarn House: its building materials, their weathering and colonization by plants. *Field Studies*, 1 (5), 89–115.

RUSSELL E.J. (1959) *The World of the Soil*. Collins.

TRIBE H.T. (1960) Decomposition of buried cellulose films. *The Ecology of Soil Fungi* (ed. D.Parkinson & J.S.Waid), pp. 246–256. Liverpool.

PROBLEMS IN THE LINKAGE OF PLANT AND ANIMAL ECOLOGY IN A UNIVERSITY SYLLABUS

G. C. VARLEY   H. N. SOUTHERN
Department of Entomology   Bureau of Animal Population

S. R. J. WOODELL
Department of Botany

all of the University of Oxford

I. INTRODUCTION

At Oxford University until recently, students who entered to read for Honours in Botany or Zoology took a Preliminary Examination rather similar to Advanced-Level Biology either from school or during their first year at Oxford. The Honours courses for Zoology and Botany were (and are) entirely separate.

After some years of discussion between the faculty boards of Biology and of Agriculture & Forestry, an entirely new joint syllabus of teaching came into force in October 1963. Students who intend to read Agriculture, Botany, Forestry or Zoology now undergo a course of instruction for a new Preliminary Examination in Biology which is taken at the end of the first year. This type of examination is, in Oxford, an unclassified pass or fail test, which can be retaken wholly or in part in September in the event of failure in June. A pass in this examination is a requirement for entry into an Honours course and the choice of Final Honours course can in fact be deferred until the end of the first year.

The chief criticism of the old Preliminary course was that it was too similar to A-level courses and the new Preliminary course is specifically devised to differ both in content and approach from school courses.

The proportion of ecology in the new Preliminary course is 12 days out of a total of 168 lectures and/or days. The rest is devoted to Physiology (24), Genetics (24), Taxonomy and Evolution (12), Organic Chemistry (16), Physical Chemistry (8), Physics (16), Mathematics for Biologists (8) and Geology (*sensu lato*) (48). Members of the staff of the four departments concerned and of the Bureau of Animal Population and the Geology Department, with some help from the Physiology, Entomology and Biometry Departments, collaborate in the lectures and in the practical

17

work. So far as possible the courses are given by biologists specially for biologists.

II. THE ECOLOGY COURSE

The ecology course extends over 12 days in the summer term. Most days begin with a lecture and continue until about tea-time with either a field class or a practical class in the laboratory, where at the moment there are facilities for a maximum of seventy students. Each year so far more than sixty have attended.

A. Aims and problems

Three main practical problems had to be overcome in designing the course.

1. It must be assumed that most students have no more knowledge than is necessary at A- and O-levels in Biology. A few may know hardly anything about the plant and animal kingdoms.

2. Field classes with seventy students require careful planning and the students must be carefully controlled to prevent undue destruction of habitats. At least one demonstrator to ten students is regarded as necessary in field work.

3. For zoological laboratory classes, each pair of students is provided with a binocular microscope and an adequate sample of the animal population or community to be studied. It is quite insufficient to provide a specimen for each student or student pair. Thus the provision of class material entails a tremendous amount of work behind the scenes.

The main aim has been to concentrate attention on the broad principles governing ecological processes. These are first expounded in lectures with carefully chosen examples and then illustrated with suitable practical observations and exercises.

There are a number of advantages in this dynamic approach. First, the general principles can be taught with reference to very common plants and animals. Second, undue stress on taxonomy is avoided since only common species are used as examples. Field work can be undertaken largely on the University's estate at Wytham and there is no need to enter or endanger the special reserves which have been designated to protect unusual restricted habitats.

Of course, there are considerable taxonomic difficulties to be overcome by the students. Many are quite uninformed about the plants and animals they encounter and know neither the names of the common animals and plants nor the features by which they are to be recognized. Instruction about the main groups is woven into the early field classes and exercises.

Thus, on the botanical side, one of the first field classes is devoted to learning the commonest woodland flowering plants and bryophytes; but it was discovered towards the end of one course that several students were still unable to identify a sycamore tree!

On the zoological side the first practical class work in the laboratory is examining samples of woodland litter animals. This sample is obtained using a Tullgren funnel and includes a bewildering variety of small animal life. A fairly simple key, worked out by Mrs Southern and Dr Whittaker and set out in the Appendix to this paper, is used by the students to identify specimens to the main taxonomic groups. They are definitely discouraged at this stage from attempting identification of species. Using identifications to the groups only, they separate the litter community into its different trophic levels, and can rank them for size, abundance, etc.

The key is also designed to cover the various invertebrates which will be met when sweeping and beating green vegetation in a later field class. At the end of these 2 days devoted to comparing the decomposer community of the litter with the community based on green plants most students have a working knowledge of the major taxonomic groups of terrestrial invertebrates.

Most of the laboratory and field exercises are designed to profit from the large size of the class by asking student pairs to make certain measurements or counts on sub-samples of the material available so that their results, when added together, give sufficient quantitative data for demonstrators to collate, analyse and expound at the end of the day.

Other exercises are designed to illustrate the general principles by the use of abundant and taxonomically simple groups. For this purpose the terrestrial isopods are selected, because they are abundant as individuals but the few species are easily identified and are particularly suited for quantitative study. A population of *Porcellio scaber*, provided in the laboratory, is measured by the students. Differences in the numbers of successive size-groups are used to describe the 'structure of the population' and it is possible to infer from this the proportion of each size-class which survives and, with suitable simplifying assumptions, to construct a simple life-table. In a separate exercise using isopods, habitat selection in the field is investigated; the half-dozen species which the class encounters can be shown to have distinct habitat preferences.

B. Outline of course linking plants and animals in ecosystem

Since the aim is to stress the principles underlying ecological processes and to display the interrelated functions of plants and animals, the course is designed to show the students how the problems of zoologists and botanists interact with each other.

The first day of the course begins with an introductory lecture dealing with the flow of energy and the cycling of matter in the ecosystem. Thus energy flow diagrams of the type to be found in the work of Macfadyen find their place in the very first lecture. Following this is a lecture which stresses the importance of animals in hastening energy flow. It describes the various types of herbivores and the animals at the third trophic level—carnivores and ecto- and endo-parasites of herbivores—and the large wide-ranging carnivores which are perhaps the most conspicuous of the many members of the fourth trophic level.

After these two lectures the class is taken out to Wytham and split into groups which are taken for an hour alternately by botanical and zoological demonstrators. The students are shown various life-forms of plants, stratification and the influence of dominants on other species; the importance of the root system is mentioned though this is given further attention later. The heterogeneity of any small area is strongly stressed. The story of the second and higher trophic levels is taken up by the zoological demonstrators, who first consider the question of habitat classification from the animal viewpoint. The students are shown how habitats can be defined in terms of lateral discontinuities (e.g. open ground, field type, scrub and woodland, each with its internal patterns) and of vertical layering. The questions are: what are the important animals in each habitat and what habitats does an animal need.

Then there are three lectures on the environment, two by a botanist and one by a soil scientist, and two field days in which the woodland community is studied floristically and the non-random distribution of plants is investigated and related to environmental, sociological and other factors. Soils also are studied in the field. A lecture on animal communities is interpolated here and a whole day is used for laboratory work examining animals extracted from litter samples.

Three lectures by a zoologist introduce populations, competition and population regulation. Here a lecture is interpolated on competition between plants, in which the similarities with respect to competition among animals are discussed. These lectures are all linked with field work or practical work in the laboratory. The botanical exercise deals with micro-environmental distribution in the field and its interpretation.

On the last day the effects of man on natural communities and questions of conservation are considered. The changes in the flora are outlined from the time of early man up to the present urban and industrial conditions with its heavy demands on the world's resources. This is illustrated by special reference to the destruction of forests. The effects of man on the population dynamics of animals can be presented in an equally dramatic way. Not only have many species become extinct, but the accidental or intentional introduction of species from one part of the world to another provide interesting case-histories. The relative stability of complex habitats and communities is contrasted with the instability of monocultures. Elton has concluded that conservation needs the cultivation of diversity so that new kinds of habitats and communities can build up natural stability.

Twelve days is a short time in which to cover the vast subject of ecology and the choice of material and example is entirely dependent on local facilities. The students are given an idea of the multiplicity of plants and animals and of the methods by which factors of the environment can be quantified by chemical and physical techniques. They are also brought into contact with current research projects in Wytham. For instance, in one of the practicals the class examines owl pellets (provided by research work in progress on owls and small mammals) and identifies the bones of the prey. The class is also given a résumé of the work on oaks and their insect defoliators; this research is perhaps particularly suitable because one of its objectives is the quantification of the relationship between the oaks and the insects which feed upon them.

III. CONCLUSIONS

A. General conclusions about integration
1. In retrospect, we consider that, although this course is carefully integrated, complete integration in the true sense of the word is not possible; there are some fields of ecology where botanical and zoological ideas are concurrent and others where there is little common ground. Botanists are best equipped to deal with primary producers and the physical background to their environment, while zoologists have the more detailed information about the population and community problems in ecology. The arrangement whereby competition, biotic effects, energy in the ecosystem and the human influences were dealt with from both zoological and botanical aspects ensured that lecturers from both sides dealt in detail with their own specialities and integrated where they could.

2. Experience has shown the advantage of the interplay between two *slightly* different viewpoints and methods in securing the continuing interest of students. There may be animal and plant ecologists in some institutions who would not integrate so well. The fact that practical work

in zoology is about equally divided between the field and the laboratory while in botany it is almost entirely conducted in the field makes for variety.

3. The problem, common to botanists and zoologists, of teaching the ignorant part of the class about the plant and animal kingdoms while occupying the attention of the whole class with the general problems or ecology is solved in rather different ways, again producing a stimulating variety in approach. The botanists concentrate on teaching the common plant species of woodland and grassland at the same time as using them for ecological study; the zoologists, having more diverse material, concentrate on recognition of the main terrestrial taxonomic groups, which should serve as a good introduction for those who go on to the survey of the animal kingdom in the Honours Zoology course as well as enabling them to make ecological observations of value.

4. Experience has shown that students who are primarily interested in plants and animals in the field automatically have a bias in favour of one or the other. The method adopted of partial integration between botany and zoology allows each student to give free rein to his own particular interest, whilst at the same time he is exposed to the ecological thinking of the other discipline.

5. It will have been noted that this course concentrates on terrestrial environments. Where marine or interesting freshwater habitats are readily available, quite different courses might prove more satisfactory. In fact, a number of other days of the Preliminary course are spent in examining flowing and standing fresh waters under the guise of zoological or botanical taxonomy. The zoologists in their second year receive a course of seven lectures on marine biology and spend a week at Swansea.

B. *The effect on the student*
Only a preliminary judgment is possible as the first Final Honours examination of students taught on the new system is in June 1966. Those who have chosen Final Honours Zoology and have wished to specialize in ecology can attend a course of lectures such as those given by Mr Elton on Animal Ecology but there are other optional courses which have considerable interest for ecologists: Dr David Lack's lectures on birds, Professor E.B.Ford's course on Population Genetics and the course on Animal Behaviour all have a strong ecological content. There is also a course on Insect Population Dynamics. Although the size of the Zoology Honours school has not greatly changed in the last 3 years, the numbers attending this last course have risen dramatically. With only eight

lectures followed by practical exercises of various kinds it has been possible to teach about modern methods for the analysis of the life-tables of insects and bring the students within reach of the frontiers of ecological research. The attitude of mind in the students resulting from their work in the first year must have played a big part in this satisfactory result.

Although the field work has involved a great deal of preparation, it has been considered well worth while because it has been so much appreciated by the students. The reactions of students who later took the Honours Botany course, for instance, suggested that they had indeed profited from the grounding provided by the Preliminary course and a satisfactory proportion took the advanced course in plant ecology seriously.

Not all the students have reacted equally well to the course. Some will have been overawed by the need to name so many organisms to their groups or species, but *they* would never have turned to ecology under any system of teaching. By demonstrating advanced concepts right from the start, the course has shown where ecology is going and has attracted very considerable interest.

It is possible that there may be a case at a later stage for further coordination of ecology teaching at the Honours level. Complete integration is bound to be difficult when the teachers are trained either as botanists or zoologists. The formation of an ecological department under a Professor of Ecology might eventually provide a solution to the problems.

APPENDIX

A KEY TO THE MAJOR GROUPS OF BRITISH
FREE-LIVING TERRESTRIAL INVERTEBRATES

KITTY PAVIOUR-SMITH* and J.B.WHITTAKER†

Bureau of Animal Population, University of Oxford

Pupae and microscopic animals have been omitted. Of the microscopic animals, the Protozoa, rotifers, harpacticoid copepods, tardigrades and some nematodes can be found in books on freshwater fauna, e.g. Macan T.T. (1959) *A Guide to Freshwater Invertebrate Animals* (Longmans, London), and on soil fauna, e.g. Kevan D.K.McE. (1962) *Soil Animals* (Witherby, London). However, the terrestrial adults of four insect orders with immature stages in fresh water have been included; these are marked with asterisks and are likely to be encountered only near fresh water. If collecting is done near an animal nest or a corpse the following ecto-parasitic orders may be found in addition: Mallophaga, Siphunculata (lice) and Siphonaptera (fleas).

The wide size-range within groups makes it difficult to give useful size limits; however, a note is made where all or almost all members of a group, when adult, are 'minute' or 'small'. Roughly these terms mean: head + body lengths < 1 mm and < 5 mm respectively.

The characters used in the key can all be seen if × 35 magnification is used, and therefore may not be those normally selected by experienced zoologists. Figures 1–4 show certain characters which have given difficulty to students; illustrations of most groups can, however, be found in e.g. Imms A.D. (1947) *Insect Natural History* (Collins, London, New Naturalist Series) and Kevan D.K.McE. (1962) *Soil Animals* (Witherby, London). The numbers and letters in the text (e.g. 'see 14b') are cross-references to other couplets or parts thereof. The superscript numbers refer to notes at the end.

1   Animals segmented (if not obviously segmented, then *either* animals
    worm-like, blunt at both ends and having minute, shining bristles
    serially arranged along length *or* animals with true jointed legs)............3
–   Animals not segmented (and not as above) 2
2   Animals soft-bodied and slimy; ventral surface of body forming a
    muscular foot..slugs and snails: MOLLUSCA
–   Animals small, worm-like, with a tough shining cuticle..........................
                                                      threadworms: NEMATODA

* Mrs. K. Southern.

† Present address: Department of Biology, University of Lancaster, England.

3 True (jointed) legs present 11
– True legs absent (Annelids and some insect larvae).......................................4
4 Body segments many more than 15 (no head capsule)..............................
                                                  worms: ANNELIDA 5
– Body with fewer than 15 segments (exclusive of any obvious head)
    (certain insect larvae)..6
5 With a terminal sucker at each end of body.........................leeches: HIRUDINEA
– Body without suckers..........................earthworms, potworms: OLIGOCHAETA
6 With distinct head capsule...7
– Without distinct head capsule..9
7 Head arranged horizontally so that mouthparts visible from above
    (head capsule usually well sclerotized and therefore darker in
    colour than rest of body)..8
– Head arranged vertically so that mouthparts not visible from above
    (head capsule usually scarcely sclerotized so that whitish like rest
    of body) ....LARVAE OF CURCULIONIDAE, COLEOPTERA (part)
8 Prothorax at least twice the length of, and usually wider than, either
    of the other 2 thoracic segments.................LARVAE OF COLEOPTERA (part—
    Buprestidae and some Cerambycidae)
– Prothorax the same length and width as other 2 thoracic segments
                  LARVAE OF DIPTERA NEMATOCERA (most), DIPTERA
9 Reduced mouthparts heavily sclerotized (but may need extruding in
    preserved material)..LARVAE OF HIGHER DIPTERA
– Reduced mouthparts only lightly sclerotized..10
10 Heavily sclerotized, anchor-shaped or toothed 'breast-bone' present
              LARVAE OF CECIDOMYIIDAE[1], NEMATOCERA (rest), DIPTERA
– 'Breast-bone' absent[1]..........................LARVAE OF APOCRITA, HYMENOPTERA
11 Three pairs of true jointed legs (insects)..19
    (also larval mites—see 14b, larval pauropods and larval millipedes—see 16)
– Four pairs of true jointed legs (and with chelicerae and pedipalps—
    e.g. in Fig. 4)..ARACHNIDA 12
– More than 4 pairs of true jointed legs..15
12 Segmentation of abdomen distinct (may need to be viewed ventrally)..............13
– Segmentation of abdomen not visible externally...14
13 Pedipalps very large with crab-like pincers (body ending bluntly;
    animals small) ....PSEUDOSCORPIONIDEA
– Pedipalps without crab-like pincers (with pair of eyes, either raised
    on a tubercle or on a flat forwardly produced projection...................
                                            harvestmen: PHALANGIDA
14 Abdomen (behind the legs) joined to rest of body by a narrow
    'waist'...spiders: ARANEIDA
– Abdomen broadly fused to rest of body (animals mostly minute,
    some small)..mites and ticks: ACARINA[2]
                                            (for larvae see 11a)

15 Appendages behind head differentiated into 6–7 pairs of walking
    legs, followed by 5 pairs of small flat plates (pleopods) and 1 pair
    of uropods ('tail-legs')..woodlice: ISOPODA, CRUSTACEA
 – Appendages behind head all (except for the first pair in centipedes)
    walking legs (N.B. 2 species of millipedes look superficially like
    woodlice)..16
16 With twice-branched antennae (animals minute)..............................PAUROPODA
                                                                       (for larvae see 11a)
 – Antennae unbranched 17
17 Body segments (after first 3) fused in pairs, giving appearance of
    2 pairs of legs on most 'segments' (larvae with fewer than 6 seg-
    ments visible behind 3 pairs of legs, see 11a)............millipedes: DIPLOPODA
 – Body segments not fused in pairs, so that only 1 pair of legs per
    apparent segment..18
18 First pair of legs modified as large jaws (maxillipeds).....centipedes: CHILOPODA
 – First pair of legs not like large jaws (animals small)........................SYMPHYLA
19 Wings absent or extremely reduced...20
 – Wings present...43
20 With antennae (though these may be much reduced in size)......................21
 – Without antennae but first pair of legs held out as tactile organs
    (first 3 abdominal segments each with a pair of minute 'styliform'
    appendages—cf. Fig. 1; animals minute)..PROTURA
21 Always with ventral tube (Figs. 2 and 3) on first abdominal segment;
    with no more than 6 abdominal segments (fourth usually with
    forked spring (furculum); animals minute or small)........COLLEMBOLA 22
 – Without these characters..23
22 Body elongate with thorax distinct and most or all of the abdominal
    segments visible (ventral tube sometimes greatly reduced (Fig. 3));
    furculum sometimes reduced (Fig. 3) or absent...
                                             'long' springtails: ARTHROPLEONA
 – Body globular, as thorax and first 4 abdominal segments fused;
    furculum always present......................'round' springtails: SYMPHYPLEONA
23 Minute appendages (styles—Fig. 1) present on at least 2 (usually on
    many more) abdominal segments, in addition to a pair of anal
    cerci (Fig. 1)..
                                                                                             24
 – No such styles, except in ♂ long-horned grasshoppers (bush crickets)
    and ♂ cockroaches, and then never more than 1 pair; (winged or
    secondarily wingless insects)...
                                                                                             25
24 Abdomen ending in a segmented median filament between a pair of
    many-jointed filament-like cerci; compound eyes present (ocelli
    may be absent); body covered by scales................bristle-tails: THYSANURA
 – Abdomen without such a median filament, but with a pair of fila-
    ment-like cerci about as long as the antennae (Fig. 1); neither

compound eyes nor ocelli present; body colourless and without
scales (animals small)...DIPLURA

25 With lateral ocelli or simple eyes only (rarely up to 30 of these per
side may be grouped into a pair of 'pseudo-compound' eyes but if
so the animal very pale and lightly sclerotized and of the following
form); form elongate, without a waist, but with clear thoracic
and abdominal segments...................remaining larvae of higher insects..............26

  – Lateral ocelli absent, but compound eyes (and often dorsal ocelli)
present; animal not of above general larval form (Rarely the compound eyes are reduced to one or to a few separate units but if
so the animal as in 36a or 35a respectively)..33

26 Pairs of abdominal false legs (prolegs) present as well as thoracic legs
(polypodous larvae)...27

  – Pairs of abdominal prolegs absent (oligopodous larvae)..........................30

27 With 5, or fewer, pairs of unjointed prolegs (these bearing apical rows
of minute hooks)...........................caterpillars: LARVAE OF LEPIDOPTERA
(except Micropterygidae, see 28a)

  – Normally with more than 5 pairs of prolegs (without such hooks)..............28

28 Size only a few millimetres; abdominal prolegs (8 pairs) similar to
thoracic in being segmented and clawed...
LARVAE OF MICROPTERYGIDAE, LEPIDOPTERA

  – Size larger; prolegs not segmented..29

29 Numerous (22–28) ocelli on each side; 8 pairs of prolegs starting with
first abdominal segment; abdomen not annulated......................................
LARVAE OF PANORPIDAE, MECOPTERA

  – Only 1 ocellus on each side; 8, or fewer, pairs of prolegs starting after
first abdominal segment; abdomen usually annulated................................
sawfly larvae: LARVAE OF SYMPHYTA, HYMENOPTERA

30 Sluggish white 'grub-like' larvae...31

  – Active larvae (or larviform adult) with elongate, somewhat depressed
body, often with a well-sclerotized head with obvious forwardly
directed mouthparts and long thoracic legs...32

31 Three simple eyes almost touching in a darkly pigmented patch;
retractile legs (3-segmented), appearing conical when retracted,
first pair very close together on either side of mid-ventral line,
second and third pairs very wide apart on ventro-lateral margins
of body; (head arranged vertically with mouthparts ventral)............
LARVAE OF BOREIDAE, MECOPTERA

  – Ocelli (up to 6) sparsely arranged; non-retractile legs not arranged
as above but all 3 pairs in similar positions on their respective
segments; (head often arranged more horizontally with mouthparts terminal).................................beetle larvae: COLEOPTERA (part)

32 Larvae fusiform (in 'snake-flies', this shape only behind the heavily

sclerotized head and pronotum); (all with very large and obvious 'jaws')............larvae of lacewings, alder flies, snake flies, etc.: NEUROPTERA

– Larvae (or larviform adult if completely sclerotized) parallel-sided, even if tapering at the ends.. beetle larvae (rest) (and larviform ♀ adult glow-worm): COLEOPTERA

33 Thorax appearing to consist of only one large segment (mesothorax) since prothorax and metathorax are small and fused with the greatly enlarged mesothorax..............................adults of wingless flies: DIPTERA[3]

– Thorax not as above 34

34 Body bearing scales which, if insect very hairy, are visible at least on the abdomen...wingless LEPIDOPTERA

– Body without scales...35

35 Mouthparts modified as long piercing and sucking stylets (usually have triangular-shaped face). (Rarely, mouthparts completely absent—see 45b)...........................nymphal and apterous bugs: HEMIPTERA

– Mouthparts present but not modified as stylets.................................36

36 With a narrow 'waist'; (heavily sclerotized, shining insects; may have club-like vestiges of wings)...

ants and other adult wingless APOCRITA, HYMENOPTERA

– Without a 'waist'..37

37 Fore legs greatly expanded, with huge teeth on tibiae and tarsi.........

nymphal mole-crickets: GRYLLOTALPIDAE, ORTHOPTERA (part)

– Fore legs not as above..38

38 Hind legs (especially their club-shaped femora) very much larger than the first two pairs of legs (and always much longer than the abdomen)..............................grasshoppers, crickets: ORTHOPTERA (part)

– Hind legs not unusually large compared with the other two pairs of legs 39

39 Head prolonged into a downwardly directed 'rostrum' (beak) bearing mouth-parts at the end...MECOPTERA (part)

– Head not as above 40

40 Anal cerci present...41

– Anal cerci absent...42

41 Dorso-ventrally flattened; cerci short and divergent............................

cockroaches: DICTYOPTERA

– Not flattened; cerci long and somewhat convergent (forceps-like in later instars) ....earwigs: DERMAPTERA

42 Long thread-like antennae (12–50 segments), prothorax usually small (front of head, between antennae, often swollen; insects small)

nymphal and apterous adult book lice: PSOCOPTERA

– Short, stubby antennae (6–10 segments), prothorax well developed (insects small–minute) ....

nymphal and apterous adult thrips: THYSANOPTERA

43 One pair of wings, the other pair modified as 'halteres' (small club-like organs) 44
 − Two pairs of wings (in a few mayflies and a few beetles, second pair of wings may be lost completely and, in the latter, hardened fore wings (see 48a) may be fused together along mid-line; in one neuropteran sp. hind wings may be minute)..46
44 Fore pair of wings modified as 'halteres' (metathorax is the enlarged thoracic segment; insects small).......................................♂ STREPSIPTERA[4]
 − Hind pair of wings modified as 'halteres' (mesothorax is the enlarged segment as in 33a) 45
45 Mouthparts present; prothorax indistinct as fused with mesothorax; (tarsi usually with 5 segments but never as few as 1; wings usually with at least 1 cross vein joining 2 long veins)................................DIPTERA[3]
 − Mouthparts completely absent; prothorax quite distinct from meso-thorax; (tarsi of 1 segment; wings lacking any cross veins joining long veins; insects small–minute)................adult ♂ COCCIDAE, HEMIPTERA
46 Mouthparts modified as long sucking stylets (usually have triangular-shaped face)..bugs: HEMIPTERA[5] (rest)
 − Mouthparts not thus modified...47
47 Fore wings forming usually hardened 'elytra' or wing covers which usually meet in the mid-dorsal line, but never overlap; mem-branous hind wings fold longitudinally and transversely under elytra or hind wings absent 48
 − Fore wings at least partly membranous, often overlapping; hind wings may fold longitudinally but never transversely under elytra.........49
48 Elytra usually covering most of the abdomen, but if short, then end of body without 'forceps'...beetles: COLEOPTERA
 − Elytra always short exposing most of abdomen; and abdomen ending in a pair of more or less converging 'forceps' (unjointed cerci).........
                                                earwigs: DERMAPTERA
49 Fore wings interlocking with hind wings by means of a ridge on the former and row of hooks on the latter (other characters which may be present: very much reduced venation, elbowed antennae, a pigmented spot on leading edge of fore wing)............HYMENOPTERA 50
 − Wings not interlocking...51
50 Body without a waist...sawflies: SYMPHYTA
 − Body with a waist..ants, bees, wasps, etc: APOCRITA
51 Both pairs of wings strap-like and fringed with long hairs on both leading and trailing edges (antennae and prothorax as in 42b; insects small–minute)...thrips: THYSANOPTERA
 − Wings otherwise...52
52 Body and wings bearing minute pigmented scales (sometimes extremely sparse on the wings or mixed with hairs on the body;

    may be visible only under high magnification)..
moths and butterflies: LEPIDOPTERA

 – Neither body nor wings with scales..53

53 First vein extending no further than half-way along wing, ending
    at a thickened joint-like cross vein; thorax distorted to bring all legs
    almost completely in front of first pair of wings (body length
    >3 cm)..dragonflies: ODONATA*

 – Venation otherwise 54

54 First 2 veins extending (unbranched) the whole length of the wing,
    parallel to each other and more or less to the front edge of the
    wing; thorax not distorted as above..55

 – Venation not thus..57

55 At rest wings held vertically above body; many 'intercalary' veins
    present which have lost basal connection to main veins but con-
    nected by numerous cross veins; (bearing 2 filamentous cerci and
    often a third tail filament)................................mayflies: EPHEMEROPTERA*

 – Wings held tentwise over body; no intercalary veins................................56

56 'Costal veinlets' numerous, giving ladder-like effect along front edge
    of each wing................lacewings, alder flies, snake flies: NEUROPTERA (most)

 – No such ladder-like effect given by costal veinlets. (Small insects
    covered with whitish waxy exudation—but this may not be
    visible in alcohol; hind wings may be smaller than fore wings)......
CONIOPTERYGIDAE, NEUROPTERA (rest)

57 Fore legs as in 37a................ mole-crickets: GRYLLOTALPIDAE, ORTHOPTERA

 – Fore legs not as above..58

58 Hind legs as in 38a................................grasshoppers, crickets: ORTHOPTERA (most)

 – Hind legs not unusually large compared with the other two pairs of
    legs 59

59 Face prolonged downwards into a 'rostrum' (beak) as in 39a (apex of
    ♂ abdomen usually scorpion-like)................scorpion flies: MECOPTERA (rest)

 – Face not thus prolonged) 60

60 Prothorax very small compared with either head or mesothorax;
    at rest, wings held tentwise over abdomen..61

 – Prothorax the same size as, or larger than, head or mesothorax; at
    rest, wings usually held flat (but never tentwise) over abdomen................62

61 Front of head obviously swollen above the upper lip (labrum);
    mandibles (biting jaws) always present (though not always easy
    to see without dissection); usually wing membrane naked between
    the veins but if not then hairs minute and colourless (small insects)
book lice: PSOCOPTERA

 – Front of head not swollen; mandibles absent; wing membrane
    between the veins always covered more or less densely with pig-
    mented hairs..caddis flies: TRICHOPTERA*

62 Shield-like pronotum much longer than the head or mesothorax or metathorax, and almost hiding the head; fore wings rather thickened and opaque (jaws at rest between the bases of the front legs)............
cockroaches: DICTYOPTERA

- Prothorax, mesothorax, metathorax and head all of about equal size; pronotum not shield-like and not hiding head; both pairs of wings transparent...stoneflies: PLECOPTERA*

NOTES

1 The paedogenetic larvae of a few Cecidomyiidae lack 'breast-bones' but are distinguished from Apocrita larvae by their burrowing *freely* in dead wood or fungi and by their producing abundant 'daughter' larvae directly.

2 Acarina. Note especially the Oribatid mites which are strongly sclerotized, usually with hair-like or club-like 'pseudostigmatic organs' of which the pits (or pseudostigmata) are usually clearly visible (under a high power) on either side of the base of the gnathosoma. The 'seed mites' (Family Phthiracaridae) belong to the Oribatei. Ticks have a toothed structure (between the pedipalps) which, together with the toothed chelicerae, forms a piercing organ.

3 Diptera. In the Sub-Order Nematocera (primitive Diptera) adults have many-jointed antennae made up of similar elements.
Adults of the Sub-Order Brachycera have short antennae made up of a small number of dissimilar elements: 2 or 3 obvious basal segments carrying a *terminal* appendage which may be jointed or bristle-like (arista).
In the Sub-Order Cyclorrhapha adults have antennae of 3 basal segments, of which the third is the largest and bears *dorsally* a bristle-like arista.

4 Female Strepsiptera are very degenerate and larviform, and are found only within the bodies of certain Homoptera and certain Hymenoptera. Their microscopic, free-living, first-instar larvae key out as beetle larvae, but see diagram in e.g. Imms A.D. (1925 and later editions) *A General Textbook of Entomology* (Methuen, London).

5 Hemiptera. Sub-Order Homoptera. Wings usually sloping in a tent-shaped fashion over sides of body, the fore pair generally of uniform consistency throughout. (The most common of these are the froghoppers and leaf hoppers, with very short antennae with a terminal bristle, and the aphids with thread-like antennae with no conspicuous terminal bristle but usually with a pair of tubular projections on the abdomen.)
Sub-Order Heteroptera. Fore wings when folded lying flat upon back, with membranous wing tips greatly overlapping (apical portion more membranous than the remainder).

ACKNOWLEDGMENTS

We are most grateful for the help and advice of Dr E. Broadhead, Dr B.M. Hobby,

Dr A.Macfadyen, Dr M.G.Morris, Professor O.W.Richards, F.R.S., Mr G.H. Thompson and Professor G.C.Varley, and for the criticisms of three successive first-year undergraduate classes.

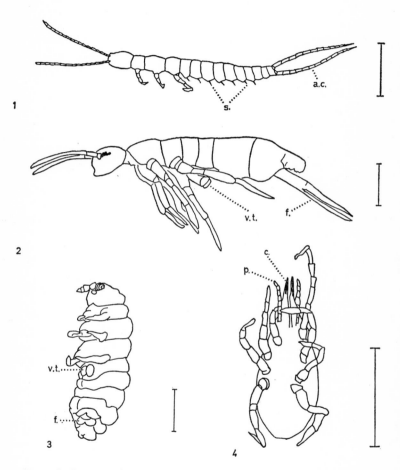

FIG. 1 Styles (s.) and anal cerci (a.c.) in a Dipluran (dorso-lateral view). Scales (each = 1 mm) are given on the right of each animal.
FIGS. 2 and 3. Ventral tube (v.t.) and furculum (f.) in Collembola (two 'long' springtails, Arthropleona).
FIG. 4. Chelicerae (c.) and pedipalps (p.) in an Arachnid (a mite, Acarina).

THE LINKAGE OF ECOLOGICAL TEACHING
WITH THAT IN THE EARTH SCIENCES

F. OLDFIELD

Department of Environmental Sciences
University of Lancaster

The title of this paper presents me with a choice between two alternative and contrasting types of treatment. It would be possible to concentrate on a factual and partly historical account of those situations where biological and geographical or geological teaching are combined or integrated at various levels in the present system of education. However, the alternative that I shall adopt here lays more emphasis on personal views about the issues of principle and method involved in the kind of linkage under discussion.

I. BASIC PREMISES

What follows stems from a series of premises which I believe must form an essential part of the basis for any consideration of the interrelationship between biological and earth science teaching at most levels, though they would perhaps not all be accepted by many geographers. My premises are as follows:

1. That at all levels as much learning as possible should be at first hand; in all the field sciences this implies venturing frequently beyond the classroom or laboratory.

2. That before using the results which the application of scientific techniques yields, all students should have an opportunity to employ a variety of appropriate techniques with some intensity of application and therefore learn at first hand the rudiments of their practice and the reality of their limitations.

3. That studies of this type do not necessarily detract from, but may on the contrary enrich, the quality of any attempt at the broader synthesis so frequently advocated in geography.

4. That the study of processes and of dynamic interrelationships, within the environment, within the organism, between organisms, or between organism and environment, holds a greater intellectual challenge and also promises results of more fundamental theoretical and practical value

33

than does the description, analysis and discussion of purely *spatial* patterns of, for example, physiographic phenomena or plant and animal distributions at a single point in time.

5. That from an intellectual point of view it is an exceptionally stimulating and rewarding experience for any devoted student to explore the points of contact and growth between conventional 'subjects', to encounter and to accept critically techniques and ways of thinking from outside his own 'subject' and so to move beyond the insularity and introversion with which many academic disciplines are practised.

6. That there is a need, on practical, aesthetic and recreational grounds to acquaint a far wider sector of the non-specialist public with the nature, workings and status of man's physical and biological environment.

II. LINKAGE PROBLEMS AT DIFFERENT EDUCATIONAL LEVELS

In schools, though no simple generalizations are completely valid, the most fundamental barrier to any true linkage would appear to lie in the nature of the examination curricula in the subjects concerned. Whereas at all levels biology and the earth sciences meet out of doors and in one's immediate neighbourhood, the syllabus too often points the biologist towards, for example, anatomy and the geographer towards regional studies of remote areas at third hand. There is also sometimes a disadvantageous feed-back from university curricula in the form of the teacher who, for example, within the context of geography, relies on unverifiable and predigested text-book material whilst totally lacking the confidence and insight to teach from the field at first hand. These two inter-related problems produce the kind of sixth-former with whom I am familiar when interviewing for university entrance and who, in spite of taking geography and a biological subject at A-level, has never been encouraged to explore the links between the two, either by example from his teacher or by his own personal insight, and who may in consequence see little relationship between them. Recently, the work of the Field Studies Council above all seems to be making the student think beyond this rigid compartmentalization.

At postgraduate level the success of the few basically interdisciplinary master's degree courses in, for example, Conservation or Ecology, is particularly encouraging. Students may approach any single one of these applied, interdisciplinary or borderline studies at postgraduate level from a variety of different undergraduate courses. Thus they come with disparate and often, in the context of their own developing interests, *com-*

plementary backgrounds. This may pose what I suspect are peculiarly English problems which must ultimately call for a rather flexible approach towards course work for master's degrees by examination. What I should like to see implemented is a larger number of postgraduate courses providing not so much a rigid M.A. or M.Sc. syllabus but rather a context within which well-qualified undergraduates from different disciplines would have the opportunity to supplement prescribed and specifically postgraduate courses with participation in work taking place at undergraduate level in those disciplines complementary to their own undergraduate studies. This presupposes (i) an expansion in postgraduate course work despite the current anxieties about duplication, (ii) increasing mobility between different departments and universities after graduation, and (iii) formal provision for flexibility in entrance qualifications and course structures. Within the context of ecology and the related fields of study in the earth sciences I believe that the overwhelming breadth of study encompassed, the increasing variety of approach between existing departments and the innumerable points of contact between many aspects of each range of disciplines point ultimately to some developments along the lines suggested above.

Within the framework of the present educational system, it is at and immediately before undergraduate level that the problems posed by developing courses based on the premises stated at the beginning of the paper seem to me to be most complex, and for this reason I have left them until last. At present in university courses, linkage of some sort takes place in three main ways:

1. Through the student studying, for example, a biological subject as ancillary to 'honours' in (say) geography, or vice versa.
2. Through the growing body of joint honours courses linking the two sides.
3. Within the context of a single 'honours' course *per se* ('biogeography' within geography, some micrometeorology in applied ecology, etc.).

The structure of ancillary courses varies across a broad spectrum from the brief, fundamental 'principles of . . .' approach at one end, to the study of more or less arbitrarily selected elements at the other. The latter extreme may achieve no true linkage whatever, as when, for example, the geographers find themselves in a minority, reading an ancillary botany course taken mainly by zoologists and comprising simply a selection of courses from the botany 'honours' syllabus.

Joint honours courses achieve real linkage only if they are in part at least expressions of the genuinely shared interests of the particular individual teachers involved. Thus, I believe that any attempt to prescribe or even simply to generalize would be superfluous except to suggest that the strong pressure of inertia in many universities, which militates against flexibility of syllabuses and changes in course structure, could perhaps be peculiarly damaging to joint honours ventures of this type.

Under the third category above, i.e. linkage achieved within a single-subject major course, I am competent to speak from only one side of the fence. I believe it would be profitable to conclude the present discussion with a brief consideration of the ecological teaching taking place within the context of geography itself.

Outside the biological sciences in British higher education at least, the teaching of plant and animal ecology as here understood is more or less restricted to university departments of geography. With the development of departments of environmental studies and environmental sciences in certain of the new universities, and with the growing urge to re-evaluate curricula in schools and Colleges of Education, this situation is bound to change in the fairly near future. Even so, it is convenient to begin by considering the part played by ecological studies in geography departments *sensu stricto*.

Most teaching of ecology in geography departments takes place under the heading 'biogeography'. As little as 10 years ago this formed often only a tiny fraction of most undergraduates studies in geography; for example, as one small section in a course of lectures on climatology. By now, very few British geography departments fail to offer a full course in biogeography at first- or second-year level to all honours students, and many now offer the subject as a final-year 'special option'. We therefore need to consider the scope and content of 'biogeography' in relation to ecology, and to consider the reasons underlying its rapid expansion as a branch of university geography.

III. THE RELATIONSHIP BETWEEN ECOLOGY AND BIOGEOGRAPHY

Many teachers of biogeography have entered the field from its pedological geomorphological or climatological margins and so the content and emphasis of biogeography varies greatly from one department to another. Lack of uniformity is reinforced by an almost equal lack of good and comprehensive text-books which in other subjects often impose some measure of standardization on the scope of lecture courses. Thus it is easier to begin by saying what biogeography is not, since all courses concur in using the term to embrace something very different from the sum of phytogeography and zoogeography as traditionally defined by biologists. The stress laid by biologists on the distribution of particular taxa, in traditional plant and animal geographies, and on extrinsic and intrinsic factors affecting such distributions, has never fitted well into the geographer's scheme of study, where recent methodological preoccupations point away from any systematic discussion of *taxonomically* related organisms (save perhaps man or economic crops).

Without implying either fine distinctions or close delimitations, biogeography as taught in most departments in fact comes much closer to ecology than to 'plant and animal geography'. Recent definitions (e.g. Deevey, 1949) and even some older ones (e.g. de Martonne, 1932) also suggest this, as does the content and approach of the few texts stemming in part from current biogeographical teaching, either in Britain (Eyre, 1963) or in the United States (Dansereau, 1960).

Even if we accept the core of 'biogeography' as overlapping strongly with much of ecology, this still leaves room for large differences of approach between departments. For instance, the extent to which marine ecology is considered varies from zero to a significant fraction of the course; some departments lay much more stress than others on soil studies as central to biogeography; world vegetation types receive widely varying treatments both in terms of quantity and of approach; historical plant and animal geography may be stressed or hardly touched upon; and the strictly biological foundations of modern ecology also receive varying emphasis.

There are good biological as well as academic grounds for supposing that variety of approach and emphasis at the outset of a new venture is of itself no bad thing. However, one uncertainty has more serious implications and is reflected both in differences in the extent to which basic biology (e.g. elementary physiology, soil minerals and nutrition, simple genetics, the species concept, etc.) figures in the courses, and in doubts about the form which the biological basis to the study should take. Here, there is a practical as well as a theoretical problem. The lecturer in biogeography may face a first-year audience with few or no A-level biologists and a preponderance of exclusively 'Arts' sixth-formers. He must either choose superficiality or grasp a curiously awkward nettle. My own experience is of being reduced to many unsatisfactory compromises by the circumstances.

Despite this kind of practical problem, and many others, the scope and conceptual framework of the subject have recently been examined in a number of papers by biogeographers (Eyre, 1964; Morgan & Moss, 1965; Stoddart, 1965) with the conclusion in each case that the central concepts of biogeography could form a new focus for a much wider range of geographical studies.

Eyre (1964) expounds the ecological approach as he sees it and commends it to wider application within geography. Stoddart (1965) points to the concept of the ecosystem as the real core of biogeography and contends that it could become the core of much of geography, thus revising and revitalizing the much-debated and sometimes debased concept of the 'region' along functional lines and also bringing geography into the broader field of 'general systems' Morgan & Moss (1965) also stress the significance of the ecosystem and the relationships within it, but they consider that the concept of community, defined in a rather flexible way, usually as a major functional component of any given ecosystem, should actually form the main unit for study.

This apparent preoccupation with form and content, scope and methodology, seems to me to be symptomatic of a fundamental problem which has implications throughout many branches of geographical study. Biogeography, despite its rapid progress to the present day, lacks the strong basis of fundamental and progressing primary research by a fairly high proportion of practitioners and teachers which has been the precursor of any new teaching development in biology or the other sciences. I believe that the philosophical and methodological preoccupations are essentially the result of this lack of an active primary research frontier. Where this latter exists, the real raw material of the teacher at the highest level comes to him, especially in the less exact sciences, in a basically chaotic form which expresses the uneven state of knowledge along an advancing front; his main concern in presenting the evidence is a striving for *objective truth* and there may be considerable tension between this aim and the need for organized presentation. Where this basis of progressing primary research is less immediate, organization, symmetry, coherence and exposition are more likely to become the prevailing concern of the teacher. We need to ask whether or not, in the case of 'biogeography', this latter, secondary level of involvement alone is to be the main aim in the future. This depends on the extent to which the geographer or earth scientist of any kind is prepared (i) to learn some fundamental biology, (ii) to acquire and use critically the research techniques available, and (iii) to accept and share the scientist's concern with processes, and with quantitative studies. Thus, advocating studies of the ecosystem as the core of biogeography and much of geography involves accepting the need for competence in the appropriate *techniques* for measuring and analysing productivity and energy flow. At this stage, many geographers would claim that in both his research and teaching the biogeographer had ceased to be a geographer. This argument seems to me to be irrelevant. What I am more concerned to suggest is that the methodological proposals made by the biogeographers referred to above must be adequately fulfilled in practice as well as in teaching. Until they are, they appear to be in some measure premature.

This digression beyond the questions of teaching to the further issues of basic research is, I believe, essential; for, at the highest level, the former should grow, in part at least, as an ever-changing articulation of the latter.

We are attempting to achieve some genuine integration of one aspect of ecology within a broader field of earth sciences, or 'environmental sciences' at Lancaster. The emphasis in the major part of the department's research and teaching is on processes and rates of change in the physical environment, including its evolution during geologically recent times and up to the present day. The nature of the techniques used in such studies enforces an intimate link between the evidence for changing physical environment and that for long-term biological change. The techniques (for example, pollen analysis) call for a combination of the stratigraphic approach of the geologist with the ecological insight of the biologist. In the teaching which is growing from such work, first-hand acquaintance with techniques of primary research forms an important element, whilst the rapidly growing volume of evidence along an exceptionally broad research front presents the joint challenges of objectivity and organization in teaching mentioned above; the ultimate aim is to attempt to present a synthesis of changing environment and biotic response right up to the present day, which will form a factual historical basis for examining the long-term context and the status of present-day plant and animal communities including man—a striving for what one might perhaps call *long-term* dynamic ecology. This type of study is one of many possible approaches to problems of conservation; and we are proposing that a study of conservation, broadly defined, will grow directly from the linked ecological and earth science teaching briefly outlined above.

IV. CONCLUSION

Accepting pragmatically, and for the purposes of a single department, fairly closely defined aims of the kind proposed above, without claiming that they form the core or basis of some hypothetical 'biogeography' seems to me to be a fruitful approach at this stage. It has the further advantage of dictating to a large extent the nature of the biological basis needed as a preliminary to the study. Ecological history, with its dependence in part on identification, and especially on insight into the nature of biological evolution and the limitations of the species concept as well as on both descriptive and dynamic ecological studies, requires a preliminary training which stresses many of the theoretical and practical aspects of taxonomy and genetics, in addition to the perhaps more obviously relevent and specifically ecological background needed.

This type of study is only *one* possible approach to integrating some ecological study into the work of a department of 'earth sciences', and this like any other approach will ultimately depend in part on a firm and relevant research basis.

REFERENCES

DANSEREAU P. (1960) *Biogeography*. New York.

DEEVEY E.J. (1949) Biogeography of the Pleistocene, Part I. Europe and North America. *Bull. Geol. Soc. Amer.* **60**.

DE MARTONNE E. (1932) Traité de Géographie Physique. T. III. *Biogéographie*. Paris.

EYRE S.R. (1963) *Vegetation and Soils: A World Picture*. London.

EYRE S.R. (1964) Determinism and the ecological approach to geography. *Geography*, **49**, 369–376.

MORGAN W.B. & MOSS R.P. (1965) Geography and ecology: the concept of the community and its relationship to environment. *Ann. Assoc. Amer. Geog.* **55** (2), 339–350.

STODDART D.R. (1965) Geography and the ecological approach: the ecosystem as a geographic principle and method. *Geography*, **50**, 242–251.

ECOLOGY IN THE MEDICAL SCHOOL

D. J. BRADLEY

Department of Medical Microbiology,
Makerere University College, Kampala, Uganda

I. INTRODUCTION

Medical schools now are not usually thought of as providing a habitat for the ecologist, least of all the population ecologist. Yet 'populos' referred to the people originally and rates of increase were first adequately understood in relation to man (Cole, 1957). Life-table analysis grew up from considering medical failures. An ecological approach is clearly seen in the work of such early epidemiologists as Snow, who literally went from οἶκος to οἶκος in his search for the habitat of the cholera agent. Since that time the paths of medicine and animal ecology have diverged. More recently, animal ecologists and the 'human ecologists' have drawn closer to each other, but this has concerned the student of healthy man— sociologists and geographers—rather than the medical workers. It is my contention that ecological thought and methodology not only should, but inevitably will, play a considerable part in the education of the student of medicine and in medical research.

There are in the medical course many topics which may be called ecology in a broad sense, and about the vague field 'human ecology' much has been written. This term has been used to describe the work of many quite different schools of geography and sociology, and also as the title of a medical Chair whose occupant covers the entire fields of preventive and social medicine. In this paper, however, I shall concentrate on population ecology. Other branches of ecology may be of equal relevance but space is limited. Population dynamics has always been a concern of the demographers; in the last few years it has also been used by cell biologists (Bertalanffy & Lau, 1962) who have studied cell turnover in the intestinal wall (Quastler & Sherman, 1959) and in immune cell populations from the thymus and elsewhere. It is with the invading populations of parasites— from viruses to worms—that use man as a habitat that I wish particularly to deal, as they have been neglected.

I shall briefly review the traditional ecological material already included in medical courses, then consider current ecological work of importance to the student of medicine, and thirdly, last, and chiefly outline the

41

relevance of ecological concepts to the future of medical science and teaching. Of necessity emphasis will be more on what to teach than on how to teach it.

II. THE KNOWN AND TAUGHT

In the tropics, the subtropics and temperate America, though rather rarely in England, the undergraduate medical student learns some descriptive ecology of the vectors of disease. For example, the cycles of transmission of both urban and jungle yellow fever are taught. From this an outline of monkey distribution and the habitat of urban, rural 'domestic', and forest canopy species of *Aëdes* follow. Again, the occurrence of sleeping sickness of the sub-acute Rhodesian and chronic Gambian varieties is correlated in teaching with the savannah and riverine species of tsetse, respectively.

Sometimes it is necessary to go into detail to make the disease pattern comprehensible. To take an example from sleeping sickness: *Lantana* has been introduced into East Africa relatively recently and has spread in the area north-east of Lake Victoria where it has been used to form hedges between fields and near houses. It now forms dense thickets. This vegetation change combined with a series of very wet years has produced an ecoclimate allowing the spread of *Glossina fuscipes* away from its usual riverine habitat to live close to human houses (Willett, 1965). This has been followed by a serious epidemic of Rhodesian sleeping sickness, normally associated with savannah tsetse. To understand how this has happened and the dangers of further spread requires detailed descriptive ecology, even at undergraduate level.

Even so, it is only the descriptions that usually get across to students, not the principles underlying them. Vector-borne disease of man is sufficiently rare in Britain for most of these topics to appear remote and academic to the English medical undergraduate and he is rarely taught about them. This is a pity, as an ecological approach helps to counteract the concept of one disease: (only) one cause—an unfortunate extension of Koch's postulates which seems ingrained in much medical thinking. In the example given above, the trypanosomes are the cause of the sleeping sickness outbreaks, but the new factor that really led to the outbreak was the *Lantana*.

Compared with Britain, populations also seem to receive more attention in the tropical medical schools, where the construction of life-tables forms part of the undergraduate course, and the effect of diseases on the population size and structure is considered though the available data may be scanty. Again this has special relevance to the doctor who is likely to have total responsibility for a 'practice' of 20,000 people, or the health of a district of 250,000, at an early stage in his career. To see the 'trees' only and not the 'wood'—as often results from the training of the English student—would be downright bad medicine here in Uganda. It is also easier to demonstrate environmental effects on disease when 95 per cent of the people live in rural areas, in an environment which may vary from tropical forest in Bwamba and Budongo, to the arid steppe of Karamoja in under 250 miles.

III. THE KNOWN BUT NOT TAUGHT

One aspect of what is really ecology has been developed considerably this century, but has never been incorporated into the main streams of ecological or medical thought; at any rate neither zoology nor medical students ever seem to be familiar with it. This is the mathematical epidemiology of parasites. Since Ross (1910) first attempted to formulate equations to account for malaria transmission and the minimal requirements for its control, malaria has been the predominant object of these studies. Perhaps because the mathematical aspect was overdeveloped (Lotka & Sharpe, 1923) they failed to make an impact in other biological fields, but the recent work of Macdonald (1957) has brought the subject back to practical realities, and work on the transmission of viral and bacterial disease has also developed considerably. Mathematical models of animal populations, such as the logistic curve or the equations of Volterra (1931) have until recently been of limited application in the field though fisheries models have been developed and used to guide fishing strategy (Beverton & Holt, 1957). The transmission equations for malaria (Macdonald, 1957) have also been adequate to explain differences between areas of stable malaria endemicity and epidemic regions, and also to provide a rational basis for planning control measures. A preliminary model of Schistosoma japonicum transmission (Hairston, 1962) suggested that an alternative mammalian host to man had been neglected: it was found that rats were in this position. Macdonald (1965b) has recently discussed the nature and purpose of epidemiological models in detail. It is remarkable how detailed and rigorous a knowledge is required of medical students in physiology whilst in microbiology and preventive medicine a comparable precision is not required of them. In the latter subject this seems to have reduced student interest: the comment that preventive medicine is just common knowledge is often heard and departments of that subject seek to gain 'respectability' by taking over beds and doing clinical work in preference to developing such quantitative and rigorous approaches as already exist. Partly this is because so few of those in preventive medicine departments are familiar with ecological work. Equally, though it is tangential to my main theme, the animal ecologist has, until recently, tended to ignore models based on field work in human epidemiology and still more obviously to avoid parasite ecology within the human host. Partly this may be because man is so complicated but also he tends not to be considered a 'proper' animal or habitat.

IV. THE FUTURE OF ECOLOGY IN
THE MEDICAL SCHOOL:
THE SCARCELY KNOWN AND NOT TAUGHT

Epidemiologists attempting to construct models of helminth transmission were forced by the population consequences of the bisexual nature of the worms (Macdonald, 1965a, b) and of the fact that most cannot complete their life-cycle within the vertebrate host and therefore the parasite load remains directly dependent on the infecting dose (Bradley, 1963), to go back from the infected host to the parasite as the basic unit. This is an extremely important change, and its application to all forms of infective disease whether due to viruses, bacteria, protozoa, or metazoa is, in my view, necessary for their proper understanding. It is perhaps first useful to point out the consequences of failure to think in this way for present medical teaching, as ways of thinking are often so deeply rooted as to be ignored.

The pyogenic bacteria are a group which are covered by every student of medicine. It is considered essential for him to know that *Staphylococcus pyogenes* can give rise to boils and other lesions, the numerous toxins it may produce, the reactions of the body to it and the occurrence of nasal and skin carriers of this organism. He should also know that certain broad groups of hosts, such as diabetics, are particularly liable to staphylococcal lesions. No one will ever expect him to know even the orders of magnitude of staphylococcal populations in boils or noses, still less their reproductive or death-rates. This is even reflected in the terminology used; the various lesions are due to 'The Staphylococcus' and any concept of population is completely foreign to the discussion. The case put in this way is an overstatement at the research level by now, but not at the stage of under-graduate teaching. Certain questions are simply not asked; such as why many are infected, some diseased and a few die in many infections. Ability to predict, except in gross terms, who is likely to suffer from complications of influenza or measles is limited.

The schistosome infections of man provide a fuller example. They cannot complete their life-cycle within man so the worm load varies greatly between people differently exposed to infection. The female worms lay eggs, some of which escape into the hollow viscera, causing damage on their way out. Other eggs are retained in the tissues and the chronic inflammatory reactions around them interfere with the functioning of the host's organs, whilst yet others may drift in the blood to the lungs, nervous system or other distant site where they can cause serious disorders. To some extent, therefore, the lesions depend on egg load which in turn is dependent on the worm load. Consequently, pathology is partly related to the worm load. Considerable difficulty was encountered in attempting to get this concept across to practising doctors—the same concept is familiar to veterinarians—and this stems from unfamiliarity with the concepts of population. The way for further analysis of schistosomal pathogenesis, in addition to the more traditional medical approaches, is to measure the rates of egg production and destruction in experimental animals, the reactions to eggs in terms of their age, and the relation of acquired immune responses to the numbers of worms and eggs infecting the host.

It seems to me, therefore, that the study and teaching of parasite population dynamics is central to the understanding of infective disease. Once the microbes infecting man, or other hosts, are thought of as reproducing populations producing various effects, whose numbers are determined by transmission intensity, reproductive rates and immune responses, and whose numbers can be artificially changed by chemotherapeutic agents, the way is open for an account of infective disease which forms a coherent whole, and also has certain practical advantages.

Firstly, the gap between individual or curative and community or preventive medicine is bridged, or rather, the chasm is filled in, if the parasite and not the host is the working unit. The effects of immunity (in the wide sense, not just antibodies) in pneumococcal infection, malaria or measles, by reducing the numbers of organisms being produced or surviving, affects the state of the habitat or host and also the extent of the emigration of parasites, or infectivity, that may occur. The effects of treatment with antibiotics, and the emergence of resistant strains, are often best understood in terms of the microbial populations involved. There is a good experimental background to these studies in extensive work on the dynamics of bacteria in the chemostat (Monod, 1950; Moser, 1957) which has not yet been fully transferred back to the situation *in vivo*.

Population studies of microbes show not only the emergence of drug-resistant populations, but also antigenic variation in each relapse strain of trypanosomes (Gray, 1964) and local variations in the pathogenicity of schistosome strains (Wright, personal communication). Population ecology is thus linked closely to population genetics and the parasites provide organisms of short life-cycles for such studies.

Secondly, a more precise account of the infection permits a more precise analysis of its causes. The study of immunity, in particular, has far outrun the study of parasite populations so that precise measures of antibodies of various sorts are always used. It is particularly remarkable that population ecology has already influenced the thinking of immunologists who speak in terms of populations and clones of immunologically competent cells. Analytical studies of immunity have been extremely successful and a multiplicity of antibodies and other mechanisms have been discovered. When, as must soon happen, attempts are made to produce a synthetic picture of the processes *in vivo* it will depend on rates of parasite destruction, or inhibition of reproduction, caused by each immune process and these will depend on a knowledge of the parasite population dynamics. Since the demographers work with human populations and some cytologists now think of cell populations, for the microbiologists and epidemiologists to work with parasite populations will result in a more even approach so that students of medicine can be taught the essentials of population ecology and find them applied to many aspects of their studies.

Conversely, the advantages of parasite studies for the ecologist have not always been realized. The parasitic Hymenoptera have, of course, been much studied, but they are rather a special case and their virtues for ecological study lie in a different direction from the microbes which multiply within their host or habitat. One of the major problems troubling ecologists is the difficulty of transferring laboratory results to the field. A particular example of this, which was first pointed out to me by Dr George Salt, and has stuck in my mind, is the way in which Gause's predator-prey system using *Paramecium* and *Didinium* (1934) worked reproducibly until a small amount of sediment was added, when it became at once relatively unpredictable: how often cows' feet stir up a cloud of mud in natural ponds! By contrast, the mammalian body provides a habitat of remarkably constant temperature, pH and size, so that whilst vertebrates of the same species differ a little among themselves, the outstanding feature of them as a habitat is their similarity. Two sheep resemble each other more closely than two lakes, and probably the susceptibility of some breeds of sheep to *Bacillus anthracis* and the resistance of others depend on rather few differences between the hosts. Many of these comments apply to other hosts: vertebrates, invertebrates and plants as well as man. I have laid emphasis on man because the subject demands it. We all have a particular interest in understanding man's relation to his parasites thoroughly: this also means that adequate resources are available. Within a given host the innate and acquired immune processes affecting the parasite are not too numerous and are susceptible to measurement. It is therefore possible to analyse the factors regulating natural populations of parasites with some precision and in a reproducible manner, and the results should be of predictive value in deciding what the effects of a particular thera-peutic or hygienic measure will be on the parasites in the individual or community. Since the number of immune mechanisms is limited and each operates against many parasites, it seems that if there are any general ecological laws to be found they may well apply to the regulation of parasite populations. Furthermore, there are parasite populations that lay eggs only in the host, the parasitic helminths, in which the basic actions of immune processes may be studied in a reproductively simple system, before proceeding to the lower forms that reproduce in geometrical progression by repeated fission, and then on to the viruses that act as templates for the infected cells.

The tools available for such investigations are powerful. Census methods have been devised in great variety for viruses (Dougherty, 1964), bacteria (Meynell & Meynell, 1965), protozoa (e.g. Russell, West, Manwell & Macdonald, 1963) and helminths (e.g. Bradley, 1967). Most parasites of man are small, manageable, and have short lives. Parts of the population may be labelled with radioisotopes (Brock & Brock, 1966) and for some helminths it is possible to label age-cohorts of eggs with titriated thymidine (Bradley, unpublished) as a lasting tracer. Methods for assessing immune processes, both cellular and humoral, are well established and very precise. Furthermore, a variety of chemotherapeutic agents and antibiotics permit of killing fractions of the population or halting reproduction.

Although studies of this general type have been followed by a few workers, such as Lurie (1964) in his studies of tuberculosis, it is surprising how often the simplest questions about parasite populations in man cannot be answered: not because they are difficult to solve, but because nobody has tried. A symposium published in 1957 (Society for General Microbiology) entitled *Microbial Ecology* almost completely lacks any discussion of microbial populations of the type I have described, as also do most of the monographs on particular parasites. For this reason the ecological approach cannot yet fill its logical place in medical teaching. But at least it can do so at once in research. The extra-host ecology, or epidemiology, of parasites has been studied more fully, as mentioned above. This can be increasingly integrated with intra-host ecology with the aim of understanding and being able to teach a single approach to infective disease in individuals and populations.

As a study, population ecology is both synthetic and rigorous and its conceptual value in medical teaching is to show that precision is not the sole prerogative of molecular biology but can be aimed at in the study of the pathogenesis and transmission of infective disease, and of human communities. Complaint is often heard of the dangers of forsaking 'hard science' for 'soft science' in the teaching of medical students. Ecology provides a 'hard' science approach to the everyday problems of infective disease. Similarly an ecological approach to environmental hygiene and other topics can provide a scientific framework for what is often taught at anecdotal level.

V. CONCLUSION

What part, then, should ecology play in the medical school? Not another department, at any rate, and few ecologists labelled as such. But the occasional one to act as leaven in the remainder of the Faculty, and perhaps to give a short course on ecological concepts and methods. Beyond that, it is as infective disease, microbiology, preventive medicine and clinical surgery that ecology can be helpfully studied and taught in the school of medicine.

ACKNOWLEDGMENTS

I am most grateful both to medical men—Professor W.D.Foster, Professor A.G.Shaper and Dr F.J.Bennett—and to zoologists—Professor D.F.Owen and Dr T.Rowell—for their comments. My debt to the thinking of Professor G.Macdonald will be apparent. I am particularly grateful to Dr P.H.A.Sneath for reading this paper at the symposium in my absence.

REFERENCES

BERTALANFFY F.D. & LAU C. (1962) Cell renewal. *Int. Rev. Cytol.* **13,** 357–366.
BEVERTON R.J.H. & HOLT S.J. (1957) *On the Dynamics of Exploited Fish Populations.* Fish. Invest. Ser. 2, 19. H.M.S.O., London.
BRADLEY D.J. (1963) A quantitative approach to bilharzia. *E. Afr. med. J.* **40,** 240–249.

BRADLEY D.J. (1967) The measurement of schistosome populations. In *Monograph on Bilharziasis* (ed. K.Mostofi). In press.

BROCK T.D. & BROCK M.L. (1966) Autoradiography as a tool in microbial ecology. *Nature, Lond.* **209**, 734–736.

COLE L.C. (1957) Sketches of general and comparative demography. *Cold Spr. Harb. Symp. Quant. Biol.* **22**, 1–15.

DOUGHERTY R.M. (1964) Animal virus titration techniques. In *Techniques in Experimental Virology* (ed. R.J.C.Harris), pp. 168–223. Academic Press, London.

GAUSE G.F. (1934) *The Struggle for Existence*. Williams & Wilkins, Baltimore.

GRAY A.R. (1964) The biological control of the antigenic characters of a strain of trypanosomes. *Proceedings of Tenth Meeting of ISCTR*, 55–59. C.C.T.A., Kampala.

HAIRSTON N.G. (1962) Population ecology and epidemiological problems. In *Bilharziasis* (ed. G.E.W.Wolstenholme & M.O'Connor), pp. 36–62. Churchill, London.

LOTKA A.J. & SHARPE F.R. (1923) Contributions to the analysis of malaria epidemiology. *Amer. J. Hyg.* (suppl.) **3**, 1–121.

LURIE M.B. (1964) *Resistance to Tuberculosis: Experimental Studies in Natural and Acquired Defensive Mechanisms*. Harvard University Press, Cambridge.

MACDONALD G. (1957) *The Epidemiology and Control of Malaria*. Oxford University Press, London.

MACDONALD G. (1965a) The dynamics of helminth infections, with special reference to schistosomes. *Trans. Roy. Soc. trop. Med. Hyg.* **59**, 489–506.

MACDONALD G. (1965b) On the scientific basis of tropical hygiene. *Trans. Roy. Soc. trop. Med. Hyg.* **59**, 611–620.

MEYNELL G.G. & MEYNELL E. (1965) *Theory and Practice in Experimental Bacteriology*. Cambridge University Press, London.

MONOD J. (1950) La technique de culture continué. *Ann. Inst. Pasteur.* **79**, 390–410.

MOSER H. (1957) Structure and dynamics of bacterial populations maintained in the chemostat. *Cold. Spr. Harb. Symp. Quant. Biol.* **22**, 121–137.

QUASTLER H. & SHERMAN F.G. (1959) Cell population kinetics in the intestinal epithelium of the mouse. *Exp. Cell. Res.* **17**, 420–438.

ROSS R. (1910) *The Prevention of Malaria*. John Murray, London.

RUSSELL P.F., WEST L.S., MANWELL R.D. & MACDONALD G. (1963) *Practical Malariology*. Oxford University Press, London.

VOLTERRA V. (1931) Leçons sur la théorie mathématique de la lutte pour la vie. *Cahiers Scientifiques*, **7**. Gauthier-Villars, Paris.

WILLETT K.C. (1965) Some observations on the recent epidemiology of sleeping sickness in Nyanza region, Kenya, and its relation to the general epidemiology of Gambian and Rhodesian sleeping sickness in Africa. *Trans. Roy. Soc. trop. Med. Hyg.* **59**, 374–386.

WILLIAMS R.E.O. & SPICER C.C. (ed.) (1957) *Microbial Ecology*. Seventh Symposium of the Society for General Microbiology. Cambridge University Press, London.

SECTION II
THE TEACHING OF ECOLOGY AT SCHOOL LEVEL

GENERAL PROBLEMS IN THE TEACHING OF
ECOLOGY IN THE INTRODUCTORY STAGES
OF A SCHOOL BIOLOGY COURSE

L.C.Comber

Formerly Staff Inspector, Ministry of Education

I. INTRODUCTION

This paper puts forward a purely personal view to which some biology teachers might not subscribe. It is imperative, therefore, that I should make my position and the purpose of this paper quite clear at the outset. With regard to the former, I should want such biology as is introduced into the first few years of the secondary school curriculum to be an integral part of a broadly conceived science course designed to give the pupils knowledge and understanding of those phenomena of nature which can be brought within their immediate experience. It should be recognized as part of their general education in its broadest sense and in its own right, and not as a preparation for any stage that is to follow. It should be concerned as much, therefore, with the development of habits of thought and attitudes of mind as with the acquisition of knowledge and the mastery of skills. As far as possible it should be an extension of the exploration of the natural environment which is a growing feature of the work of many primary schools and which contains the seeds of a thoroughly sound scientific education.

I should not want to teach ecology at this stage. Rather, I would want to place the pupils in situations where they can learn about living plants and animals and their interrelations, and the relationships between them and their physical environment, by first-hand experience in the field and through their own observations. I am in fact arguing for an old-fashioned natural history approach to biology, which I believe to be the proper starting-point, not only from the point of view of the pupil but in the best interests of the subject itself. The kind of course I have in mind would go further, however, in that rigorous scientific modes of thought would be introduced and systematically nurtured while the aesthetic and linguistic aspects of the experience would not be neglected. I should want the pupil to develop his powers of observation and experimentation, to be able to

53 E

recognize problems arising from his observations and to formulate hypotheses as an aid to their elucidation; but I should want him also to enjoy the beauty of, for example, the kingfisher's flight and the intricacy of a spider's web and to feel an urge to write about them or to record them in a variety of other ways. Perhaps, above all, I would want him to develop wholesome attitudes to living creatures generally.

Later in the course, possibly from the point at which pupils begin to identify their main lines of academic interest and to narrow the curriculum they follow accordingly, more deliberate teaching of ecology would be appropriate; but it would still, I hope, be an integral part of the whole biology course, feeding material into it and receiving support, in terms of subject-matter, practical techniques and experimental methods, in return. The purpose of this paper, therefore, is to examine the problems arising from the introduction of pupil-experiences of this kind into the secondary school curriculum. Many primary schools have already solved similar problems at their level satisfactorily, and a number of secondary schools have gone a long way towards a solution.

II. THE PROBLEMS THEMSELVES

The problems fall into two main categories, administrative and pedagogical. I will deal with them in that order.

There was a time when 'to give instruction away from the school premises', to use the then current phrase, was a major undertaking. Various authorities had to be informed well beforehand and previous permission obtained; insurance cover had to be arranged by the school, and often an unsympathetic and reluctant Head had to be won over. These difficulties have now been largely removed, although they are often quoted as excuses for limiting the pupils' biological experiences to the school building. Work away from the school is now accepted as a desirable feature in the teaching of most subjects and no problems peculiar to biology need arise, except that, ideally, expeditions should be fairly frequent and they are subject to postponement and subsequent rearrangement because of bad weather. The main administrative difficulties appear to be that field work absorbs a large amount of time, without any very obvious returns in terms of the subject-matter assimilated, and it is not always easy to fit into a school timetable organized in teaching periods of relatively short duration for each subject. Neither is a very real difficulty. The first requires for its solution only the faith that this is a good thing to do and the willingness on the part of the teacher to prepare the expedition so thoroughly that the educational returns justify the time expended. The second is a matter of previous planning; the timetable should be arranged to meet the needs of the pupils and the subject. In my own teaching days I was always able to arrange the lessons for certain classes to be at the latter end of the afternoon so that we could, if necessary, run on after school hours. This may not always be possible and problems certainly arise when biology becomes alternative to other subjects timetabled alongside it, or when the pupils travel to and from school by special transport. I have no doubt, however, that a satisfactory solution to this problem can usually, if not invariably, be found.

A point worth making here is that one well-planned expedition can provide the material for several weeks' work in the laboratory, but two further problems arise in this connection.

The first is concerned with the collection of living material in the field and the consequent risk of depleting the population of certain species and upsetting the biological balance in the working areas. Once the need for wise and restricted use of an area and for active measures for protection and conservation has been recognized, however, the situation can be turned to good effect. Good attitudes towards the conservation of our natural heritage can be built up.

The second involves the provision of suitable spaces and adequate facilities for maintaining and using living material in the school. Many school buildings are woefully inadequate in these respects and suitably qualified technical assistants in school biology departments are still the exception rather than the rule. But these needs are recognized; new secondary schools are normally provided with heated greenhouses and they occasionally have well-planned animal rooms as well. The problem of laboratory assistance is now one of recruitment and training rather than one of establishing the principle. The recent publication by the Organization for Economic Co-operation and Development (1966) of *Biology Today: Its Role in Education*, drew attention to these requirements and made strong recommendations concerning them as well as advocating the establishment of field centres with adequate facilities.

One further administrative problem is that connected with external examinations, which still, unfortunately, dominate the work of many schools and the effects of which tend to spread downwards even to the work of the lower forms. The difficulty, if traditional examination methods are to be employed, lies in producing questions which, while preserving the measure of standardization required by an external assessment, provide for the very different opportunities and working areas open to schools in a wide range of localities. Some progress has been made in recent years in devising questions which encourage rather than inhibit good field studies, but there is a very long way to go before this problem is solved satisfactorily. In the meantime ecology at this very important and formative stage suffers, either from total neglect in examination syllabuses, or, what may be even worse, from the wrong kind of purpose and emphasis. The solution to this problem would seem to lie in the introduction of entirely new methods of external assessment. Experimental examinations conducted in connection with the new Certificate of Secondary Education, in which continuous assessments of course work by the teachers themselves, suitably moderated by external examiners, contribute to the pupils' final examination score, are throwing some light on the problems that arise and offer some hope of an eventual solution. The immediate problem is to persuade a sufficient number of biology teachers that an ecological approach to school biology is the most satisfactory one and to encourage them to work out a solution to the examination question. That leads me to my second category of problems —the pedagogical ones.

The problems fall into three groups, namely, those arising from the pupils, the teachers and the availability of working areas. A fourth group, related to the nature of ecology itself, and its relation to biology as a whole, might also be distinguished; but the natural history approach I have advocated has the advantage of providing for steady progression through the different stages of the course so that the sophisticated ideas and methods proper to ecology are encountered only when the pupil has acquired the necessary preliminary knowledge and maturity of mind.

Most boys and girls in the lower forms are intensely curious about the world in which they live and they are naturally interested in living things, particularly in animals. This interest furnishes strong motivation in biological studies and especially those in the field. At this stage of development, however, the span of a child's attention is normally short and natural high spirits coupled with the removal of the restraints imposed by the normal classroom atmosphere may face the teacher of a large class with some difficulties. This is particularly true if the field study situation is a novel one. The solution to this problem clearly lies in adequate preparation and careful organization. As long as the pupils are fully aware of the nature and purpose of the expedition and they have been given sufficient to do within the compass of their individual powers, no serious difficulties are likely to arise. There is a growing tradition for this method of working in the programmes of many schools and pupils soon become accustomed to it; they readily accept responsibility for the organization of their own work if given the opportunities, and many of them develop surprising qualities of leadership when the class is organized to work in groups. The development of these qualities is good in broad educational terms as well as being beneficial to the study of biology. Nevertheless, adequate supervision on the part of the teacher is essential; extra pairs of hands are extremely valuable and outside volunteer help can sometimes be obtained. A useful arrangement is to organize field trips when students in training are attached to the school for their teaching practice because, as well as providing extra help and supervision, it gives the student valuable experience in what should be an important aspect of his training. This is, however, only a temporary relief; in the main the teacher must expect to cope with his whole class of perhaps thirty pupils single-handed and he must plan his programme accordingly. The secret undoubtedly lies in giving the pupils enough that they can do without assistance to demand their full attention.

Probably more serious than the problems arising from the nature of the pupils are those related to the training and consequent attitudes of the teachers. Few teachers of biology at present have had sufficient experience and training in field study methods to make them confident in what is without question a more difficult and demanding teaching situation than that of the classroom or the laboratory. The good natural historian and field ecologist will feel impelled to take his classes out of doors; but these teachers are relatively rare, and for the others field work imposes an additional burden which many are reluctant to shoulder. The answer to this question clearly lies in the nature of the initial training, and especially in the courses of direct preparation for teaching in University Departments of Education and in Colleges of Education. Progress in this direction is being made but not sufficient to meet the needs of the schools.

There is an urgent need, too, for courses of in-service training in ecological methods and in field teaching for serving teachers. There are welcome signs that the Field Studies Council are prepared to offer more courses for both teachers and students in training, but recruitment to the courses organized so far has not been sufficient to justify immediately the considerable expansion that is required to meet the school situation. Greater incentives to attend such courses, whether they are provided by the Field Studies Council or by other bodies, appear to be necessary and this problem demands attention. Fortunately there are indications that the whole question of refresher training generally is being recognized as an urgent problem.

The availability of suitable working areas is for many teachers the most serious obstacle to be surmounted, but the problem may be more imaginary than real. It is, of course, an advantage to have favourable working sites close at hand, although it must be admitted that many schools which are fortunately placed do not take sufficient advantage of their opportunities. Part of the trouble is that we have grown accustomed to selecting especially attractive areas for field study purposes and have largely neglected the possibilities of more restricted but, from the point of biology teaching, often more rewarding localities. Some 30 years ago Dr Rose Bracher produced a little book called *Ecology in Town and Classroom* (Bracher, 1937) which greatly influenced my own early teaching, and more recently the Nuffield Biology Project has drawn the attention of teachers to what can be done in the most unpromising surroundings. Other sources of ideas are not difficult to find, although it would be valuable if the British Ecological Society, or some other body, collected together suggestions for biological field study and field ecology appropriate to urban and other unfavourably situated schools. References to this problem, and suggestions for its solution, are made elsewhere in this volume, and it is not in my brief to pursue this aspect further here.

There is, however, one important final point, and that is the place of residential field centres in the school programme of field study. I regard this as critical, not only because these centres can provide skilled field teaching in favourable surroundings, but because residential experience for a specific educational purpose is a valuable ingredient in a pupil's general education. Such experience comes best as the climax of a progressive course in field biology in which skills and knowledge have been systematically built up. This will be begun by studies made in the immediate vicinity of the school, perhaps even within the school grounds, on waste ground near by, or in a neighbouring park, and will spread further and further afield as the course progresses. Fortunately a pattern of work, and the provision of physical facilities to meet it, are beginning to emerge.

My object in preparing this paper has been to show that although problems in the teaching of ecology in the introductory stages of school biology exist, they are by no means insoluble. The important element in the whole situation is that biology teachers should want their courses to be based upon the study of living organisms in their natural surroundings and that this should lead, amongst other things, to the fundamental ecological principles upon which the solution of many of the world's most pressing problems depends.

REFERENCES

BRACHER R. (1937) *Ecology in Town and Classroom.* Arrowsmith, Bristol.

ORGANIZATION FOR ECONOMIC CO-OPERATION AND DEVELOPMENT (1966). *Biology Today: Its Role in Education.* Prepared by P.Duvigneaud; English version ed. by L.C.Comber. O.E.D.C., Paris.

THE PRACTICAL TEACHING OF ECOLOGY IN THE INTRODUCTORY STAGES OF A SCHOOL BIOLOGY COURSE

JOHN H. GRAY

Manchester Grammar School

I. INTRODUCTION

Charles Elton (1927) at the very beginning of his book on animal ecology writes: 'Ecology is a new name for a very old subject. It simply means scientific natural history.' Eugene Odum (1963) refers to ecology as 'the study of the structure of nature'. These are elementary and all-embracing descriptions of ecology. They suit my present purpose well. They allow me to emphasize the diverse and unsophisticated ecological studies which I believe we should encourage. It is important to remember that we are concerned here with children in the age range of 11–16 years. We would not be justified, therefore, in attempting to teach any of the specialist approaches to ecology in a strict sense of that term.

II. AIMS

Our dual responsibility as schoolteachers is, firstly, to develop the children's enthusiasm for natural history. If the enthusiasm does not exist already, we must generate it as best we can, and use it in the interests of the biological and general education of our pupils. Secondly, we are responsible for a programme of class teaching which must match our overall educational aims and the examination requirements.

Field studies in the school biology course, far from being strictly ecological in emphasis, should have a broad outlook which links field observations with the appropriate laboratory work, and biology with other subjects. Man is an animal and it seems important that we should show not only that man is influencing his surroundings both in the town and in the country, but that he is also influenced by his environment.

Field work provides the store of first-hand experience of organisms which is an essential component of any biology course. It is, to my mind,

61

the proper starting-point for the course. It contributes to the development of skill in making and recording observations, and in hypothesis-making. Through field work, pupils can be trained in the methods of recognizing and attacking scientific problems at a very elementary level. Field work is also important because it provides a means for developing the emotional side of a pupil's character, i.e. his aesthetic appreciation of nature and the attitudes he adopts towards natural phenomena.

III. THE GENERAL PROGRAMME

When planning the field work of a biology department, the scope and the depth to which the work can be taken is largely a matter for the teacher, who must judge the practical and intellectual capabilities of the age-group or class. It is for the teacher to devise the best means of promoting the right level of field activities. Complicated techniques of investigation generally obscure rather than reveal the underlying principles. In some school circumstances, and for some children, great effort is needed merely to stimulate interest and to provide for the most elementary activities. In other schools, and for other children, it is largely a matter of ensuring that the right facilities are available for individuals whose interests are already well established. A good tradition of field work is a precious asset to a school, well worth the trouble involved in developing and sustaining it. Even in fortunate schools which have the tradition of field work, it is important to recognize that there are years when the impetus seems to be slackening and timely help from the teacher may be needed so that the new generation, just arriving in the school, picks up the tradition and the impetus is not lost.

There is a variety of methods by which a teacher can promote field studies. Choice depends upon circumstances. In some schools the easiest method is to run a Natural History Club in out-of-school hours. Another method is to base much of the class work in biology on field studies. It is ideal to have both programmes, but they must generally be kept rather separate because different groups of children are involved. I have found both methods helpful.

Our chief duty is to ensure that interest and enthusiasm are stimulated and that the right facilities are available when they are wanted. This aspect of a biology teacher's work requires time and energy. The expenditure of these is normally very well rewarded, both in terms of pupils' developing interests and in terms of the support which all kinds of field studies can give to the biology course.

IV. THE NATURAL HISTORY CLUB

The Natural History Club with weekly or twice-weekly meetings provides excellent opportunities for pupils to do their own work in a fairly informal atmosphere but with the necessary personal encouragement and advice. The interests of children are so diverse that the Natural History Club seems to me the best way of encouraging young people to work in their own way and at their own pace. Children readily share their interests, to mutual advantage in a club.

I have sometimes tried to impose my own views of what the Natural History Club should do. The attempts have usually been frustrated. It is better to take the interests of a pupil or group of pupils and develop these as time proceeds. On occasions the group will want to work together; more often the individualists win, as they probably should.

Children love collecting things. We should let them do so, channelling the instinct so that it soon becomes a properly disciplined activity. There is generally no difficulty in getting children to understand the need for conservation. Given the right stimulus, they progress to keeping caterpillars, growing plants from seeds, and managing aquaria. Valuable experience in handling and looking after organisms is gained in this way, and pupils begin to develop a feel for organisms.

V. EXAMPLES OF NATURAL HISTORY CLUB ACTIVITIES

The following examples show what can be done within a club. One boy had a particularly strong interest in collecting and rearing Lepidoptera. His industry set an example to other children who copied him. Arising from this, the club made a survey of local moths. If I had this opportunity again I would encourage a programme of trapping by means of mercury vapour lamps. These traps are relatively easy to set up and a study of, for instance, the incidence of melanism in moths would be possible. We may, at the present time, and in some parts of the country, be experiencing a change in environmental conditions due to the Clean Air Act. A careful record of the incidence of melanism over the years might even be of research value. In any event, it is a good introduction for a pupil into an important aspect of both ecology and genetics.

Starting with the interests of one pupil, a group programme can be developed. The experience of working in a team is most valuable. The teacher will need to guide and support the activities with background information in the form of talks and films. Ford's books (Ford, 1945,

1955) in the New Naturalist series on *Moths* and *Butterflies* suggest other lines of investigation for young entomologists.

Another pupil was a botanist who contented himself with collecting and recording the distribution of local plants, especially orchids. He did little more than this, despite encouragement to embark on more intensive and experimental project work. I was delighted to find that later in his school career he used his records as part of a survey of the effects of myxomatosis on the chalkland flora. The foundations of his botanical knowledge were well laid during the early years of unambitious collecting and recording. This example also points to the desirability of retaining copies of the records of pupils' work, so that comparisons can be made over the years.

A third pupil enjoyed collecting freshwater organisms and keeping aquaria. He was very successful in persuading friends to work with him. These boys gained a sound general knowledge of freshwater organisms which stood some of them in good stead when they came to Sixth-Form Project work. Their specialist study would otherwise have lacked the requisite broad foundations.

None of these activities is novel or ambitious. Extensive programmes demand disproportionate time and energy from the teacher and, to the pupil, the results become obscured by the techniques. In each case I utilized the enthusiasm of one boy or a group of boys, helping them to exploit a local situation. I helped to give coherence to their work and encouraged them to write up reports.

Rural schools are undeniably in a favoured position. For urban schools there are nevertheless opportunities within many school grounds. Books in the New Naturalist series contain helpful suggestions for investigations. Those by Salisbury (1964), Turrill (1948), Fitter (1945), Ford (1945, 1955) and Smith (1951) are especially relevant.

Formal weekly meetings of the club allow the papers presented by members on their own field work to be read and discussed. Visitors and films introduce fresh interests. Occasional exhibitions give members a chance to show some of their work to the school and help recruitment.

Most clubs depend upon personal encouragement from the teacher. By maintaining a Natural History Club which functioned out of class-room hours, I was able to encourage a great many of the activities which I wanted to see and was able to establish the sort of personal contact which allowed my own enthusiasms to be transmitted. I never had any doubt that this was a most important part of my job and I rarely regretted the hours spent in this way.

VI. CLASSWORK IN THE FIELD

There are, however, schools and teachers who cannot establish a Natural History Club, with the expenditure in energy and time out of school hours which this necessarily involves. For such teachers it seems to me to be especially important to orientate the conventional classroom teaching more strongly towards the field.

The case for teaching a high proportion of the biology syllabus through field work is a good one and does not depend merely upon the lack of a Natural History Club. Pupils are readily stimulated and interested by outdoor work. They meet the organisms in natural or semi-natural surroundings and their experience is inevitably first hand and extensive. Training in making and recording observations in the field is of fundamental importance to a biology student. The skills of recognizing problems, erecting hypotheses and testing these in the field are ones we should start to develop early. Laboratory and literary studies acquire a new significance when they arise from field experience.

A field teaching programme is not so difficult to run as may at first appear. I propose to show how, by selected pieces of field work, the biology teaching for examination purposes can be founded in field studies.

My own practice was to start the course in science teaching in Form 1, that is to say for the 11-year-old children, by a series of lessons in the field. Any habitat would have served my purpose—a park or playing field, some waste ground or a pond. For an urban school it may be necessary to contrive suitable habitats by establishing, for example, water butts, compost heaps and fallen logs in a corner of the school grounds. In addition, a useful range of wild plants can be grown in a plot near the laboratory.

My concern was to get pupils to examine carefully some of the habitats close to the school. The variety of organisms is usually a revelation to children, and they enjoy mapping the distribution of plants and comparing results from year to year. Organisms can be collected and kept in the laboratory, providing material for wet days. Pairs of pupils can adopt a species and find out as much as possible about it. There is ample opportunity during this work for instruction on the techniques of searching for organisms, keeping them alive and recording observations on them. Man's influence on these habitats is usually very obvious; it is neither to be regretted nor ignored.

This introductory course appeals to children and through their work and discussions they gain an appreciation of what biology is about.

The pupils learn about organisms at first hand, and not through books and preserved specimens. It is often arranged that the General Science course of Forms 1 and 2 has a high proportion of biology. It is at this stage that I would choose to meet some of the examination requirements, such as the study of a particular habitat through the seasons. The time which this necessarily involves is readily conceded by children at the ages of 11 and 12. Work on a habitat through the seasons will give that sound background of field experience which is needed to bring any biology course alive. Pupils will meet a wide variety of organisms and gain practice in identifying them. They will begin to see how organisms are adapted to their particular habitats, how they move and are distributed in characteristic patterns. The pupils will see the way in which communities change through the seasons and the ways in which organisms adapt themselves or change their habits to meet the challenge of successive seasons. These topics should not be taught from the text-book: a valuable opportunity to bring pupils face to face with the living material itself would be lost, and the experience would become second hand or even third hand. When pupils have become familiar with local habitats, they frequently undertake work on their own, beyond the immediate demands of class work. It is easy for them to do so.

Teaching can proceed logically: the initial investigations reveal phenomena which can be re-examined in later seasons, or in future years at an appropriate stage in the curriculum. The following examples may be compared with the teaching of the same topics through text-books and preserved specimens.

VII. EXAMPLES OF CLASS WORK IN THE FIELD

1. *Perennation*

It is easy to find a variety of plants which are exhibiting the various modes of perennation. A good field note-book account of a limited range of perennating structures is worth very much more to a pupil than a comprehensive account taken from a text-book. The functions of such structures as bulbs are best appreciated if they are examined in the living state at different times of the year. It is only by such methods of study that the important relationships amongst organisms and between organisms and their environment can be established in pupils' minds.

Questions can arise from the phenology of the vernal plants. For example, what features have they in common which permit their early appearance? Sampling of subterranean portions reveals their variety of form. It suggests a periodic examination throughout the year of, for instance, bulbs and corms, with appropriate chemical and gravimetric investigation and a study of shape and structure of the food storage organs. The plants can also be cultured in the greenhouse or garden plot, thus giving also a valuable lead into reproductive habits.

A suitable range of aerial and subterranean perennating devices should be studied. It is useful to plant additional examples in the patch of ground near the laboratory which every biology teacher should feel himself able to demand for the proper teaching of his subject.

2. Dispersal mechanisms

The facility of organisms for geographical dispersal readily becomes apparent to the pupil in the field. Static traps furnish ample evidence of the movements of animals and plants. Pitfall traps, made from jam jars sunk to soil level, will collect wandering soil crganisms. The traps should be examined at different times of the day. Vaselined boards, placed face upwards on the soil surface, will collect aerial propagules as they settle and this investigation can be linked with the results of exposing trays of sterilized soil in similar fashion. A net, fixed across a stream, will collect both active and passive travellers. Man's role can be partially investigated by collecting the soil from shoes, turn-ups, car mudguards and lorry or truck sweepings. These diverse investigations can be organized on a class basis, with the results of each team of investigators entered on wall charts for evaluation and discussion. A consideration of experimental designs and sampling techniques is essential, both before and after the work has been done.

The study of dispersal mechanisms provides many opportunities for comparing plant and animal biology, and the degrees of interdependence which may be seen between the two groups. The adaptability and adaptedness of organisms is well demonstrated by work on this topic and the next.

3. Colonization and succession

If small habitats are temporarily sterilized, then the processes of colonization and succession may be observed. Much can quickly be learned about the organisms concerned. Taxonomically they are diverse, but they share some habitats of dispersal and reproduction. Suitable habitats are water butts, leaf compost piles and ordinary earth.

The colonization of bare earth by weeds and soil animals can be charted easily. An elementary appreciation of the biology of organisms such as thistles and aphids is readily gained. The links between structure, function and life history are apparent, and susceptible to experimental investigation in the field and in the laboratory.

These three examples illustrate ways of teaching some topics of field ecology. Other writers who have discussed the problems involved include Perrott (1963), who has reviewed current aims and practice in schools, while Lambert (1964), writing also in the *School Science Review*, makes important observations on the nature of ecology as a discipline for school biologists. The Nuffield O-Level Biology Course (Nuffield Foundation 1966) incorporates much ecological work and offers a most valuable and exceptionally detailed account of the techniques involved in teaching the course.

VIII. CONCLUSION

My view of the practical teaching of ecology at lower and middle school level may seem rather restricted. It does not encompass the teaching of much that is commonly called ecology. The practice of making extensive fauna and flora lists and leaving the work at this point is much to be regretted. Such lists should be made only when a need for them is felt, and when they lead directly to further inquiry and experiment. Conventional biology syllabuses are already overloaded so that the teaching of many topics tends to be didactic. Ecology is a subject which could particularly suffer from such a style of teaching. By planning the right programme of work for our pupils, however, we can develop their enthusiasm and curiosity and establish in their minds sound methods of investigating biological pheomena. We should teach only those aspects of biology which we can make real to pupils through their personal observation and experiment. We must teach for understanding.

REFERENCES

ELTON C. (1927) *Animal Ecology*. Sidgwick & Jackson, London.
FITTER R.S.R. (1945) *London's Natural History*. Collins, London.
FORD E.B. (1945) *Butterflies*. Collins, London.
FORD E.B. (1955) *Moths*. Collins, London.
LAMBERT J.M. (1964) Ecology as a biological discipline. *Sch. Sci. Rev.* **45,** 568–575.
NUFFIELD FOUNDATION. (1966) *Science Teaching Project 'O'-Level Biology Course*. Longmans, London.
ODUM E.P. (1963) *Ecology*. Holt, Rinehart & Winston. New York.
PERROTT E. (1963) The teaching of field biology. *Sch. Sci. Rev.* **45,** 44–53.
SALISBURY E. (1964) *Weeds and Aliens*. Collins, London.
SMITH M. (1951) *The British Amphibians and Reptiles*. Collins, London.
TURRILL W.B (1948) *British Plant Life*. Collins, London.

AN APPROACH TO THE TEACHING OF
ECOLOGY AT A-LEVEL

CLIFFORD J. SMITH

Bootham School, York

I. BASIC CONSIDERATIONS

The main purpose in teaching A-level ecology must obviously be related to the requirements of the examination boards, some of which place more emphasis on the importance of ecology than others. Visiting examiners may interview candidates wishing to present field work, or ecology note-books may be sent for inspection to the headquarters of some boards, while in others it is possible for a candidate to reach the highest grade without having done any ecological work at all. There has been a recent increase in the amount of ecological work in most British universities, and it is regrettable that this pattern has not become more apparent in some A-level requirements.

Boarding schools and day schools have quite different time allocations for various activities, but it is noticeable that the latter are now following the practice of using more half-holiday and weekend time to study ecology. The demands of sporting, musical and other types of extra-curricular activities vary much from school to school, but it is true to say that there is a more liberal approach to the proper use of leisure time than there was a few years ago. The general status and tradition of biology and natural history in a school are often also of great significance. Financial considerations can likewise play a decisive part, for instance, the amount of laboratory assistance available for the preparation of ecology apparatus, the ability of the school to afford rather special items of equipment such as a pH meter, the willingness of the Local Education Authority to finance the costs of holiday field-work courses, and so on.

The interests of the pupils themselves are also important. We all have 'good' years when ecology appeals to the temperament and abilities of our pupils, but at other times we seem to be saddled with a batch of un-enterprising pupils whose only aim is to pass the examination with a minimum of effort and interest. Members of the teaching staff, too, have their own interests and abilities, so that a person who is primarily interested in conservation or taxonomy is bound to have a different approach from that of the experimental physiologist.

The geographical location of the school itself is bound to have a profound influence on the approach to ecological work, particularly its nearness to good open countryside. Only the ardent ecologist can stimulate enthusiasm in his pupils in the heart of a smoke-begrimed city-centre habitat. Schools in such situations often find it best to organize weekend or vacation courses, even if such arrangements prevent observations over a complete annual cycle.

II. DESCRIPTIVE AND EXPERIMENTAL APPROACHES

It will be seen that every school has its own special problems, but by and large an ecological study will comprise three stages:

1. There must be a period of initial recording and analysis involved in the *description* of a living community.

2. Based on these studies, the pupil is led to frame a *hypothesis* to explain what he has seen and recorded.

3. Finally, he will conduct *experiments* to test out his ideas.

The descriptive and experimental stages are, of course, quite complementary. Some pupils are more interested in one than the other, and the planning of an A-level ecology course should allow for the pupil who is a competent experimental ecologist as well as for the more descriptive type of worker.

III. CHOICE OF SITE AND SUBJECT

The choice of a suitable site for descriptive work poses many problems. I think that the best results are obtained if a particular site is used by as many students as possible and for as many years as possible. In this way an immense background of data is available for almost any new project that is undertaken, and there must be few schools where such a site is not available. There is a danger inherent in this practice of an area being over-collected, but provided the teacher is aware of this, it represents no more than an additional biotic factor.

A few fortunate schools possess their own nature reserves; some are very attractive sites which any naturalist would enjoy visiting, while others are small parts of the school grounds of no great natural value but quite suitable for basic ecological study. Many schools are not so fortunate, but there must be many cases where boards of governors, local authorities or school managers would be prepared to help if they were approached in the right way.

Considerable use can be made of nature reserves owned or administered by bodies such as the local County Naturalists' Trust. These organizations now cover most of Britain, and part of their purpose is to provide educational facilities for ecological work. Many of their reserves are already available for schools, and some are designed for the almost exclusive use of educational bodies. Recently a number of local education authorities have begun to establish nature reserves for the use of schools in their districts and would, I am sure, respond to specific requests for more such areas to be established.

If the more traditional type of site is not available, the following examples of much more limited projects indicate a few of the many possible methods of tackling A-level work. (1) Bird-box ecology, using boxes attached to trees and buildings; this study profitably leads to interesting work on the ecology of ecto-parasites and commensals. (2) Sewage ecology with the co-operation of the local sewage works; quite apart from the descriptive analysis of the flora and fauna of filter beds and settling tanks, this study lends itself to the establishment of miniature sewage systems under laboratory conditions. (3) Spider ecology in urban areas, possibly with emphasis on their population cycles in compost heaps, buildings and derelict sites. (4) The autecology of species ranging from the starling to the stinging nettle.

There is never any lack of descriptive material in the centre of an industrial area, but it still remains true that for most pupils the open countryside is the most attractive and stimulating environment for ecological work.

IV. METHOD OF STUDY

It is probably advisable for a pupil to undertake two distinct types of A-level work in ecology. Firstly, he should undertake some basic descriptive recording to become acquainted with fundamental techniques in ecological survey—the quadrat, transects, population sampling, soil analysis and elementary taxonomy. There is a tendency to regard the quadrat and the transect as ends in themselves, but, although many pupils enjoy the accumulation and presentation of this type of factual knowledge, such recording should always form part of an integrated project.

Secondly, the pupils should be given, or encouraged to choose, a problem of more limited scope, involving initial descriptive techniques on which can be based suitable experimental work to test any deductions that may be made. This type of inquiry is the subject of Mr A.K.Thomas's paper, which follows.

The amount of time available for ecological work at A-level is very limited for the average student. It is usually impossible for a single individual to undertake all the necessary work in describing a community and its environment and it is therefore essential to have a group of observers working together—possibly over a number of years—and pooling their results.

At this stage it might be helpful to illustrate my suggestions by referring to a current project in which I am engaged. Based on a recently formed Sixth-Form Biology Society, work has been started on one of the County Naturalists' Trust's nature reserves. Although this is situated some 8 miles from the city, the schools between them will make frequent visits to the area. The local training college (mathematics department) undertook the task of surveying the whole area, and they have now produced a duplicated, detailed map which has been gridded to correspond with stakes on the nature reserve itself. Four LEA grammar schools, three public schools, two other independent schools and a secondary modern school are co-operating to manage the reserve, together with a small number of interested amateur naturalists.

The area is a lowland heath, with typical heathland vegetation and a wealth of insect and bird life. Extensive areas of heath and heather, with occasional islands of coarse grass and birch scrub, form the major vegetation of the terrain. The wetter parts carry a wealth of bog plants such as species of *Drosera* and *Gentiana pneumonanthe*. One of the problems confronting those responsible for the management of this reserve is the invasion of birch scrub, and the disappearance of the gentian. These problems provide an excellent incentive for detailed descriptive ecology, involving transect, quadrat and valency recording, the investigation of edaphic variations, and research into the history of land usage involving changes in biotic factors. Work along these lines has already been carried out for many years now. Since the nature reserve seems to be slowly drying out, continuous descriptive recording is essential for the proper study and management of the area.

In addition to the basic descriptive ecology that has been suggested, each pupil (or a small group of pupils) will be undertaking special individual investigations. Boys taking A-level in biology, chemistry and geography will probably specialize on the origin of the soil particles, the effects of adjacent land usage, the history of the site as revealed in pollen analysis, and so on. There are unlimited 'pure' biological problems such as the distribution of vipers on the reserve, the autecology of the heather, the curlew, the hoverflies or any other of the innumerable taxonomic entities inhabiting the area. Pupils who have no special interest before tackling the descriptive field work often develop more specialized interests and with a certain amount of guidance will soon embark on personal projects. At every stage there is the stimulus of previous work having been done, of other schools doing similar work, and of some purpose behind the investigations quite apart from any examination requirement. Meetings between the various schools are planned both at the reserve and elsewhere for informal discussion.

Perhaps most essential of all, the pupils can see that the teachers themselves are joining in the basic work with enthusiasm, being anxious to obtain reliable results for a practical purpose. With nature conservation as the ultimate aim, most pupils see their A-level ecology as something more than an academic exercise.

V. OTHER TYPES OF PROJECT

For many schools it may not be possible to rely on A-level candidates being available for regular visits throughout the year to a near-by study area. Other projects will need to be undertaken involving a short but more intensive period of observation, either at week-ends or during one of the school vacations.

The Field Studies Council provides excellent and expanding facilities but, by their nature, it is rather an expensive way of introducing ecology to sixth-form pupils. Commercial organizations (such as Bio-Probe) to some extent take the place of field centres in supplying travelling laboratories and accommodation at a fairly reasonable cost. Special centres like the marine laboratories at Port Erin and Millport provide excellent though specialized centres for study. Cheaper accommodation is available at selected Youth Hostels, at certain County Trusts' centres such as those at Gibraltar Point, Bardsey Island and Spurn Promontory, and at a wide variety of associated places.

One solution to the problem of inexpensive accommodation for a week's intensive course makes a compromise between economy and the desire for time unoccupied by household chores. Many university departments and schools use the facilities of countryside organizations such as the Holiday Fellowship and the Co-operative Holidays Association which are willing to lease their guest houses during out-of-season periods such as early May. Temporary laboratories can be set up in converted lounges and reading rooms, with the help of a van-load of apparatus from school. Very often the building can be taken over completely for such a special ecology course.

In working a habitat intensively for a short period—often at a place which cannot readily be revisited—two requirements should be met for successful ecological work. In the first place, the terrain to be studied should contain only a limited number of species, so that the student does not spend too much time on taxonomic details. Certain types of seashore, or hill-tops over 2000 ft, can provide excellent habitats in which the pupil can gain a working knowledge of most species in the area within a short time, and he will then be able to explore the various techniques for describing such a community. Secondly, each pupil should have the chance to revisit the same type of habitat in two successive years, in the first of which he can undertake purely descriptive ecology, while in the second he can perform experimental work to test out hypotheses he has formulated in writing up and thinking out his first season's work. It is, of course, most helpful for the leader of the party to have a sound working knowledge of the ecology of the region before taking a party there.

VI. THE PURPOSE OF TEACHING A-LEVEL ECOLOGY

Quite apart from the direct help that the study of ecology can provide in getting a pupil through his examinations, I feel that two special purposes are served by a sound field approach to ecology. Firstly, pupils come to realize that the study of biology is that of living organisms and their interrelationships. Too often we tend to teach biology with little reference to living specimens, and I think it is essential to keep reminding ourselves that we are dealing all the time with living things.

Secondly, that only through the proper treatment of ecology can we direct our pupils to the proper study of mankind and his many economic problems. More and more professions are entered from an A-level study of the biological sciences together with geography, and perhaps it is not too much of an over-simplification to suggest that the proper study of mankind is essentially that of the trained ecologist.

ECOLOGY AT A-LEVEL:
THE EXPERIMENTAL APPROACH

A.K.THOMAS

Dauntsey's School, West Lavington, Devizes

I should like to approach the subject of experimental ecology rather gradually, if I may, for it seems to me that one cannot really jump into experimental work of an ecological nature *in vacuo*. It is clear that descriptive work in the sixth form can lead to the formulation of hypotheses; such a general background of knowledge of the area around one's school is important. However, it is wise for pupils to select some very restricted topic for intensive study, once they have seen something of the vegetation and commoner animals around them.

Such a restriction can be achieved in various ways. Pupils may observe some zonation in vegetation, for example, which can be correlated with a single habitat factor. Although most ecological situations are multifactorial in nature, we can often find correlations with single factors, such as the availability of light in relationship to the ground flora of a wood, or the zonation of the larger algae on the seashore in relationship to the degree of exposure between tides.

Another way of restricting the scope of any intensive study is to select a single, commonly occurring species and examine some aspect of its life and interaction with its environment. For example, at Dauntsey's we have looked at the rates of growth of *Limnaea pereger* in the wild, and at the incidence in that species of the oligochaete *Chaetogaster limnaei* during the course of a year; at the reproductive capacity and vegetative performance of bluebells (*Endymion non-scriptus*) in the local woods; at the epizooites found on the gills of *Gammarus pulex*; and at the rates of filtration of some common lamellibranch molluscs. All these investigations began as purely observational studies: they often suggested particular problems and hypotheses of a causal nature, which needed to be tested experimentally.

To take but one example: if bluebells set more seed and grow more vigorously in open conditions than in shaded areas of a wood, can we test the hypothesis—a very likely one—that it is the total amount of light energy reaching the plants during the past which has caused the observed differences? By shading some of the 'open' plants with diffuse screens, we could deliberately alter the light intensity reaching them. However, screens may well divert some of the rainfall, and a more satisfactory arrangement is to use two types of screen, one of transparent material and one of translucent material, and to compare the performance of the plants under these two for some years. We also tried transplant experiments, bringing both 'shaded' and 'open' plants into a garden bed side by side, and arranging for half of each group to be shaded and half fully exposed to light. Unfortunately, the plants did not survive, and I mention this particularly as a warning that we must expect a certain amount of mortality amongst experimental organisms; any research biologist is aware of this, but pupils at the beginning of their sixth-form projects will often need encouragement, and where necessary diverting to an alternative topic.

However, we are not limited to problems of the performance and distribution of organisms. Many topics of a more physiological nature, often studied formally in the laboratory and sometimes only theoretically at this level, can be taken out of doors to enliven our presentation of biology. I would mention first the problems of studying the exchanges of materials and the flow of energy in a habitat, some aspects of which can be examined even at sixth-form level without a great deal of elaborate apparatus.

The uptake and loss of carbon, particularly of carbon dioxide, by organisms in a community can be followed at the following points. If we take first a terrestrial community—such as a lawn—then it is relatively simple to estimate the following:

(a) The upward flux of carbon dioxide from the bare soil during a given period. Monteith et al. (1964) describe how this flux of carbon dioxide can be estimated by exposing oven-dried soda-lime in dishes at least 14 cm in diameter under inverted tanks at least 400 cm^2 in area, their edges being pressed firmly into the soil. The soda-lime needs drying at 100° C for 2 hours before and after exposure. Its increase in weight has indicated fluxes of carbon dioxide from the soil varying from a winter minimum of 1 g m^{-2} day^{-1} to a summer maximum of about 7 g m^{-2} day^{-1}.

(b) The concentration of the carbon dioxide in the soil atmosphere can be estimated colorimetrically by exposing tubes containing a pH indicator mixture in the soil; the contents of the tubes are protected from the effects of other constituents of the soil, and from contamination by micro-organisms, by a PTFE (polytetrafluoro-ethylene) membrane (Martin & Pigott, 1965).

(c) The balance of carbon dioxide between any one leaf and the surrounding atmosphere can similarly be studied by enclosing it in a test-tube with a little of the same pH indicator mixture (Nuffield Biology Project, 1966). Rates of change of carbon dioxide concentration around the leaf can be determined by comparison against colour standard discs (Lovibond), either visually or by using a simple colorimeter with a sodium source, provided that the temperature of the air inside the test-tube is known.

(d) For any one leaf, the compensation period—the time elapsing from dawn until the carbon dioxide given out in overnight respiration has been recovered in the net photosynthetic uptake—is easily determined using the same simple apparatus (Hosokawa & Odani, 1957; Thomas & Field, 1962).

All these are, of course, purely descriptive exercises. But they can easily be used in experimental situations. Does the carbon dioxide balance of sun and shade leaves alter in the same way when pairs of leaves are exposed to the same range of intensities of light? How do the compensation points of shade plants from a wood compare with those of plants growing at the wood margin or in meadows? How does the rate of production of carbon dioxide by a natural soil vary with temperature? (We have obtained results suggesting a Q_{10} of about 3.) Do more mature soils in the later stages of succession have a higher output of carbon dioxide than the more barren soils in the younger stages?

Turning to aquatic habitats, we can follow the diurnal pH shifts and the variations in the concentration of dissolved oxygen in the water of a stream or a rock pool. These seem to be clearly correlated with the availability of light energy to the photosynthetic organisms in the water; but it is a simple matter, at least in static water, to test this hypothesis by shading the pool with opaque materials, or by removing some of the larger plants.

Estimates of the productivity of the vegetation of an area should not be too difficult to obtain. A lawn offers as simple a habitat as any. We can determine the dry-weight production of unit areas of a lawn during a whole growing season by collecting all grass cuttings, taking a sub-sample and determining its dry weight on each occasion, and then finding an approximate calorific value for the dried material. A simple calorimeter has been developed which gives approximate results (Nuffield Biology Project, 1966), so that such a measure of productivity, converted to kcal m^{-2} $year^{-1}$, can be compared with the visible radiation falling on the lawn during the year. There are certain difficulties in using photographic light meters, concerned with their spectral response and angular sensitivity, but Powell & Heath (1964) have devised a simple integrating light meter which can be exposed for some weeks at a time to allow estimates to be made of the total light flux reaching it.

Theoretically it should be possible to discover what densities of herbivores (primary consumers) will subsist on the annual production of unit
area of vegetation. How does the rate of feeding of cabbage white caterpillars in captivity correspond with their observed density on cabbage
plants? What is the total dry weight and calorific value of a fully grown
caterpillar? What fraction does this represent of the energy intake in
food? Can we attempt to construct an energy balance sheet for caterpillars, estimating respiratory losses by measuring the rate of consumption
of oxygen, and allowing for the dry matter present in the faeces? What
fraction of the energy value of the production by cabbage plants finally
becomes trapped as energy stored in fully grown caterpillars? Such studies
have been carried out by professional ecologists (see Odum, 1963;
Macfadyen, 1964), but some attempt is surely worth while for an interested
sixth-form boy or girl.

The production of plant material by primary producers is largely
diverted to decomposer organisms in the soil; Macfadyen (1964) quotes a
value of five-sevenths for the fraction trapped by soil organisms in pasture
land grazed by beef cattle, which only acquire one-seventh in their food.
The rates of decay of fallen leaves can be followed fairly simply by
exposing equal fresh weights of newly fallen leaves of a single species in
fine nylon bags (we use nylon stocking material) and determining the
dry weights of sub-samples regularly during the year. We found considerable differences in the rates of change in dry weight between bags
sited in different areas, and this appeared at first to be related to the degree
of waterlogging of the soil. We wondered whether this in turn might have
affected the availability of oxygen to the micro-organisms responsible
for the decay, and tried analysing samples of air taken from the centre of
the mass of decaying leaves. The results did not support this idea, but we
hope to repeat the experiment on a larger scale, and to keep some bags
under partially or completely anaerobic conditions.

The concept of competition is an important one in ecology, and several
investigators have shown in simple experiments how the yield of mature
organisms in an area varies considerably with the density of sowing,
planting or stocking with seeds or other young stages. Le Cren (1961)
describes how by stocking different reaches of a beck with different
densities of trout fry, the optimum density (about 8 fry per m^2) was
determined. Below this density the beck was understocked; at 8 fry per
m^2, each animal had an optimum area of feeding territory around it,
and any extra fry were unable to compete for space. Harper (1960) has
shown how the yield of some common crop plants or their weeds is

affected by the density of sowing, and also by competition between different species such as poppies and wheat when mixed in different proportions and at different densities. Since many species show delayed germination, it is necessary, however, to test any sample first for its percentage germination within any given period of time from sowing.

The influence of the height of the water table in the soil on the performance of plants growing in it has been shown by many workers. Brierley (*in litt.*) has described experiments in which potted plants were grown in a device which permitted the water level around the pot to be maintained at any required height. Plants which had their roots submerged in waterlogged soil grew in a stunted manner, while progressive lowering of the water level gave far more vigorous plants; one presumes that this could be due to the improved aeration of the soil. Could we not test this hypothesis further by arranging for the pots to be supplied with an atmosphere depleted of oxygen—perhaps by passing the air stream first through pyrogallate solutions?

The pollination mechanisms of plants offer a rich field for experimentation in the wild. Are insects necessary for seed to be set in any one species? We have attempted to test this hypothesis for snowdrops (*Galanthus nivalis*). On one occasion the plants outside our muslin cages set no seed either—it was the very cold winter of 1963 and there appeared to have been few if any suitable insects on the wing. This points clearly to the necessity for adequate controls in any experiment.

In brief, we find from descriptive work that a number of correlations can often be detected. These can only be converted into causal relationships by experiments designed specifically to test the hypotheses.

The problems which pupils tackle should ideally stem from their earlier experience of biology in the field, and preferably have been thought out by the pupils themselves.

Great care has to be taken to ensure that pupils select only the most limited of problems if they are to achieve any chance of finding valid solutions. Any experiments should be designed so as to allow the proper use of simple statistical techniques and tests of significance to be applied to them; this must be built into the planning at an early stage, and not superimposed upon the results as an afterthought. The material facilities for work of this kind will vary considerably with the type of work undertaken. One essential is the provision of adequate bench and cupboard space where long-term project materials can be stored, or experiments left running, without interfering with normal teaching in the laboratory. We are fortunate in having a small third laboratory which can if necessary be set aside for long-term work, and this is essential at certain periods of the year. We find it necessary to construct much of our own apparatus, as commercially produced items, such as thermistor thermometers, light meters and oxygen probes, are particularly expensive especially when more than one may be required for use at one time. So workshop facilities, and a supply of raw materials, are very useful.

The amount of time spent by boys on experimental project work in ecology varies considerably with the interest shown by individuals. We devote three periods each week for the 2 years in the sixth form to individual project work; this may be in biology, practical physics/engineering, or geography. In biology the completed reports are submitted to the Cambridge Syndicate in connection with their optional field studies scheme, and boys are given a *viva* some time before their A-level examination by a visiting examiner. They begin this work by January of their Lower Sixth year, although not every week is given over to this. An early start is thought to be essential for various reasons: many projects have involved tracing events through whole life-cycles, or during a critical period such as the pollination phase of spring-flowering plants; if work is to be repeated 12 months later in confirmation, then it is important to have the second investigation finished in time to allow a final report to be written during the Easter holidays. It is interesting to note that our physics and engineering departments, having seen the value of such project work in biology, are now running a similar pilot scheme for project work in practical physics.

Perhaps the most pressing need for the future is for the wider dissemination of the details of experimental project work in schools which has proved successful. Some schools publish accounts in the journals of their departments or natural history societies, but these have a limited circulation. The *School Science Review* could well become a vehicle for accounts of experimental work in ecology, as most biology teachers read it as a matter of course.

If work of this kind is to spread, the assessment of its quality for examination purposes poses considerable problems. It may well be that some form of internal assessment, externally moderated, will come to be recognized as the only possible way of dealing with large numbers of pupils. I understand that this is being actively explored by the Nuffield A-level team, and their findings will be considered with a great deal of interest by those teachers for whom work of this kind is one of the most stimulating parts of their teaching.

REFERENCES

HARPER J.L. (1960) Factors controlling plant numbers. In *The Biology of Weeds* (*Symp. Brit. ecol. Soc.* **1,** 119–132). Blackwell, Oxford.

HOSOKAWA T. & ODANI N. (1957) The daily compensation period and vertical ranges of epiphytes in a beech forest. *J. Ecol.* **45,** 901–915.

LE CREN E.D. (1961) How many fish survive? *River Boards' Assn. Year Book,* **9,** 57–64.

MACFADYEN A. (1964) Energy flow in ecosystems and its exploitation by grazing. In *Grazing in Terrestrial and Marine Environments* (*Symp. Brit. Ecol. Soc.* **4,** 3–20). Blackwell, Oxford.

MARTIN M.H. & PIGOTT C.D. (1965) A simple method for measuring carbon dioxide in soils. *J. Ecol.* **53,** 153–155.

MONTEITH J.L., SZEICZ G. & YABUKI K. (1964) Crop photosynthesis and the flux of carbon dioxide below the canopy. *J. appl. Ecol.* **1,** 321–337.

NUFFIELD BIOLOGY PROJECT (1966). *Students' Text* and *Teachers' Guide* (Years 3 and 4). Longmans, Green and Penguin Books, London.

ODUM E.P. (1963) *Ecology.* Holt, Rinehart & Winston, New York.

POWELL M.C. & HEATH O.V.S. (1964) A simple and inexpensive integrating photometer. *J. exp. Bot.* **15,** 187–910.

THOMAS A.K. & FIELD J.A. (1962) Estimation of daily compensation period. *Sch. Sci. Rev.* **43,** 711–712.

THE PLACE OF ECOLOGY
IN THE NUFFIELD SCHEME

W.H.DOWDESWELL
Winchester College

I. INTRODUCTION

My brief in this symposium is to speak as one of the organizers of the Nuffield Science Teaching Project. Since there are now several schemes which involve the teaching of biology, let me explain at the outset that I shall be concerned here only with the O-level Biology Project. The purpose of this has been to develop a 5-year course suitable for those children within the age range 11–16 who normally take GCE O-level—in grammar-type schools and the upper streams of secondary modern schools. Many of these schools lie in the heart of industrial areas and in devising a course based on the study of living organisms, the organizers have had to bear this fact constantly in mind. At the same time, it is obviously important that, in attempting to cater for the needs of the less fortunate, the legitimate claims of schools situated in more favourable circumstances should not be disregarded. The need to steer this delicate passage has proved both a challenge and a fascination.

I suppose it is a truism, particularly in the company of ecologists, to assert that the ecological approach lies at the heart of all biology teaching. One of the misconceptions that has all too often confounded efforts to reform school biology teaching in the past been the belief that mere factual information about living plants and animals is sufficient to achieve an understanding of them. Nothing could be further from the truth.

In essence the Nuffield Biology Project has been concerned with two main issues—what is taught and, far more important, how it is taught. Concerning the former, little need be said here, for what is taught is to a considerable extent a matter of personal opinion. Some topics such as respiration and photosynthesis select themselves; others, such as the role of DNA, are more debatable. But when we consider teaching methods and the way in which biology is presented to children of all ages the position is very different, for few would deny that much of what passes at present for the science of living things is, in fact, most unscientific. How often,

83

for instance, do our students perform a genuine experiment to which the result is not already a foregone conclusion? How often do we ourselves accept, and expect our students to accept and memorize, dogmatic assertions made in text-books without a shred of evidence to support them? If any one of our aims has stood out above all others it has been to encourage a more genuinely experimental attitude and a more critical approach to evidence—both first hand, obtained in the field and laboratory and second hand, derived from the literature. We believe that the study of ecology provides unrivalled opportunities for achieving these ends.

How, then, are we to present children within the O-level age-group with a more truly scientific view of living organisms? There is no simple answer. But one thing seems clear; they must be afforded better opportunities of handling, examining and learning about plants and animals, not only in the classroom and laboratory, but also in the natural circumstances in which they are found. At O-level we believe that such work should not require the specialized facilities of a nature reserve, nor do we subscribe to the view that much elaborate apparatus is needed. Most of the equipment required already exists in school laboratories and much of what is needed in addition can be made at little cost. The investigations that we have suggested in the Nuffield course can mostly be carried out within the confines of a school garden or on any piece of waste ground near by.

II. ECOLOGY IN THE INTRODUCTORY PHASE (11–13 YEARS)

Early in the 2-year introductory course we aim to show that biology, like other branches of science, is an experimental subject and that the study of living things in their natural environment poses the same sort of problems as occur in physics and chemistry, except there are more of them. Since the school year starts in the autumn, earthworms provide the obvious choice (although animals such as woodlice provide an excellent alternative) and the kind of investigations we have devised enable children to relate what they can observe outside in a lawn or garden to what they can study more closely and experimentally in a wormery set up under laboratory conditions. A close relationship between field work and laboratory investigation is one of the features of the whole Nuffield biology course at all levels. Experience of living organisms in the first year embraces a wide variety of approaches, particularly that relating to growth and life-cycles. Among animals, locusts provide splendid subjects for study since their development is rapid and easy to control, and they are easily kept in a school laboratory. In the second year, the study of plants and animals extends to their sizes, shapes and movement, with particular emphasis on the use of simple models. An innovation at this level is the introduction of microbiology with the many opportunities it provides, both for experimental work and for emphasizing its close relationship with the applied side of the subject, particularly human health and disease. The introduction of bacteria so early and in an experimental context provides a sharp reminder to advocates of project work in biology that this does not always have to be done out of doors—as is commonly supposed. Much experimental work of a semi-ecological kind is far better done indoors, particularly when, as is so often the case, it can be related to what goes on outside.

III. ECOLOGY IN THE INTERMEDIATE PHASE (13–16 YEARS)

As they get older and their fund of experience widens, children are able to view scientific problems in a more objective and analytical way. In the Nuffield course, a gradual change-over occurs during the first 2 years from a purely descriptive approach to a more quantitative one. By the beginning of the third year, many of the problems posed have a strong quantitative flavour. This is true of the ecological side which occupies the equivalent of a term (mostly done during the summer) in each of years III and IV.

As I have explained earlier, the principle we have adopted throughout this course is that ecology at O-level should be studied largely within the precincts of the school. This is undoubtedly possible except in a small minority of urban areas. Such a notion is in marked contrast to the attitude in many existing GCE examination syllabuses which demand the study of a 'well-defined habitat'—whatever that may mean. Ecology begins on our front doorstep—or even inside it (see the Nuffield film 'Camp Followers of Man') and the sooner children come face to face with this reality the better.

In attempting to implement these ideas, it seemed to us that tinkering with existing syllabuses and teaching methods would get us nowhere. We must go right back to the beginning. Moreover, in devising a new approach it was important to consider what came before and what was to come after, so that the ecology could be placed in its right perspective. This meant paying particular attention to the relationship with physiology, and it is significant that the first chapter on ecology which deals with spatial distribution in *Pleurococcus* and factors affecting it is preceded

G

by chapters on 'The Organism and Water' and 'Plants and Light Energy'.

The fact of distribution provides a logical starting-point for any course in ecology; it is particularly relevant in a Nuffield context as the pupils will already have become aware of it at the beginning of Year I. Opportunities abound for setting up hypotheses demanding investigation. For instance, the belief widely held that the distribution of *Pleurococcus* on the trunks of trees or palings provides a means of finding the north can be easily tested; factors other than light which may affect distribution must be considered, such as aspect and the run-off of water. Many other plants provide equally good material for this sort of work; for instance, mosses and lichens, both of which tend to be somewhat overlooked in school teaching.

A study of distribution leads on to the question of how organisms reach their habitats in the first place. Clearly, we can consider propagules under two headings—those that are moved passively and those that move themselves. Studies concerned with the former need not be based, as they usually are, only on the well-known dispersal mechanisms found in flowering plants (which, incidentally, are all too frequently considered from a structural rather than an ecological point of view). Fungi such as *Saprolegnia* provide splendid opportunities for experimental work in laboratory aquaria and under natural conditions. For more elaborate laboratory investigation, *Euglena* provides a good example of a 'plant' with a limited power of movement and hence the ability to disperse itself to some extent.

Dispersal in animals presents peculiar problems associated with the fact that most of them can move on their own. The behaviour of woodlice and their reactions to different environmental conditions are relevant here, and lend themselves well to study both in a laboratory and outside. Moreover, these are well suited to quantitative treatment and can provide exercises in simple statistical analysis. Other animals which have proved admirable for this sort of work include the freshwater shrimp (*Gammarus pulex*), the freshwater 'louse' (*Asellus*), and Planarians. These can be subjected to a variety of conditions in an 'artificial stream' in the laboratory and their reactions compared with similar situations in the natural state. Again, boards covered with a sticky substance such as petroleum jelly and placed in different positions can provide valuable quantitative evidence of dispersal both in small, flying insects and among plants.

Once a community of plants and animals has become successfully established in a habitat, what happens to them then? This question raises a further one of equal importance. What do we mean by success and what adaptations in plants and animals are needed in order to achieve it? Here again there is a great variety of practical work that can be done in the vicinity of a school. We can create an artificial animal habitat—for instance, by putting down a piece of raw meat or a carcase (suitably protected against the local dogs). Subsequent colonization by blowflies such as *Calliphora* can then be studied, records kept and the results assessed quantitatively. Jam jars inverted over patches of garden soil provide a good way of studying competition among weeds and, incidentally, serve as a useful introduction to experimental design. In the laboratory, competition between fungi such as *Penicillium* and *Mucor* on a piece of bread also illustrate problems of survival in a restricted habitat.

Competition and differential survival in organisms inevitably leads on to succession, and this forms the next topic in our course. This is a subject which is difficult to present in a dynamic manner using examples out of doors since, among the larger organisms, succession usually takes place so slowly. However, the problem can be readily overcome by setting up artificial habitats. Troughs of water can be put out in a variety of places under different environmental conditions and subsequent colonization and succession studied both qualitatively and quantitatively. The problem of identification is bound to arise here, and we have attempted to meet it by providing a key to the commoner organisms, both plant and animal, likely to be encountered in such conditions. An alternative approach is to study the progressive colonization of glass plates suspended in an aquarium containing pond water, or the colonization of cellophane sheets inserted in soil contained in plant pots. In the aquarium we may even introduce herbivorous animals such as the liberty fish (*Mollienisia*) as an additional factor influencing plant survival.

The various influences discussed so far together contribute to the eventual establishment of a community; and the study of a community provides the climax to this section of our course. As always, we were faced with the problem of finding appropriate material in close proximity to schools. Soil seemed to us the obvious choice. Apart from the more obvious investigations of soil structure and zonation, there is a wealth of experimental work to be carried out. The use of various methods for extracting soil arthropods, such as Tullgren and Baermann funnels, raises once again the problem of identification, and we hope that the elementary keys which we have produced may prove useful in this respect. It is sometimes claimed that little experimental work of any value can be carried out on soil organisms at school level. This is not the case. For instance, a whole series of investigations on food relationships can be conducted by burying pieces of leaves (litter) of known size and number enclosed in nets of varying mesh so as to exclude different portions of the animal community. The amounts of material extracted from each sample can then be compared at intervals on a quantitative basis. Again, with a little ingenuity, it is perfectly possible to establish a model food-chain under laboratory conditions and to study the changes that take place over a limited period of time.

The study of food preferences (also carried out with earthworms in Year I) and food relationships leads on conveniently to the idea of a climax as their end-product. Here, again, experimental evidence derived from natural sources is not easy to obtain in a reasonable time. However, laboratory communities can change quickly and we find that the process of colonization of glass plates in an aquarium, mentioned earlier in connection with competition, provides a ready means of showing that a state of equilibrium is eventually reached.

In this brief account I have followed through the sequence of the ecological section of our course starting with the fact of spatial distribution and ending with the climax community. But we believe that no such course for schools can be regarded as complete without the addition of two further items.

The first of these concerns parasitism—a condition in which the bodies of the living organisms themselves provide the habitat for other plants and animals. Practical work here is inevitably restricted to observational exercises, but we have attempted to provide students with as wide a selection of examples as is reasonably possible. These range from plant galls and root nodules to protozoans and insects. In addition we have produced a unique 8 mm film loop of the life-cycle of *Apanteles glomeratus* in the larvae of the large white butterfly (*Pieris brassicae*).

In the final chapter on ecology we attempt to place man in his ecological environment and to show how the principles we have introduced in the preceding work on animals and plants can be applied to human societies. This raises a number of important issues—the effective use of soil, farming practice and rotation of crops, the influence of weeds, parasites and disease. The problem of pollution is important, too, and its detrimental influence on plants and animals both in the wild state and under domestication. At this point we ask the question—how are we going to maintain the countryside (viewed in its widest sense) in a condition in which we can enjoy it and utilize it to the full? The answer, of course, is by understanding more about conservation. A section on conservation then follows and concludes this part of the course.

IV. MAINTAINING A BREADTH OF VISION

It might be argued that a course of this sort, which relies to a considerable extent on experimentation using specialized examples, could lead to a rather narrow outlook on the range of plant and animal communities as a whole. We have attempted to avoid this deficiency in two ways: (i) By providing an extensive *Teachers' Guide* which is closely cross-referenced to the text. This includes not only notes on teaching, the construction of apparatus, etc., but it also suggests a wide range of approaches and experiments as alternatives to those described in the text. In this way we hope that a teacher using the course may be encouraged to make the best possible use of any local facilities at his disposal.
(ii) By providing at the end of each chapter a short section (two or three pages) of Background Reading. This is material intended for out-of-school use (possibly in Preparation) and covers a diversity of topics each related to the chapter in question. For instance, at the end of a chapter on dispersal we have an account of 'History and Plant Dispersal' telling the stories of the spread of the Oxford ragwort (*Senecio squalidus*), the rayless camomile (*Matricaria matricarioides*) and the Thanet cress (*Cardaria draba*). 'Becoming Established in a Habitat' is illustrated by the activities of sexton beetles, while 'Climax and Feeding' concludes with 'The Loudest Noise on Earth' —the story of Krakatoa and its subsequent recolonization.

V. THE SIGNIFICANCE OF ECOLOGY IN AN O-LEVEL COURSE

I began this paper with the suggestion that an ecological approach lies at the heart of all good biology teaching and, perhaps, this is a suitable theme on which to end. In the previous pages I have attempted to show how ecology, treated as an experimental science at an elementary level, can provide pupils with a dynamic insight into the lives of plants and animals which they could not obtain in any other way. By linking it closely to physiology, as we have tried to do in the Nuffield course, I believe two sides have benefited. Ecological relationships such as food-chains have become more understandable, while physiological processes such as photosynthesis have become more realistic once their ecological significance and survival value are apparent. But there is a final point perhaps the most important of all. Throughout this course we have returned repeatedly to such concepts as variation, adaptation, competition and differential survival. These are the raw ingredients of evolution and, by introducing them early and often, we have provided the lead-in to the concept of natural selection and all that follows from it. The right way to teach evolution, at any rate at O-level, is surely through ecology and not through fossil horses. For this reason we have left evolution until the end of Year V when the ecology course is over and the stage has been set for a more genuine understanding.

THE PLACE OF ECOLOGY IN THE BIOLOGICAL
SCIENCES CURRICULUM STUDY

ELIZABETH PERROTT

Department of Education, University of Keele*

I. INTRODUCTION

The Biological Sciences Curriculum Study was set up in 1959 by the American Institute of Biological Sciences, with financial support from the National Science Foundation totalling more than four million dollars, 'to seek the improvement of education in the biological sciences' at school level.

As a result, during three successive summers, 1960, 1961 and 1962, three parallel sets of course materials for American High School Biology were prepared by teams of writers working at summer writing conferences. The publications, which include texts, laboratory manuals and teachers' guides, were released through commercial publishers in the United States in the autumn of 1963, and since this time the BSCS materials have been adapted for use in many other countries by recognized groups of teachers.

The writers' primary purpose was to produce biology courses suitable for wide use in the average high school with average classes. The aim of the courses was to give pupils a basic understanding of science and of scientific processes and, in doing so, to build scientific literacy in order to aid in the preparation of the pupil for responsible citizenship. They were prepared for the 10th Grade (i.e. for pupils of 15–16 years attending the comprehensive-type American high school), because most high school pupils take biology courses during this year in American school systems (Perrott, 1965).

II. THE GENERAL PATTERN

These BSCS course materials are unlike conventional treatments of high school biology in several ways:

A. Basic emphases

All three versions of the BSCS course materials have significant unifying threads. This unity arises from the agreement of the writers that certain

* Now at: Department of Education, University of Stirling.

basic emphases should be woven into and through each of the three versions. These are:

1. Change of living things through time—evolution.
2. Diversity of the type and unity of pattern of living things.
3. Genetic continuity of life.
4. Complementarity of structure and function.
5. Biological roots of behaviour.
6. Complementarity of organisms and environment.
7. Regulation and homeostasis: the maintenance of life in the face of change.
8. Intellectual history of biological concepts.
9. Science as inquiry.

B. *The product of team work*

They are the products of a well-organized large-scale project in which there had been close co-operation, on a work party basis, between two main groups of people—on the one hand, research biologists, university teachers, high school biology teachers and school science supervisors, and on the other, educationists with varied interests in science education. For instance, by this latter group, the position of biological education in the schools was surveyed and the problems pin-pointed before the first writing conference (Hurd, 1961); school exercises in logical thinking called 'Invitations to Inquiry' were devised to test pupils' understanding of biological principles and concepts by discussion methods (Schwab, 1963); and special multi-choice tests for these courses were devised by a team of biologists working closely with a specialist testing agency.*

C. *Large-scale testing*

This curriculum study also differs from others previously undertaken in the extensive and thorough testing it has undergone in the schools. It was used in both large and small schools, in rural and urban areas, in every section of the United States. Some 1000 teachers, who received special courses of training, tested the materials on 165,000 pupils. During the first 2 years of testing, teachers sent back weekly reports on their classroom experience with BSCS courses and made suggestions for improvements and modifications. The materials were also tested against traditional programmes taught in control groups of schools.

D. *Science as a process of inquiry*

BSCS courses also differ markedly from traditional courses in the teaching methods employed, for the emphasis is on reasoning rather than recall, and away from laboratory and field work concentrated on verification towards laboratory work involving real investigation. The writers aim

* Psychological Corporation, 304E 45th Street, New York, N.Y. 10017.

to teach science as a method of seeking answers and to do this they stress underlying concepts. Work is centred in the laboratory and field where real problems are explored, open-ended experiments and other materials being used as the media for conveying an understanding of science. Through emphasis on basic concepts and the illustration of such concepts in a variety of ways, the pupil is given practice in drawing generalizations, in seeking relationships and in finding his own answers; in other words, he is given experiences which aim to provide an understanding of the methods of science.

E. *New content*

In addition, the different emphasis given in terms of content reflects modern biology more adequately than do conventional approaches. For example, where traditional texts emphasize the organ and tissue level of biological organization, BSCS texts place greater emphasis on other levels, viz. the molecular, cellular, individual, population, community and world biome (Figs. 1, 2 and 3).* It should be noted, however, that not one of the versions has its major emphasis on the level preferred by traditional texts.

F. *Variety of treatment*

The production of three separate versions of the course materials emphasizes that there is more than one approach to the teaching of biology, and that it is for the teacher to choose the approach which is best suited to his own background and interests and to those of his pupils. For example: the Yellow Version (Moore *et al.*, 1963) puts its emphasis on the cell as the most elemental, independent structural and functional unit of living organisms (Fig. 1), while the Blue Version (Welch *et al.*, 1963) puts main emphasis on molecular biology as the fundamental area of biology upon which all other biological knowledge is based (Fig. 2). In the Green Version, on the other hand (Kolb *et al.*, 1963), a course is presented which gives the ecological and behavioural aspects primary importance (Fig. 3). In the context of this symposium, it is the Green Version which chiefly concerns us here.

III. THE GREEN VERSION

The neglect of the ecological and behavioural aspects of biology in most high school texts at this level is considered unfortunate by the writers of the Green Version, since the problems created by growing human

---

* The figures are based on an analysis of the content of traditional and BSCS texts in terms of the emphasis given to different levels of biological organization when estimated on a five-point scale. They are reproduced from the *BSCS Teachers' Handbook* by kind permission of the BSCS.

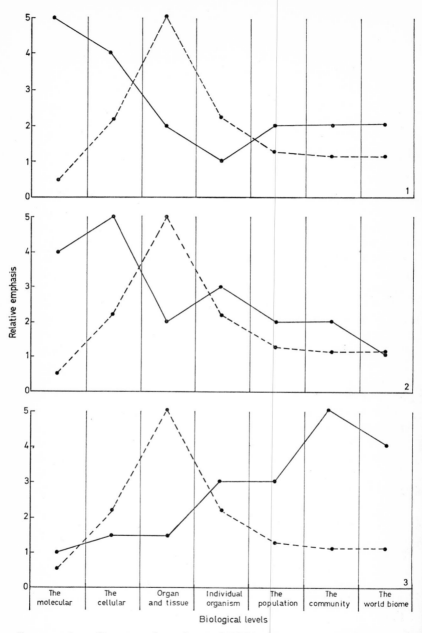

FIGS. 1, 2 & 3. Content and emphases of BSCS texts (———— BSCS version; ----- conventional text). 1. Blue version. 2. Yellow version. 3. Green version.

populations, by depletion of resources, by pollution, by regional development and the like, all require intelligent community or government
action for solution and are, in part at least, ecological problems of which
every citizen should have some background knowledge.

The course is divided into six sections:

Section 1. The Living World. The Biosphere

(a) The Web of Life

This subsection begins with a consideration of the interdependence of
plants, animals and protists in the transfer of energy, the cycling of
matter and the interdependence of living systems and the physical
environment. The related laboratory and field work is based on
observation of living organisms, and on the interrelationships of
producers and consumers. Experimentation on seed germination introduces the pupil to experimental methods. The basic units of ecology
which form a series from the individual, as the most concrete, to the
ecosystem, as the most abstract, are considered.

(b) Individuals and Populations

Individuals and various groupings of individuals which can be called
populations are dealt with and the quantitative study of populations
and the idea of density is explored. The effect of biotic and abiotic
factors on population densities and the importance of the species
population as an entity of practical and theoretical importance in
biology is discussed. There is related laboratory work on yeast populations and on factors limiting populations.

(c) Communities and Ecosystems

The actual field study of a community is basic to this subsection.
Much of the text material is concerned with the kinds of ecological
relationships which exist in communities. Finally, the concept of
an ecosystem is introduced. This subsection is also related to laboratory
investigations on competition and field work on a comparative study
of habitats.

Section 2. Diversity in the Biosphere

Some idea of the diversity of organisms and of their classification
is now given before going further into patterns of ecological organization.
This is not, however, a 'type-study' of representative living things. The
emphasis is on the variety of forms in which life can occur and on aspects
of form and function which are relevant to a useful and meaningful
organization of such diversity.

Section 3. Patterns in the Biosphere

Afetr divergence into taxonomy in Section 2, ecological considerations are returned to with patterns of distribution which are discussed from the ecological, historical and biogeographical standpoint.

(a) Patterns of Life in the Microscopic World

The soil as an ecosystem is considered first and related laboratory work deals with the decomposing action of soil microbes, nodule-forming bacteria, and the investigation of a plant disease.

(b) Patterns of Life on Land

Environmental conditions are considered here and laboratory work is focused on limiting factors in distribution and on exercises involving the making of climatograms as a means of summarizing temperature and precipitation measurements. Field work in the school area is recommended to support this subsection.

(c) Patterns of Life in Water

The principles of ecological distribution considered in the previous section are extended to aquatic environments and are related to practical work on a pond community. Laboratory studies include 'Succession in a freshwater community', 'The effects of salinity on living organisms' and 'The measurement of pH in aquatic ecosystems'.

(d) The History of Life

The sweep of biological events through time and the continuity of life processes is presented here. Fossils are seen as the tangible evidence for the existence of organisms in the past, from which palaeontologists are able to provide more than a description of extinct organisms, the reconstruction of biotic communities, of climates and even of whole ecosystems being possible.

(e) The Geography of Life

The geographical distribution of most species cannot be explained on ecological grounds alone. As organisms vary in ability to disperse, the structural and physiological characteristics of a species are considered in relation to the physical barriers that it may have had to cross in spreading from its area of origin. The influence of man on the distribution of organisms is also discussed and laboratory work includes experiments on the effects of barriers on dispersal.

Section 4. Within the Individual Organism

The writers of this version feel that traditionally this aspect of biology has been magnified out of all proportion of its lasting value to the student. Therefore, subsections on (a) The Cell, (b) The Functioning Plant, (c) The Functioning Animal, (d) Reproduction and Development and (e) Heredity, and related laboratory work, which together form the bulk of conventional courses, are concentrated into one section here.

Section 5. Adaptation

(a) Evolution: Genetic Adaptation
The chief objective of this subsection is to give an explanation of how evolution operates.
(b) Behaviour or Individual Adaptation
Laboratory exercises include a study of population genetics, effect of population size, social behaviour in fishes and photo-periodic control of plant behaviour.

Section 6. Man and the Biosphere

The whole course is brought into focus in this section. Here, topics which will concern the pupil in the future as a citizen are dealt with. These are topics in which biological information has some relevance but which also extend into other areas of knowledge. A primary aim of the whole course is to provoke the student into continuing to think about them. To this end the following ideas are explored:
(a) A consideration of man—the human animal.
(b) Man's shifting position in the biosphere.
(c) The rapidly increasing world density of human population and related problems.
(d) The living world not only as an entity which demands study yielding understanding, but also as an experience that demands appreciation, yielding aesthetic pleasure.

IV. AID FOR THE TEACHER

This change of emphasis from traditional courses makes considerable demands on teachers, and with this in mind, not only has it been BSCS policy to organize teacher preparation programmes, but a great deal of help has also been provided for the teacher in the form of teachers' guides and films; these give practical help on techniques, methods, laboratory organization and background materials, and also outline the philosophy behind the approaches employed and give guidance on teaching methods.

In order to avoid the rigidity which such detailed guidance could give to the courses taught, each text and laboratory guide contains more materials and experiments than can possibly be covered in the time available, hence the individual teacher is given a measure of choice. For example, of the eighty-five laboratory or field exercises in the Green Version students' manual, forty-five are basic, while the rest are 'highly recommended' or 'optional'.

V. LABORATORY BLOCKS

An element of choice is also provided by the laboratory blocks. These are intended to supplement any of the versions of the BSCS course and provide for 6 weeks' continuous experimental work. They give students the opportunity to work on a long-term problem, thus recognizing and making provision for one of the difficulties of problem-solving in biology, i.e. the length of time involved in the completion of some types of experiment. Each block is centred around one area of biology. The one on 'Field Ecology' (Phillips, 1964) is based on a more extensive field study. Other titles include: 'Animal Behaviour' (Follansbee, 1965); 'Microbes, Their Growth, Nutrition and Interaction' (Sussman, 1964); 'Life in the Soil' (Pramer, 1965) and 'Genetic Continuity' (Glass, 1965). Each school makes its own choice of one laboratory block and this is yet another means of giving individuality and flexibility to a BSCS course.

VI. INVESTIGATIONS FOR THE SPECIALLY INTERESTED PUPIL

Flexibility is also encouraged by the provision of four volumes of long-term investigations (Brandwein et al., 1965), based on research problems, to be used by the specially interested pupil on a voluntary basis. Facilities are provided for these investigations to be undertaken outside school hours, usually through the medium of the science clubs. Many of these problems are ecological in nature, e.g. 'The Effects of Flooding on Seedlings of Upland Tree Species', 'Analysis of Bird Territory', 'The Seedcoat as a Possible Source of Predaceous Nematode-capturing Fungi' and 'The Role of Light and Temperature in the Seasonal Distribution of Microcrustacea'.

VII. THE RELEVANCE OF THE BSCS GREEN VERSION COURSE TO BRITISH EDUCATION

Although at first sight it seems that a course of study devised for 15–16-year-old pupils to be taught in 1 year on the basis of 1 hour per day or

5-6 hours per week has little relevance to the British system of education. On closer analysis, however, one finds that our situation does not in fact differ markedly from this. The results of a survey of 10 per cent of the schools in England and Wales carried out by the author and her co-workers in 1962 on behalf of the Nature Conservancy's Study Group on Field Biology and Education (Perrott *et al.*, 1963), show that considerably less than half the secondary school pupils are taught biology as a separate subject below the age of 15 years.

The situation is not, therefore, very different from that in the United States where general science is also commonly taught in the junior high school (Perrott, 1965). The main difference is that the majority of pupils in England who study biology below the sixth-form level do so for 2 years. But the time allocation during this period is only equivalent to that allocated to biology in American high schools during 1 year.

This survey also showed that very little time is spent on the teaching of ecology to pupils below sixth-form level in British schools, the average time being approximately $2\frac{1}{2}$ hours per annum, and that experimental or problem-solving work of the type devised for the BSCS Green Version course was undertaken by less than 10 per cent of the schools (Perrott *et al.*, 1963).

The feasibility of teaching this type of course in English secondary schools was tested by the author and her co-workers when an experimental programme was carried out, with 500 pupils from Staffordshire secondary schools, at the University of Keele in 1964.* Lessons, laboratory work and field investigations, including many which were adaptations of the BSCS Green Version, were arranged. The topics taught were taken from the GCE and other syllabuses followed by the schools and included such subjects as the relation of plants and animals to their natural environment, the interdependence of plant and animal life, and the formation and composition of the soil.

The aim of the programme was critically to assess the part which ecology can play in the learning of biology under normal school conditions at the pre-sixth-form level, and to estimate whether ecological investigations which are suitable for secondary school pupils at this stage are able to serve both the investigatory as well as the illustrative aims of science teaching.

The results of testing show that the ecological approach can be effectively used to teach topics included in the GCE O-level syllabus and other

* Author's unpublished work on an investigation supported by the Nature Conservancy.

terminal courses and that such teaching can be integrated into the normal school programme of biology teaching as in BSCS courses. It is to be hoped that the raising of the school-leaving age to 16 years will provide even more opportunities for this type of course.

REFERENCES

BRANDWEIN P. et al. (1965) Research Problems in Biology. Series 1, 2, 3 and 4. Harrap, London.
FOLLANSBEE H. (1964) Animal Behaviour. Heath, Boston (Distrib. Harrap, London).
GLASS B. (1965) Genetic Continuity. Heath, Boston (Distrib. Harrap, London).
HURD P. (1961) Biological Education in American Secondary Schools 1890–1960. American Institute of Biological Sciences, Washington, D.C.
KOLB C.H. et al. (1963) High School Biology. Rand McNally, Chicago (Distrib. Murray, London).
MOORE J.A. et al. (1963) Biological Science: An Inquiry into Life. Harcourt Brace & World, New York (Distrib. Hart Davies, London).
PERROTT E. et al. (1963) Science out of Doors. Longmans, London.
PERROTT E. (1965) Biological Sciences Curriculum Study: its relevance to British education. Science Teacher, 9, 14–17.
PHILLIPS E.A. (1964) Field Ecology. Heath, Boston (Distrib. Harrap, London).
PRAMER D. (1965) Life in the Soil. Heath, Boston (Distrib. Harrap, London).
SCHWAB J.J. et al. (1963) Biology Teachers Handbook. Wiley, New York and London.
SUSSMAN A.S. (1964) Microbes, Their Growth, Nutrition and Interaction. Heath, Boston (Distrib. Harrap, London).
WELCH C.A. et al. (1963) Biological Science: Molecules to Man. Arnold, London.

SECTION III

METHODS AND TECHNIQUES IN ECOLOGICAL
TEACHING AT UNDERGRADUATE LEVEL

H

THE APPROACH THROUGH THE ECOSYSTEM

K.H.MANN

Department of Zoology, University of Reading

I. INTRODUCTION

At an early stage of planning a course of scientific instruction a decision has to be made about whether the approach is to be deductive or inductive, i.e. whether to begin with broad generalizations and seek their verification in nature or whether to begin with facts and attempt to unite them in a synthesis. It is probably true to say that most ecological teaching begins with facts about plants and animals. This is no doubt very sound, but at Reading and probably at other universities instruction in ecology is spread over more than 1 year of a student's course, during which time a proportion of the students give up ecology in favour of other branches of biology or turn to non-biological subjects. There is, therefore, a danger that if the synthesis is reserved for the later part of the course it will be presented only to advanced students.

The view presented in this paper is that the broad principles of the subject should be taught to elementary students even if there is not enough time to support all the generalizations by a full quota of facts. So many human activities of economic and social importance follow naturally from a few basic ecological principles that to teach them to as wide an audience as possible is surely an important duty. By comparison with chemists and physicists, who have been enunciating principles in their subjects for something like 200 years, biologists tend to be unwilling to commit themselves to generalizations. Yet general theories are important, both as a framework on which to hang a multiplicity of facts which otherwise might be incomprehensible to students, and as a stimulus to further research. Taxonomy and comparative anatomy have had their great generalization—the theory of evolution—for more than 100 years and gene theory has been at the core of teaching and research in genetics for about half that time, but until recently the basic principles of ecology have been far from clear. It is not long since ecology could with some justification be described as 'the study of the incomprehensible by the incompetent'.

With these points in mind, the following account of the approach to ecology through the concept of the ecosystem is offered as the basis of a satisfying general theory of ecology. It is not, of course, an original idea; it derives from the ideas of Elton, Lindemann, Odum, Macfadyen and many others. However, its use in the teaching of ecology does not seem to be very widespread, at least on this side of the Atlantic, so that a restatement in the present context may not be out of place.

II. THE ECOSYSTEM AS A FUNCTIONAL UNIT

Let us begin with a very simple concept, that of a food-chain. Some plant material is eaten by a herbivore, which is eaten by a carnivore, and this may in turn fall prey to another carnivore. Natural situations are seldom as simple as this; most predators have several sources of food and most animals have several predators. A diagram expressing this relationship for a community becomes a food-web rather than a food-chain, and a complete food-web for a particular habitat is often a very complex thing indeed. How can food-webs be simplified so as to make them comprehensible? The concept of trophic levels comes in here. If we distinguish between primary producers, herbivores, carnivores and decomposers, we can break up our food-web into groups of organisms where all members of a group are performing the same kinds of feeding activities. Omnivores are a little difficult to fit into the pattern, but by analysing diets it is possible to say what proportion of the omnivore biomass should be assigned to each category. We then find that in most situations the biomass of the various trophic levels can be fitted to a pyramidal diagram, with the primary producers forming a broad base on which rests a smaller biomass of herbivores and an even smaller biomass of carnivores. In many cases not only the biomass but also the energy content of the trophic levels fall into the pyramidal pattern.

This is a static model describing things as they are at a particular time; but just as classical botany and zoology have moved from a descriptive to a functional approach by incorporating the findings of physiology, so ecological thinking can become functional by taking into account the production of each trophic level and the flow of energy and materials from one level to another. The community of plants and animals, including micro-organisms, and the inanimate environment in a particular place are in a continual state of interaction and together constitute an ecosystem. On this view the ecosystem is the functional unit in ecology. Ecosystems may be as large or as small as we care to make them, but it is highly convenient to draw their boundaries at points of environmental discontinuity. Thus a pond is a convenient ecosystem to study; it is possible to consider it as part of a larger ecosystem, but the properties of the pond are sufficiently different from the properties of the terrestrial habitats surrounding it for there to be little advantage in doing so. An area of reasonably uniform grassland, or woodland, or an area of the North Sea, are also conveniently considered as ecosystems.

Figure 1 represents a generalized ecosystem. It is constructed by taking the successive trophic levels of a pyramid of biomass, separating them a

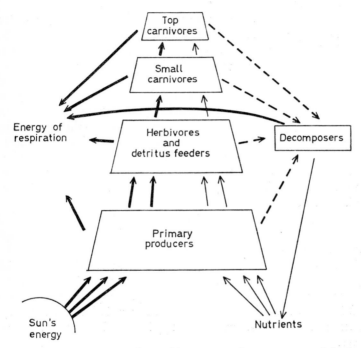

FIG. 1. Diagram illustrating the trophic structure of an ecosystem and the flow of energy (thick arrows), materials (thin arrows) or both (broken arrows).

little and considering how energy and materials move between them. There is a separate box for decomposers. The primary producers fix energy and materials to form new organic matter, and the arrows on the right show some of this material being transferred to the herbivores and detritus feeders. The remainder of the primary production dies and decays so that energy and materials are transferred to the decomposers, as illustrated by the broken arrows. Materials are transferred from level to level through the system until they reach the top carnivores which, by definition, have no predators. It is therefore axiomatic that the whole of their production ends in death and decay and is led to the decomposers. These last organisms reduce organic matter ultimately to its inorganic constituents and a proportion of these are taken up again by the primary producers. Thus there is a cycling of nutrients in the system and if the cycle were interrupted, as for instance by the erosion of soil containing decomposers, the functioning of the ecosystem would be impossible.

The thick arrows on the left show the sun's energy being transferred to the primary producers, which lock it up in the products of photosynthesis. A good proportion of this energy is used by the plants for their own purposes, being released in respiration. The remainder is stored as net production and is available to the next trophic level. Of the energy taken in by the herbivores, some is respired and some is stored in new growth and in this manner the process continues through the system. The energy of metabolism is dissipated as heat and not fed back, so the flow of energy is a one-way process and the magnitude of the flow is a measure of the activity of the ecosystem. Plant nutrients which recirculate are like the wheels of the mechanism, transmitting the energy. Since the mechanism cannot function without the wheels, conservation of plant nutrients is of vital importance.

These are the properties which all ecosystems have in common. Once they are established, the reasons for a number of activities in applied ecology become apparent. For instance, soil is seen as the repository of nutrients and decomposer organisms and its conservation is essential to the continuance of a terrestrial system. Toxic chemicals which enter the plants or the herbivores may pass through the system and be concentrated in a much smaller biomass at each trophic level. They may be harmless to large animals when first applied and later become a serious menace.

III. DIFFERENCES BETWEEN ECOSYSTEMS

Let us now consider the differences between ecosystems rather than the properties which they have in common. Each trophic level is made up of a variety of species and the composition varies from place to place. The primary producers of chalk upland are different from those of a valley bog and the consumers of a lake are different from those of a stream. These differences are determined partly by the physical and chemical properties of the environment. Organisms have tolerance ranges for temperature, water content, pH, etc., of their environment, and if the conditions are beyond the tolerance range of a particular species it is excluded. Much valuable teaching and research centres on the study of factors limiting the distribution of plants and animals, and this is one of the areas where physiological studies in the laboratory are a necessary complement to field investigations.

In any given habitat, not all the organisms that could exist there will in fact be present. In a particular set of physical and chemical conditions, some species will find them ideally suited to their requirements, while others will be near the edges of their tolerance ranges. In the course of competition for essential requisites, some species will be less effective than others and will be excluded. This aspect of ecology, the study of competition, is essential to the understanding of the structure of ecosystems.

When we reach the point of understanding, however imperfectly, the reasons why some species occur and prosper in a given situation while others do not, we are ready to consider single-species populations. The important principle to teach here is that populations tend to be self-regulating, i.e. to have homeostatic mechanisms which match the size of the population to the resources of energy and materials available to it. The field of population dynamics is a wide one and there are many conflicting theories, but a consideration of the ecosystem as a whole sheds light on some vexed questions. Since the surface of the earth is not deeply covered with organic detritus, it is clear that decomposers consume most of it as fast as it is produced and their numbers are presumably limited by the energy resources of their food supply. Grazing animals, on the other hand, cannot exploit green plant tissue to the limit or they would denude the surface of the globe of its chlorophyll-bearing tissue. Hence, their population density must be regulated by some factor other than food, most likely predation. For carnivores, however, there is a fair amount of evidence to suggest that they increase their numbers to the limit of the energy available to them in the form of production by prey species. Sometimes there is direct contest for food or living space, but in many cases numbers appear to be limited by social convention. In consideration of this question the subjects of ecology and animal behaviour are closely intertwined.

When the physical and chemical features of an ecosystem remain reasonably constant for a long period, the organisms themselves have a modifying effect on the environment. This changes the balance between species and enables new species to enter the system, colonizing every possible ecological niche. A system which has matured in this way appears to be buffered against change. Because there are many species present, it is unlikely that a fall in numbers of one member of a trophic level will be matched by an increase in some other. The food-web is complex, so that the pathways of energy-flow through the system are very diverse, and if one route is constricted it will not make much difference to the total flow. Studies of ecological succession and quantitative studies of species diversity acquire a new significance when viewed in this context.

There is a growing body of knowledge in the field of production ecology and comparisons have been made between the production of populations of algae, of fish, and so on, in a variety of different situations. If production is seen as the process whereby energy and material are handed on through the trophic levels, it is possible to think of an ecosystem as a kind of supra-organism with its characteristic metabolic rate and its own brand of biological activity. One way of defining the aims of conservation would be in terms of maintaining the metabolism and the distinctive character of the ecosystems being conserved.

IV. PRACTICAL WORK

Much of the practical work which accompanies a lecture course along these lines is of the kind which is familiar to most ecologists. The aim is to acquaint students with the characteristic fauna and flora of various habitats and show how the distribution of species is influenced by physical and chemical factors. The results of competition are demonstrated in the field and laboratory and attention is drawn to the evidence of ecological succession. But in addition to all this it is possible to investigate the structure and function of ecosystems in a more specific way. Figures 2 and 3 illustrate the results of two class exercises which have been carried out by Reading students.

The first is a generalized result of an exercise which has been carried out many times by third-year students as part of their freshwater ecology course. An area of 100 m² is marked off in a chalk stream which is about 10 m wide and 30 cm deep. Quadrats are placed at random and the contents removed by means of hand nets which are kept facing upstream. All organisms are identified, counted and weighed and the population of each species in the study area is calculated. Gut contents are investigated and a food-web is constructed. The organisms are sorted into trophic levels and pyramids of numbers and of biomass are prepared. The students are invariably surprised by the large numbers of organisms present. There is no measurement of metabolism but the structure of the ecosystem is clearly seen and it is therefore much easier to comprehend the workings of some of the processes that have been described above.

The second exercise was carried out by a class of about forty first-year students in the course of 4 afternoons in the early summer. Soil temperature, incident light, percentage of light reaching the soil and percentage reflected by the vegetation were measured on more than one occasion. Quantitative samples of the vegetation were taken at intervals of 1 week and the relative growth-rates of various types of plant were calculated. The fauna above and below ground was sampled by means of Tullgren

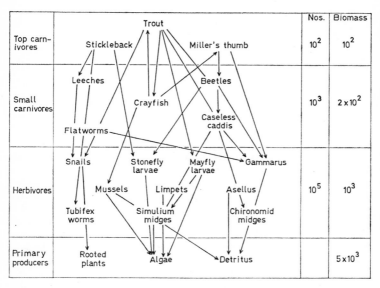

FIG. 2. Diagram illustrating in a simplified manner the trophic structure of a chalk stream ecosystem. Biomass figures are wet weight in grammes.

funnels, cores, quadrats, sweep-nets and small mammal traps, and the catch was sorted into carnivores and herbivores. The rates of respiration of soil samples, litter samples and representatives of the various categories of consumers were measured by determining the rate of CO_2 production, using Pettenkofer tubes. At the end of the exercise it was possible to produce the energy-flow diagram in Fig. 3. It brings out well the relative proportions of the energy-flow in different directions. These figures are, of course, very approximate, but they indicate that truly functional studies of ecosystems are not beyond the capabilities of elementary students.

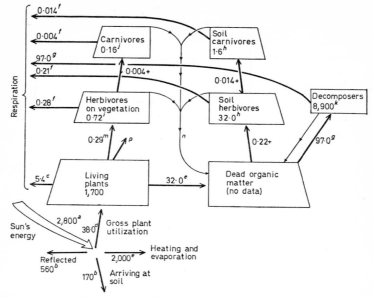

Fig. 3. Energy-flow diagram for a meadow in Southern England in early summer. Standing crops in kcal/m² and energy-flow in kcal/m²/day. *a*, calculated from total hours of sunshine for Reading area by the standard (Penman) formula; *b*, measured on site; *c*, calculated as one-sixth observed net increase in plant weight; *d*, observed increase in plant weight plus respiration and grazing; *e*, that not otherwise accounted for; *f*, calculated from animal biomass and rate of respiration; *g*, respiration of total soil sample, less that of animals; *h*, amalgamated data from Tullgren extraction, o. dichlor. benzene extraction, cores, and three-fifths of estimates of carnivorous birds; *i*, tins placed over vegetation and all animals caught and sorted; *j*, as in *i*, plus two-fifths of estimate of carnivorous birds; *k*, calculated from rate of respiration assuming 1 cal/g/h; *m*, only 0.9 per cent of plant production; *n*, production of dead organic matter not estimated; *p*, production to beef and hares, not estimated; +, something to be added for animal growth, which was not measured.

V. CONCLUSIONS

Macfadyen once wrote (pers. comm.): 'The primary purpose of teaching ecology is to equip people to understand what goes on in ecosystems and to anticipate the probable outcome of changes, both natural and artificial, in such systems.' It is difficult to see how this aim can be achieved unless the properties of ecosystems are presented in a systematic way and the principles on which they work are brought out as clearly as possible. A tentative formulation of these principles is given below.

1. The ecosystem is the functional unit in ecology.

2. Energy flows through successive trophic levels of the system and is not recycled.

3. Plant nutrients are constantly recycled and without them energy cannot flow.

4. The kinds of organism present in an ecosystem are determined in part by the physical and chemical factors of the environment.

5. Of the organisms that could exist in the physical and chemical conditions obtaining, many will be excluded by competition for resources.

6. Populations tend to be self-regulating, having homeostatic mechanisms which adjust population size to the resources of energy and materials available.

7. When environmental conditions are reasonably stable, ecosystems tend to change towards a more mature condition in which there is a greater diversity of species, a greater stability in population densities and more regularity in the flow of energy and materials.

ACKNOWLEDGMENTS

The author is indebted to Professor A.Graham, Mr A.Macfadyen and Dr T.B.Reynoldson for criticism of the paper and to Dr R.M.Wadsworth and Professor G.Williams for stimulating discussions and for permission to use data obtained in a field class under their supervision.

THE DESCRIPTIVE APPROACH TO
VEGETATION STUDIES

M.C.F.PROCTOR

Department of Botany, University of Exeter

I. INTRODUCTION

Ecology grew up largely as a descriptive science, and even now descriptive work makes up a substantial part of the ecological literature. In the last few decades, quantitative and experimental work have taken an increasingly prominent share of the subject, and it has become possible to feel that ecology is emerging from a pioneer qualitative and descriptive phase into a quantitative and analytical maturity. But this antithesis, if it is an antithesis at all, represents only a part of the truth. Study of the regularities in the composition of vegetation is a legitimate scientific object in itself, and one to whose attainment the preliminary reconnaissance of Tansley's *The British Islands and Their Vegetation* (1949) only points the way. The ecological hypotheses that are tested in the laboratory are made in the field, and ecological work that loses touch with the field—the *oikos* of the plant—ceases to be ecology. Descriptive ecology provides the context within which laboratory results can be interpreted in the field, and a powerful tool for generalizing the results of autecological studies. Thus, apart from its intrinsic worth and interest, the student should learn something of descriptive ecology as part of the historical background of his subject, as a tool for the generation of ecological hypotheses, and as a framework for the interpretation of experimental results.

II. FIRST BEGINNINGS

The student's first direct contact with vegetation during a university course will often be through a series of day or half-day excursions into the surrounding countryside. Excursions of this kind may be planned with a variety of purposes in mind; to learn to recognize species, to see some of the main local vegetation types, to study the effect of various habitat factors, or to see examples of the evidence for plant succession. It is worth planning some of the excursions primarily for the purpose of studying examples of communities differing in overall composition, and not

merely in physiognomy or in the occurrence of dominants or other conspicuous species. In the Department of Botany at Exeter, we run a series
of six excursions for our first- and second-year honours students. Two of
these are particularly adapted to consideration of differences in composition between neighbouring pieces of vegetation.

About 8 miles east of Exeter the Triassic Pebble Beds form a prominent
heath-covered ridge. The flattish top of the ridge is occupied by a dry
heath, dominated by varying proportions of six species: *Calluna vulgaris,
Erica cinerea, E. tetralix, Ulex gallii, Agrostis setacea* and *Molinia caerulea.*
The grasses are favoured relative to the other species by burning, so that
conspicuous fire-lines can often be seen in the heath; inspection of these
quickly shows that their visual impact belies their relatively trivial and
transient vegetational significance. The spring-lines in the valleys are
marked by an abrupt change to a characteristic wet heath, lacking
Agrostis setacea and *Erica cinerea,* but with a very constant assemblage of
species including *Sphagnum compactum, S. tenellum* and *Trichophorum
cespitosum.* In the area we usually visit, on Aylesbeare Common, this
zone of wet heath passes at its lower edge into either a valley-bog community on shallow peat, with abundant *Sphagnum papillosum* and *Narthe-
cium ossifragum,* or into a rather species-rich wet heath showing some
influence of calcareous water, with *Cirsium dissectum, Succisa pratensis,
Carex hostiana,* etc.

Many east Devon hills show very clearly the contrast between the soft,
fertile New Red rocks of the lower slopes and the harder, infertile Upper
Greensand and Clay-with-flints above. This appears in the geomorphology
as a change in slope, and in the vegetation as a sharp line between arable
cultivation or improved pasture, and uncultivated heath or conifer plantations. We see hills of this character in the course of another excursion,
en route to Branscombe. At Branscombe Mouth itself, the lowest parts of
the cliffs are made up of Triassic red marl and 'Head' in the valley bottom.
Above this is a substantial thickness of Upper Greensand, of which the
uppermost bed is a hard calcareous sandstone, the Calcareous Grit.
Above this again is the Chalk, capped with Clay-with-flints. Land use
has been influenced by, and in its turn accentuated, the effect of the differences in the underlying rock. Climbing from Branscombe Mouth to the
crest of the cliffs to the east we cross three fields, each separated from the
next by a hedge, and a change of slope (Plate. 1). The lowest field is an
improved pasture, with abundant *Lolium perenne, Cynosurus cristatus,
Trifolium repens, Achillea millefolium, Cerastium holosteoides,* etc. The next
field, on the Greensand, is a relatively poor, mildly acid grassland, with

PLATE. 1. The cliffs above Branscombe Mouth, showing differences in vegetation associated with differences in underlying geology, slope and land use.

PLATE. 2. An area in Donegal, consisting of rocky outcrops, bearing dry heath surrounded by blanket bog, used in a phytosociological exercise.

much *Anthoxanthum, Agrostis tenuis, Veronica chamaedrys*, etc. Above this, the path climbs steeply over typical calcareous grassland on the Calcareous Grit and Chalk, to improved grassland again on the Clay-with-flints plateau at the top.

I have commented on these areas in some detail because they satisfy a number of criteria as good teaching sites for descriptive ecology. At both, the ecological situation is reasonably stable and not too complex. It is reflected in a pattern of well-defined plant communities; these do not at first sight differ too strikingly in physiognomy, so that a full appreciation of their differences requires a close examination of their floristic composition. Both provide substantial areas of reasonably *uniform* vegetation: as Braun-Blanquet (1932, 1951) wrote: 'Uneinheitliche Flächen sin vom Anfänger auszuschalten'—non-uniform areas are to be witheld from beginners.

III. 'TYPES OF BRITISH VEGETATION'

We all recognize and name some vegetation types in a rough-and-ready way, and use such terms as 'heath' and 'chalk grassland' with little conscious thought. How can we go further than this? The problem is analogous to the problem of teaching plant systematics, with a comparable set of difficulties. In both cases, a thorough grounding in the subject requires a grasp of its theoretical fundamentals, a knowledge of established methodology, and a familiarity with those parts of the accumulated body of knowledge in the subject that are relevant to the student's needs.

I am very doubtful of the value of describing plant communities in lectures in a manner analogous to 'doing the families'. This kind of knowledge is more easily and effectively acquired incidentally to other things. A wide range of plant communities can be introduced into a lecture course in the process of illustrating various ecological principles. Woodlands will illustrate climatic climaxes, regeneration, the effects of management régimes on semi-natural vegetation or the catena concept. The hydrosere, leading from open water via reedswamp and fen to woodland or raised bog, provides the example *par excellence* of autogenic succession (see, e.g. Lambert, 1951; Lambert *et al.*, 1960; and the evidence of succession available in many papers on peat stratigraphy and pollen analysis). Calcareous grasslands provide excellent material for a consideration of the effects of slope and aspect (Perring, 1959); together with acid grasslands and heaths they provide obvious examples of the effects of animals on vegetation (see references in Tansley, 1949), and an essential background to consideration of the calcicole-calcifuge problem (Balme, 1953; Steele, 1955; references quoted by Clarkson, 1966; etc.). Dune systems provide fascinating examples of succession (Ranwell, 1958, 1959; Willis *et al.*, 1959), and the allogenic succession of the saltmarsh (see again references in Tansley, 1949) provides a good contrast to the autogenic succession of the normal hydrosere. Vegetational patterns determined by patterns of environmental factors are aptly illustrated by heaths (e.g. Coombe & Frost, 1956) or mountain vegetation (Watt & Jones, 1948; Poore & McVean, 1957; McVean & Ratcliffe, 1962). The student will no doubt have seen some vegetation types in the ordinary course of the term's work; field courses in suitable areas can be made the opportunity to widen his experience in this direction also.

IV. PHYTOSOCIOLOGICAL METHODOLOGY

An invaluable account of the various schools of phytosociology is given by Whittaker (1962); it is important that the student should learn something of the presuppositions and methods of working of the main schools whose work he is likely to want to consult. It is a great pity that controversy over the Braun-Blanquet system ever became a quasi-ideological issue. Whatever one may think of some aspects of the theory and practice of Zürich–Montpellier phytosociology, the fact remains that it has been responsible for a vigorous and coherent descriptive ecology over much of central and western Europe, and it has produced a rich literature full of value to the British ecologist if he is prepared to take the trouble to understand it. For this reason, I think some familiarity with the ideas and methods of the school is essential to the training of an ecologist. An account of Braun-Blanquet's ideas will be found in his own text-book (1932, 1964), though this leaves much unsaid that the outsider would like to know. The most useful succinct introduction to the Braun-Blanquet system for English-speaking readers is still provided by Poore's papers (1955a, 1955b). Poore is quite reasonably critical of the apparent circularity of argument in Braun-Blanquet's (ostensible) manner of establishing plant associations; his papers should be read in conjunction with the admirable and sympathetic paper by Moore (1962), and Poore's own more recent ideas on 'successive approximation' in ecology (Poore, 1962).

A great deal can be learnt about phytosociology and (paradoxically) about British vegetation from phytosociological books and papers dealing with neighbouring parts of the Continent. The following is a brief (and no doubt idiosyncratic!) selection of those that we have found useful, for one reason or another: Allorge (1920–21), Barkman (1958), Braun-Blanquet et al. (1951), Dahl (1956), Duvigneaud (1949), Géhu (1961), Lemée (1938), Oberdorfer (1949), Tüxen (1937, 1955). Braun-Blanquet & Tüxen's account (1952) of the plant communities of Ireland is, in spite of some understandable shortcomings, a paper of exceptional interest and value to British ecologists. We now have an excellent phytosociological monograph of the Scottish Highlands by McVean & Ratcliffe (1962), and the more uneven treatment of Scotland as a whole edited by Burnett (1964); a recent addition is the account of the plant communities of the Burren, Co. Clare, by Ivimey-Cook & Proctor (1966a).

V. PRACTICAL TECHNIQUES

Practical phytosociological methods are best learnt in the field, and in the process of analysing field data. Our field methods are generally similar to those of Poore (1955a) and McVean & Ratcliffe (1962), and are summarized briefly by Ivimey-Cook & Proctor (1966a). We use Domin's ten-point scale for cover/abundance assessments. Students seem to have no difficulty in using this, but Braun-Blanquet's simpler scale would do equally well, and there are substantial arguments in favour of adopting the more widely used scale. A group of students can readily produce an 'association' table from a more or less uniform area of vegetation, or from a number of comparable stands, which will give a very fair idea of the composition of the community and allow generalizations to be made about the constancy and cover-values attained by the various species. Comparison of two or more such tables will provide material for consideration of differential and faithful species. It is in many ways more rewarding for students with some experience of describing vegetation to collect quadrat lists from a suitable area of country (aiming to describe uniform stands), and to try afterwards to analyse their results into a series of communities, which they can subsequently go back and re-examine in the field. Table 1 shows the results of an exercise of this kind in the area around Portnoo, Co. Donegal. The landscape is made up largely of a mosaic of patches of dry heath on thin peaty soil over well-drained rock outcrops, with areas of thin, usually rather flushed blanket bog in the valleys and on the more extensive and flatter summits (Plate 2). The students worked in pairs, distributed around an area a couple of miles across. Thirty-six lists were assembled in a preliminary table in two rough groups, 'wet' and 'dry'. Examination of this table showed that a group of correlated species tended to occur in the 'wet' half of the table, and a

I

TABLE I. Two noda extracted from vegetation data from Portnoo, Co. Donegal (species occurring in only one or two samples are omitted from the table)

(a) Species occurring principally in Nodum 1

Erica cinerea	4	4	×	3	2	5	5	4	6	—	—	—	—	—	—	1	—	2	3
Dicranum scoparium	×	2	2	2	1	×	×	1	2	—	—	—	—	—	—	×	2	—	1
Lotus corniculatus	3	3	3	2	4	4	4	—	3	—	—	—	—	—	—	—	4	—	—
Pseudoscleropodium purum	×	3	3	2	1	—	×	4	2	—	—	—	—	—	—	×	4	—	2
Stieglingia decumbens	—	3	2	4	3	5	—	5	3	—	—	—	3	—	—	2	—	—	—
Antennaria dioica	2	3	—	3	3	—	—	4	—	—	—	—	—	—	—	—	—	—	—
Viola riviniana	1	—	2	—	1	2	—	3	—	—	—	—	—	—	—	1	—	—	—
Euphrasia sp.	1	1	1	—	—	—	—	3	—	—	—	—	—	—	—	1	—	—	—
Hypericum pulchrum	1	—	3	—	—	—	—	3	—	—	—	—	—	—	—	—	—	—	—
Juniperus communis	5	—	—	1	—	—	2	2	2	—	—	—	—	—	—	—	—	—	—
Koeleria cristata	1	2	—	2	—	—	—	1	—	—	—	—	—	—	—	—	—	—	—
Lathyrus montanus	2	3	—	—	2	3	—	—	—	—	—	—	—	—	—	—	—	—	—
Frullania tamarisci	×	2	3	—	—	—	—	2	—	—	—	—	—	—	—	—	3	—	—
Anthoxanthum odoratum	1	1	—	—	—	—	—	1	—	—	—	—	—	—	—	—	—	—	—
Carex caryophyllea	—	2	4	—	—	—	3	—	—	—	—	—	—	—	—	—	—	—	—
C. pulicaris	3	—	4	—	—	—	—	1	—	—	—	—	—	—	—	—	—	—	—
Gentianella campestris	—	2	—	—	3	—	—	1	—	—	—	—	—	—	—	—	—	—	—
Plantago lanceolata	—	3	—	2	—	—	—	2	—	—	—	—	—	—	—	—	—	—	—
P. maritima	—	2	1	—	—	—	—	3	—	—	—	—	—	—	1	—	—	—	—
Polygala vulgaris	—	2	—	1	—	—	—	2	—	—	—	—	—	—	1	—	—	—	—
Solidago virgaurea	1	2	—	—	—	—	—	2	—	—	—	—	—	—	—	—	—	—	—
Campanula rotundifolia	—	3	—	—	2	—	—	—	—	—	—	—	—	—	—	1	—	—	—

(b) Species occurring principally in Nodum 2

Erica tetralix	—	—	—	—	2	1	—	—	4	5	4	4	3	4	4	3	4	1	2
Narthecium ossifragum	—	—	—	—	—	×	—	—	2	7	—	5	6	6	6	6	4	4	5
Breutelia chrysocoma	—	—	—	—	×	×	4	—	3	2	2	3	3	×	3	2	3	3	—

Species	1	2	3	4	5	6	7	8	9
Cirsium dissectum	3	1		4				5	3
Diplophyllum albicans	1				3	3	4		
Sphagnum plumulosum	5				4			2	3
Nardus stricta	3					3	7	4	6
Carex panicea				1	3				
Anagallis tenella	2		7	4			2	3	
Schoenus nigricans		3			2	4	3		
Leucobryum glaucum	2		4			5			
Sphagnum papillosum			5		4	3	4		
S. capillaceum					4	1			
Saccogyna viticulosa			1		1				
Drosera rotundifolia									

(c) Other species

Species	1	2	3	4	5	6	7	8	9
Molinia caerulea	3	4	5	4	6	8	9	6	7
Potentilla erecta	2	1	3	3	4	2	3	3	3
Calluna vulgaris	6	2	5	1	3	5	4		4
Succisa pratensis	5	2	4	4	4	2	3	3	2
Carex flacca	6	4	4	4	5			4	3
Hypnum cupressiforme	1		3	x		4	1		
Salix repens	3	3		6	2	4	1		2
Agrostis canina	1						5		4
Hylocomium splendens	1	1	1			2	1		
Pedicularis sylvatica	2			3			4		
Festuca rubra									1
Cladonia impexa	3	2	4						
Drepanocladus revolvens				x					
Scapania gracilis									
Thuidium tamariscinum									

x = present, cover value not recorded.

second correlated group tended to occur in the 'dry' half of the table. Each list was then scored for the number of 'wet' and 'dry' species it contained, and the lists were rearranged into a second table, excluding from the two main blocks those lists containing a large number of *both* correlated groups of species, or containing very few of either. In the light of this classification of the samples, it was possible to revise the groups of 'differential' species, and to examine the distribution of the remaining species within the two major groups of lists. In Table 1, two groups of nine lists—noda *sensu* Poore—have been extracted from the original thirty-six. The species are arranged in three groups: first, those occurring principally in the drier heath community, arranged in descending order of constancy of occurrence within the nine samples; second those occurring principally in the flushed blanket bog; and third, those showing no well-defined preferences. Both communities so defined follow 'Raunkiaer's Law'; in each, many more species occur in eight or nine samples than occur in six or seven. This is not true of the original data, and might be taken as evidence for a high degree of homogeneity or constancy of composition within each nodum.

The remaining eighteen samples from the original data include some which might be regarded as mixtures or transitions between the two noda we have extracted, and some which, with further field work, would almost certainly be found to fall in additional noda. There was, for instance, an obviously coherent group of quadrats containing *Trichophorum cespitosum* and *Nardus*, but lacking *Lotus corniculatus*, evidently representing a wet-heath type significantly different from either of the communities of Table 1.

The noda, once delimited and characterized, can be compared with those described from other areas and their ecological relationships explored. We were able to make such a comparison with the results of a similar but more extensive study of the area round Errigal Mountain where our series of noda showed a striking and satisfactory similarity to noda described from the comparable quartzite mountains of the north-west Highlands by McVean & Ratcliffe.

In the two examples quoted it was convenient to start the analysis with a rough ecological division of the field data—a division which was in part confirmed and in part rejected by the subsequent analysis. We could equally well have started simply by looking for groups of correlated species, or correlated lists, and then continued by the same process of successive approximation. 'Raunkiaer's Law' can be very useful in the final stages of delimiting communities; if the lists responsible for gaps in the distribution of species of constancy-class IV are noted, obvious misfits can quickly be eliminated.

IV. PHYTOSOCIOLOGICAL THEORY

I have deliberately left this aspect of descriptive ecology until last. It bristles with controversy, poses substantial conceptual difficulties, and can only be satisfactorily discussed when the student has a good deal of familiarity with vegetation and phytosociological ideas. For that reason, I think it is largely for the final honours year, when it can provide very stimulating and thought-provoking material for discussion. Phytosociology aims to produce a taxonomy of vegetation—which is not to imply a belief that plant communities are in any way biologically comparable with species. Whether such a taxonomy is possible or desirable (Webb, 1954), and if so, how it can best be attained, can be discussed in relation to the literature of traditional phytosociology and the geometrical models that have become much more familiar in recent years through the development of multivariate classification and ordination techniques (Goodall, 1963; Dagnelie, 1960; Williams & Lambert, 1960, 1961; Greig-Smith, 1964; Williams & Dale, 1962; Lambert & Dale, 1964; Orloci, 1966; etc.). The incipient phytosociologist should read Sokal & Sneath's *Principles of Numerical Taxonomy* (1963); conversely, some people will probably find that ecological data provide an easier approach to multivariate methods than plant taxonomy. The association-analysis technique of Williams and Lambert, with its correlation-weighted monothetic classification system, provides a particularly useful model for a discussion of the theory of phytosociology (Ivimey-Cook & Proctor, 1966b).

My own belief that a classification of vegetation is both possible and desirable is implicit in the writing of this paper; for reasons outlined elsewhere (Ivimey-Cook & Proctor, 1966a, b) I consider ordination methods inherently complementary to classification rather than a potential substitute for it. I would hope and expect to see such a classification achieved by a developing traditional phytosociology, using numerical methods as tools wherever they were appropriate. I think the achievement of such a classification, or rather its continuing growth, would be of immeasurable benefit to ecology.

REFERENCES

ALLORGE P. (1920–21) Les associations végétales du Vexin français. *Rev. gén. bot.* **33–34.**
BALME O.E. (1953) Edaphic and vegetational zoning on the Carboniferous limestone of the Derbyshire dales. *J. Ecol.* **41,** 331–344.

BARKMAN J.J. (1958) *Phytosociology and Ecology of Cryotogamic Epiphytes.* Van Gorcum, Assen, Netherlands.

BRAUN-BLANQUET J. (1932) *Plant Sociology.* Trans. Fuller & Conard. McGraw Hill, New York.

BRAUN-BLANQUET J. (1951) *Pflanzensoziologie,* 2nd edn. Springer, Vienna.

BRAUN-BLANQUET J. (1964) *Pflanzensoziologie,* 3rd edn. Springer-Verlag, Vienna.

BRAUN-BLANQUET J., ROUSSINE N. & NEGRE R. (1951) Les groupements végétaux de la France méditerranéene. C.N.R.S.

BRAUN-BLANQUET J. & TÜXEN R. (1952) Irische Pflanzengesellschaften. In *Die Pflanzenwelt Irlands* (ed. W.Lüdi). *Veröff. geobot. Inst. Rübel,* **25,** 224–415 Bern.

BURNETT J.H. (ed.) (1964) *The Vegetation of Scotland.* Oliver & Boyd, Edinburgh.

CLARKSON D.T. (1966) Aluminium tolerance in species within the genus *Agrostis. J. Ecol.* **54,** 167–178.

COOMBE D.E. & FROST L.C. (1956) The heaths of the Cornish serpentine. *J. Ecol.* **44,** 225–255.

DAGNELIE P. (1960) Contribution à l'étude des communautes végétales par l'analyse factorielle. *Bull. Serv. Carte Phytogéogr.* Sér. **B5,** 7–71, 93–195.

DAHL E. (1956) *Rondane: Mountain Vegetation in South Norway and its Relation to the Environment.* H. Aschehoug, Oslo.

DUVIGNEAUD P. (1949) Classification phytosociologique des tourbières de l'Europe. *Bull. Soc. Roy. Bot. Belg.* **81,** 58–129.

GÉHU J.M. (1961) Les groupements végétaux du bassin de la Sambre française. *Vegetatio,* **10,** 69–148, 161–208, 257–372.

GOODALL D.W. (1963) The continuum and the individualistic association. *Vegetatio,* **11,** 297–316.

GREIG-SMITH P. (1964) *Quantitative Plant Ecology,* 2nd edn. Butterworth, London.

IVIMEY-COOK R.B. & PROCTOR M.C.F. (1966a) The plant communities of the Burren, Co. Clare. *Proc. R. Irish Acad.* **64 B 15,** 211–301.

IVIMEY-COOK R.B. & PROCTOR M.C.F. (1966b) The application of association-analysis to phytosociology. *J. Ecol.* **54,** 179–192.

LAMBERT J.M. (1951) Alluvial stratigraphy and vegetational succession in the region of the Bure Valley Broads. III. Classification, status and distribution of communities. *J. Ecol.* **44,** 493–516.

LAMBERT J.M. & DALE M.B. (1964) The use of statistics in phytosociology. *Adv. ecol. Res.* **2,** 59–99.

LAMBERT J.M., JENNINGS J.N., SMITH C.T., GREEN C. & HUTCHINSON J.N. (1960) *The Making of the Broads: A Reconsideration of Their Origin in the Light of New Evidence.* Royal Geographical Society, London.

LEMÉE G. (1938) Recherches écologiques sur la végétation du Perche. *Rev. gén. bot.* **50.**

MCVEAN D.N. & RATCLIFFE D.A. (1962) *Plant Communities of the Scottish Highlands.* H.M.S.O., London.

MOORE J.J. (1962) The Braun-Blanquet system: a reassessment. *J. Ecol.* **50,** 761–769.

OBERDORFER E. (1949) *Pflanzensoziologische Exkursionsflora für Südwestdeutschland und die angrenzenden Gebiete.* Ulmer, Stuttgart.

ORLOCI L. (1966) Geometric models in ecology. I. The theory and application of some ordination methods. *J. Ecol.* **54,** 193–215.

PERRING F.H. (1959) Topographical gradients of chalk grassland. *J. Ecol.* **47,** 447–481.

POORE M.E.D. (1955a) The use of phytosociological methods in ecological investigations. I. The Braun-Blanquet system. *J. Ecol.* **43**, 226–244.

POORE M.E.D. (1955b) The use of phytosociological methods in ecological investigations. II. Practical issues involved in an attempt to apply the Braun-Blanquet system. *J. Ecol.* **43**, 245–269.

POORE M.E.D. (1962) The method of successive approximation in descriptive ecology. *Adv. ecol. Res.* **1**, 35–68.

POORE M.E.D. & McVEAN D.N. (1957) A new approach to Scottish mountain vegetation. *J. Ecol.* **45**, 401–439.

RANWELL D.S. (1960) Newborough Warren, Anglesey. II. Plant associes and succession cycles of the sand dune and dune slack vegetation. *J. Ecol.* **48**, 117–141.

SOKAL R.R. & SNEATH P.H.A. (1963) *Principles of Numerical Taxonomy.* Freeman, San Franciso.

STEELE B. (1955) Soil pH and base status as factors in the distribution of calcicoles. *J. Ecol.* **43**, 120–132.

TANSLEY SIR ARTHUR G. (1949) *The British Islands and Their Vegetation.* (Reprinted with corrections from 1st edn., 1939). Cambridge University Press.

TÜXEN R. (1937) Die Pflanzengesellschaften Nordwestdeutschlands. *Mitt. flor.-soz. Arbeitsg. in Niedersachsen,* **3**, 1–170.

TÜXEN R. (1955) *Das system der nordwestdeutschen Pflanzengesellschaften. Mitt. flor.-soz. Arbeitsg.* N.F. **5**, 155–176.

WATT A.S. & JONES E.W. (1948) The ecology of the Cairngorms. I. The environment and the altitudinal zonation of vegetation. *J. Ecol.* **36**, 283–304.

WEBB D.A. (1954) Is the classification of vegetation either possible or desirable? *Bot. Tidsskr.* **51**, 362–370.

WHITTAKER R.H. (1962) Classification of natural communities. *Bot. Rev.* **28**, 1–239.

WILLIAMS W.T. & DALE M.B. (1962) Partition correlation matrices for heterogeneous quantitative data. *Nature, Lond.* **196**, 602.

WILLIAMS W.T. & LAMBERT J.M. (1960) Multivariate methods in plant ecology. II. The use of an electronic digital computer for association-analysis. *J. Ecol.* **48**, 689–710.

WILLIAMS W.T. & LAMBERT J.M. (1961) Multivariate method in plant ecology. III. Inverse association-analysis. *J. Ecol.* **49**, 717–729.

WILLIS A.J., FOLKES B.F., HOPE-SIMPSON J.F. & YEMM E.W. (1959) Braunton Burrows: the dune system and its vegetation. I. *J. Ecol.* **47**, 1–12; II. ibid. 249–288.

THE STUDY OF ANIMAL DISTRIBUTION
AND MOVEMENT IN THE FIELD

A.MACFADYEN

Zoology Department, University College of Swansea

I. INTRODUCTION

It is probably unnecessary to state at this point in the volume that I do not believe that the teaching of ecology should be dominated by a single set of ideas or a single teaching method. We hope, or we should hope, for far too many different results from ecological teaching and we are certainly expected to teach too many different kinds of people. On the other hand, it seems clear that the main purpose of teaching ecology, as distinct from other branches of biology, is to give people insight into the mode of operation and the characteristics of ecosystems. For this reason, and not because I do not value their own characteristic potential contributions to a biological training, I believe that ecology courses should exclude work which is primarily directed towards studies in systematics, behaviour, genetics and evolution. Certainly, we should remind our students of the overlap between different biological disciplines but we have too much to do in the ecological field for us to dilute our courses with work adequately covered in other fields.

The study of whole ecosystems at a theoretical level is an important part of ecology and it would probably be valuable to include experimental ecosystem work with micro-organisms in a laboratory course, although I am afraid I have not had any success in this direction yet. However, it seems clear that the only way to involve a class in field ecosystem projects is to fragment the work, probably not only between students but even between successive year-groups. The result of this is likely to be a feeling of confusion and a lack of purpose in some students, and a failure to provide adequately for the student himself to learn to plan and take responsibility for his work. I find that students usually work better when faced with a clearly understood problem and a challenge to solve it. Also, of course, students vary in their appreciation of more theoretical ideas and some at least, who would not otherwise be interested, can be truly stimulated by outdoor work amongst organisms. The ecology course, therefore, should surely not attempt to teach all aspects of the subject through all available media (lecture, tutorial, laboratory and field exercise), but should concentrate on teaching each aspect in its most appropriate setting, whilst ensuring that as many approaches as possible are exploited. I suggest that one of the least satisfactory ecological teaching activities is the conduct of field classes and I want to face up to this situation in the paper which follows. I submit that the subject is worth consideration if only because we must help to train ecologists who can understand and advise about ecosystem structure, function and management if we are to prevent wrong practical decisions being made by people who lack ecological training (Odum, 1964). But I must admit here that a major reason for exposing my own often unsatisfactory experiences is the hope of suggestions from others who have been more successful.

II. GENERAL CRITERIA FOR FIELD EXERCISES

Four essential criteria of a field exercise appear to be: (1) that it can be effectively performed by the students being taught in the light both of their numbers and their abilities; (2) that it catches the imagination and promotes the enthusiasm of the student; (3) that it is relevant and provides an insight into valid ecological situations and principles; and (4) that it avoids the twin dangers of over-simplification on the one hand and nebulous confusion on the other.

The first criterion of practicability is, of course, frequently invoked as an excuse for doing no field ecology at all, or for confining field work to a kind of conducted tour in which the student is supposed to be a passive gleaner of simplified facts. Timetable difficulties are real enough, but they can be overcome either by running intensive field courses, usually in vacations, or else by arranging that ecology practicals come at the end of the week and can be extended into the weekend if necessary. Such practicals should be repeated over a number of weeks throughout, for example, the summer term.

Each of these approaches has its advantages. The former can exploit the stimulus of unfamiliar territory whilst the latter permits extension of work over at least a couple of months and thus covers a wider range of topics and permits the study of seasonal effects, which are otherwise difficult to cover. In both, I strongly favour the use of small groups working successively on clearly defined projects which can be completed in about a day. If, however, one can combine this, as we do at Swansea, with some long-term project which continues for many weeks, I believe this provides more useful training in how to plan one's work, to devise techniques and experiments, to summarize data and generally to take responsibility for seeing the project through to a finish. In practice, we find that we can run a hybrid course for second-year students, during the summer term, using 6 or more weeks based on Fridays. Some projects require night work, and this is carried out, usually from tents, on the Friday to Saturday night. The more enthusiastic students tend to continue the work over the weekend and into the summer vacation, and we deliberately keep the programme very flexible. We never fail to discover students who develop a real flair for field work in this way.

By working with small groups and a variety of projects based on different localities, we find that the problems, both of logistics and of morale, are much less than they were with larger groups.

III. SPECIFIC FIELD PROJECTS

I will turn now to the ecological projects in the light of the principles that I have mentioned. These are many, but I have only chosen for this talk to concentrate on those which are concerned with distribution and movement. In addition, we have successfully carried out productivity studies with salt-marsh pools because the fauna is simplified and there are innumerable replicates; we have used various corpses (both natural and 'artificial') in order to study carrion food-chains; and we have carried out microclimatic studies, especially in sand-dunes, woodland clearings and in relation to the bark of trees and fallen trunks. The above projects are ones which we have evolved for use with classes of up to twenty or thirty second-year students, and they have produced useful results. Others have tended to fall by the wayside, especially those of which the only justification seems to be that they have demonstrated techniques, whether chemical, physical or biological, at the expense of illustrating distinct biological ideas. For this kind of reason we have abandoned surveys of freshwater habitats in which we attempted to correlate the distribution of certain animal species with chemical or physical or even botanical factors. We have done this in spite of the relative ease with which one can devise such projects and show that different species occur in different places, because the implication of the causal relationship between certain environmental factors and the occurrence of particular species is probably specious: it hardly seems fair to leave the student uncertain about what kinds of conclusions he ought to draw if one is not prepared to face up to this situation. Studies on the estimation of animal numbers are another type of exercise which I have tended to cut down in the field, this time because they can be so much more efficiently illustrated in the laboratory, either with inanimate objects such as beads or counters, or alternatively with laboratory populations in the way that has been so thoroughly expounded by Andrewartha (1961). The principles and the limitations of methods such as the Lincoln Index method can be so much more clearly and quickly understood from laboratory studies of this kind that it hardly seems worth supporting them by more than, perhaps, a single population study on a population of grasshoppers, for instance.

Among the distribution studies we have made, the following may be specifically mentioned:

1. *The vertical distribution of woodland invertebrates in space and time*

The theme of such studies is not new, having come to me from Professor Thomas Park of Chicago by way of the Bureau of Animal Population at Oxford. Students use a variety of methods to census the fauna in the different vertical woodland layers as they are classified by Elton and Miller (1954). These authors proposed a very straightforward structural classification of habitats which was specifically designed to enable naturalists to localize their captures according to a meaningful, simple and uniform system.

Samples are taken at intervals during the day and night. Essential points are that the method should be simple and identification as far as possible carried out upon the spot, so that mainly records and not vast collections of mechanically collected material are brought home. The litter within a quadrat is examined simply by first sitting still and watching the surface of the litter, then by hand-picking and subsequently by sieving. Surface fauna is caught in traps and vegetation layers are sampled by beating into a tray. It can be shown in this way that many species are present which are not normally seen by the casual observer.

By comparing collections in different vertical layers at different times of the day and night, the probability of movement between the layers is indicated. This can then lead on to longer-term projects, such as experimental attempts to demonstrate movement by observation and by the use of various kinds of traps and to correlate activity with environmental conditions. One of the most useful traps is simply a piece of brown paper tied like a skirt around a tree trunk so as to allow animals to creep up from below: many animals such as harvestmen, spiders and woodlice collect in these traps and we have been more successful with these than with sticky bands such as are used to control codlin moth on apple trees. The descent of animals from leaves and branches can be measured by catching animals (as well as their faeces) in open trays.

If different groups of students do similar studies at sites with different vegetation, the co-ordination of their results can be done in the laboratory using demonstration material and figures. I deliberately choose a deciduous woodland for such a study because it brings the students up against a really complicated ecosystem but, by concentrating on a few features, we can even then show that some understanding of what goes on is possible. Of course, it also raises taxonomic problems. These can only be met in two ways. Firstly, we use type material which is collected beforehand, is named and is preferably available in the field. It is surprising how few species are really common and, if studies are continued over several years, it is not difficult to amass a really useful collection in this way. Newer methods for preserving in Perspex are very valuable here, although satisfactory methods for the fragile, easily bleached forms, like spiders and harvestmen, are still urgently needed. Secondly, one must stress that this is not a faunistic exercise. Some taxonomic confusion will be inevitable, but the student provisionally uses names such as 'striped springtail X' or 'shiny ramshorn snail Y', and supports these epithets with a selected voucher collection. This is then worked up in the laboratory as far as possible and the categories are used for analysis.

2. Investigations involving the use of pitfall traps

The use of these traps has provided a second type of spatio-temporal distribution study which has proved practicable. A transect of such traps can be used to correlate faunal variation with plant zonation and vegetation structure in, for example, sand-dunes; alternatively, it can be used simply to obtain data on what species are active at different times of the day and by arranging for frequent visits at, say, 3-hourly intervals. The two studies can be combined together, different students working on different aspects.

The second aspect, diurnal activity, is of course subject to weather conditions and for valid results the study should ideally be continued for several months. But the realization that this is so is of value in itself and, when prolonged over a season, a study of this kind becomes even more useful.

A practical point about repeated sampling is the use of traps which consist of jam jars with inner linings. For example, the Metal Box Company make an aluminium can which just fits a standard half-pound honey jar, and the linings can be pulled up quickly for emptying and inspection without disturbing the traps. A trap line of a hundred such jars can be readily managed by a group, or even by a single student after some practice. Of course, the long-term pitfall trap requires the use of rain shelters and preservative solutions, but for class use involving frequent visits, these are not needed.

Once again, as little material as possible should be returned to the laboratory. Material from a preliminary survey can be used for identification purposes and then only voucher specimens are required to support the new finds.

The main theoretical objections to such trapping studies is that they do not measure the population sizes, but depend on many variables which

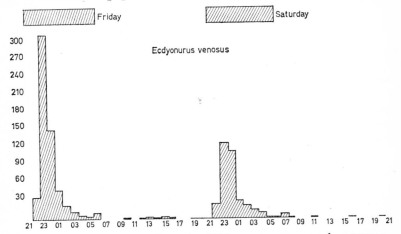

FIG. 1. Diurnal variation in the catch of *Ecdyonurus venosus* at a dam across a stream near Swansea. The shaded area at the top indicates night period. (Data from an unpublished report by C.H.Garvey and associates, Zoology Department, Swansea.)

influence activity. On the other hand, activity itself is well worth investigation and the very clear-cut changes in the fauna, which are active at different times of the day and night, provoke reflection on interspersion of species as well as on the technical shortcomings of limited sampling.

3. *The drifting activity of stream fauna*

This line of study, which has been the subject of several recent papers (see references in Anderson (1966) and Waters (1961, 1962)), provides a fruitful source of interesting data, provocative of experiment.

Such a study is best treated as a long-term exercise, but the apparatus required is minimal. One simply dams a stream so as to conduct the surface water into a bolting silk net and collects the drifting animals at regular intervals. The time in between is spent sorting and counting these and we have not failed to obtain evidence of very distinct diurnal activity peaks in this way. In one such study, very clear peaks in numbers washed down were discovered in the may fly (*Ecdyonurus venosus*) just before midnight (Fig. 1) and in *Ephemerella ignita* a little earlier in the evening. Less distinct peaks but significantly more activity during the night than in the daytime was shown by *Gammarus pulex*. Such a discovery is quite a challenge and it raises all kinds of questions about the nature of the rhythmic activity of the animals and whether, or how, the downward drift is balanced by upstream movement. These problems can then be carried further both in the field and in the laboratory.

4. Diurnal patterns in plankton movement

A somewhat similar exercise to the last is based on the use of a floating plankton sampler drawn over a sizeable body of fresh water at intervals through the day. The most readily accessible pond for us is rather choked with vegetation and is very shallow, but in spite of this it has given distinct diurnal patterns leading once more to experiments. A flooded gravel pit might be a better area to use for this type of work.

IV. THE PLACE OF STATISTICAL WORK IN FIELD EXERCISES

Most of the exercises described so far raise quantitative problems which are most appropriately answered with the aid of statistics, and one of the fallacies which experience of such project work has exploded for me is that biologists do not like, or will not do, statistics. A high proportion of students, faced with a distinct problem to answer, are fully prepared to master statistical techniques and much enjoy the glamour of operating with figures and using calculators. I am convined that such training is remembered much better than that given in formal statistics courses.

Of course, one can set out to devise exercises which have a more high-powered statistical content. I have not so much experience of these, but I can report success with soil samples from which selected, easily recognizable invertebrates were used to demonstrate the use of the Spearman rank correlation method and non-random distribution. Another successful exercise involved similar samples taken along a clear physical gradient (soil moisture level) which were used for correlation analyses. These were both rather lengthy projects and are best given to students with an initial interest in statistics or in the soil fauna. In general, it seems to me the introduction of statistical methods should come as a natural consequence of problems raised by the field work, rather than be a major objective of the ecological programme.

V. PROJECTS SUITABLE FOR LARGE ELEMENTARY CLASSES

In addition to relatively advanced topics for small groups of honours students, there is, of course, the demand for exercises which can be carried out by a much larger number of first-year students. These very large first-year classes seem to me a regrettable result of the coincidence of particular practices at school and the university and their evil effects are manifold. I have encountered only a very few realistic ecological projects which can be undertaken by such classes, especially if animals are to be studied; in practically every case these involve the collection of relatively straight-forward distribution data by individual students or small groups, followed by the synthesis of the distribution pattern by the class as a whole.

We have done exercises of this kind with seashore zonation to produce descriptive data of what species occur where. Mr Goodman and I have also taken Dr Lambert's lead (Williams & Lambert, 1959, 1960) and have asked first-year students to carry out association-analyses between plant species; this has sometimes worked very well but depends on preliminary trials of sample size and thorough preparation on the taxonomic side with fresh specimens brought into the laboratory. We have studied zonation of plants and invertebrates on sand-dune transects and attempted with some success to correlate the two, although here there is a danger of over-simplification. We have had pairs of students collect earthworms by the formaldehyde method (Raw, 1959) from a large area of lawn gridded into half metre square plots by means of string as first suggested to me by Dr T. Reynoldson. The data thus acquired can be used to illustrate the distribution patterns of single species and the association between species at various levels of sophistication. Of course, the demonstration that earth-worms do in fact occur in numbers approaching 100 per m^2 is worth making and never fails to impress. The success of this exercise, however, depends on suitable weather beforehand; this can usually be relied upon in Wales but we have once resorted to the use of a lawn sprinkler some days before the practical class and certainly obtained good yields on that occasion.

We have also studied the distribution patterns of lugworm casts on a sandy shore by throwing wire quadrats of different sizes and have thus illustrated how their fit to a Poisson distribution is highly dependent on quadrat size.

All such projects are practical propositions with large classes and demand little equipment, but they are concerned with rather similar problems of distribution and exploit to only a limited extent the potentialities offered by living creatures in the field. We have attempted with less success to bring members of large classes closer to the ecology of living organisms by splitting classes into small groups each of which searched a defined layer or micro-habitat of the same woodland for invertebrates. The material was worked up, classified by feeding groups, and displayed to the whole class. Success depends on the availability of enough competent demonstrators.

VI. GENERAL CONCLUSION

Large class exercises seem to work fairly well with still docile first-year students, but when we come to those further on in their courses, I am now convinced after a decade of trying to run steadily expanding ecological field classes that something more challenging is required of them. People of that age respond magnificently to being given responsibility and made to think things out for themselves. If merely treated as cogs in a mass-data-collecting machine, they would usually contrive to wreck it. Further, a field course which is run in the field and brings students into contact with living animals never fails to call forth enthusiasm in at least some students. Among these are often some less academically gifted people who genuinely look back on such courses as important stages in their development as biologists.

This is my justification for maintaining that field ecology courses are worth running, despite the need for much effort on the part of the staff and for the modification of some of the more restrictive types of university timetable.

REFERENCES

ANDERSON N.H. (1966) Depressant effect of moonlight on activity of aquatic insects. *Nature, Lond.* **209**, 319–320.
ANDREWARTHA H.G. (1961) *Introduction to the Study of Animal Populations.* Methuen, London.
ELTON C.S. & MILLER R. (1954) The ecological survey of animal communities: with a practical system of classifying habitats by structural characters. *J. Ecol.* **42**, 460–496.
ODUM E.P. (1964) The new ecology. *Bioscience,* **14**, 14–16.
RAW F. (1959) Estimating earthworm populations by using formalin. *Nature, Lond.* **184**, 1661.
WATERS T.F. (1961) Standing crop and drift of stream bottom organisms. *Ecology,* **42**, 532–537.

K

WATERS T.F. (1962) Diurnal periodicity in the drift of stream bottom organisms. *Ecology*, **43**, 316–320.

WILLIAMS W.T. & LAMBERT J.M. (1959) Multivariate methods in plant ecology. I. Association-analysis in plant communities. *J. Ecol.* **47**, 83–102.

WILLIAMS W.T. & LAMBERT J.M. (1960) Multivariate methods in plant ecology. II. The use of an electronic computer for association-analysis. *J. Ecol.* **48**, 689–710.

THE TEACHING OF EXPERIMENTAL
PLANT ECOLOGY

JOHN L. HARPER

Department of Agricultural Botany,
University College of North Wales, Bangor

I. INTRODUCTION

Increasing numbers of the papers in ecological journals are concerned with experimental studies and it therefore seems appropriate that experimental ecology should begin to play an important part in the teaching of ecology in universities.

Traditionally, the teaching of ecology has centred around field classes of one sort or another. The field class, however, even when associated with laboratory practicals, is limited in the number of aspects of ecology which it can present to the student and it may succeed in giving a wrong impression of the range of interests and questions with which plant ecologists are concerned. The main values of field teaching would seem to be that it permits confrontation with the variety of living organisms within and between habitats, that it can be conveniently linked with the teaching of taxonomy and that correlation between species distribution and features of the habitat may be shown. One of the most striking results of a good field class is that it raises a superabundance of questions. When field teaching is linked with the use of specialized equipment or sophisticated sampling techniques, it is possible to demonstrate correlations and so pose questions with precision. Unfortunately, the field class cannot normally go further than establish the correlations and pose the questions. Attempts to answer the questions of causation must involve experimentation.

There is a striking development in both school and university teaching in which the project, particularly the open-ended project, is coming to play a significant part in the programme of practical classes, particularly in the final Honours year. The *rationale* behind this is that much of the excitement of biology lies in the posing, and then answering, of questions to which no right or wrong answers can be given in advance. Research is exciting to many, perhaps most, university entrants, judging from the frequency with which they quote this as their hoped-for career. If they can be given some preliminary experience of the nature of research, it is common experience that they find it an intensely exciting part of the course, generating great enthusiasm and on which they are prepared to spend much more time than in classical practical classes. Such project teaching must involve the posing of a question, the design of an experiment, the growing of the material, the performance of necessary treatments, the analysis of experimental results, the writing up of the results and ideally, some sort of miniature scientific meeting in which the results obtained by the individuals are presented verbally and a discussion between the students is encouraged. Experimental ecology is ideal material for project teaching.

II. THE MAIN FEATURES OF EXPERIMENTAL PROJECT WORK

(a) *Posing of a question*
The best questions for project teaching are those asked by the students themselves rather than those presented as formal class instructions. Whether the experiments are to be done by individuals, pairs or the whole class, there is a great deal to be gained from arguing at some length about the nature of the question that is being asked, and the feasibility of asking specific questions in view of shortages of equipment, growing space, time and competence. There are obvious and grave limitations on the sorts of questions that can usefully be posed for experimental solution, but, within the possibilities, the range is enormous. There is obviously much to be gained by encouraging problems for experimental study to develop from the student's experience in field classes.

(b) *Design*
Many, if not all, experimental studies benefit greatly from careful experimental design, and this offers an opportunity for the student to practise a part of statistics that is normally denied to him: *t*-tests, randomized blocks, Latin squares, replicates, randomization, are concepts that have very little bite or meaning in a lecture course, but in the actual design of an experiment discussions about lay-out, size, the need to foresee harvesting difficulties and predict workloads, give an extremely vivid experience of the role of statistics in experimental design.

There may be a real value in an 'experimental ecology' that goes no further than (a) and (b). A question arises. What procedure might be adopted to answer the question? A class discussion of a project that is never to be performed can make a very valuable seminar!

(c) *The preparation of experimental material*

Much or all of the growing of plants for experiments should be the responsibility of the student. It has often been commented that Botany students, at the time of graduation, do not know how to grow plants. To produce a set of uniform seedlings, successfully to transplant a turf, to apply a nutrienttreatment evenly, to overcome problems of dormancy, are just a few of the ecological experiences which are usually denied to Botany students, but which might be argued to be more fundamental knowledge for a botanist than calibrations of manometers or extracting an enzyme. There are few exercises that expose the problems of plant/water relations so vividly to a student as the need to prevent his own experimental material from wilting or becoming waterlogged!

(d) *Analysis of results*

At the end of an experiment a student may be expected to have obtained quantitative data which, providing the earlier phase of design has been adequately done, should be susceptible to statistical analysis. Undergraduates (and postgraduates) seem prepared to learn and use statistics for analysing their own data, with a readiness that is scarcely ever achieved with sets of second-hand data used in formal statistics classes. The principles of, for example, the analysis of variance can very easily be taught on the results of a simple ecological experiment, and the potency of statistics as a tool for unravelling the nature of interacting factors becomes particularly clear when an ecological question is posed. There may be something to be said in favour of delaying the teaching of statistics until some experiments have posed the question of repeatability or interaction and the need for statistics has been experienced first hand.

(e) *Writing up*

It is clearly desirable that experimental projects of this type should be written up, and written up with an appropriate background of literature. A period spent working on a project should drive the student to the library. He can then, even in a project or experiment lasting only 1 afternoon a week through 4 weeks, but with some spare reading time, produce an account of an experiment and its results in the context of some of the relevant literature. At this stage, he should gain experience of how to handle and present information and in the choice of types of graphs, histograms or tables to be presented.

(f) *Public presentation*

It is surprising how few students, by the time they graduate, have had to stand on their feet and talk. The results of an experimental project provide excellent material for practice in public speaking, because on the subject of their own project students can expect to be more knowledgeable than any of their colleagues, to have some degree of authority and eventually to be ready to face criticism. It is particularly important, where individuals or pairs in a class have been doing different experiments, that sufficient time be given to such 'micro' scientific meetings, for each member of a class ought to discover the difficulties which his colleagues have had to face, and have a chance to make suggestions how the experiment could have been done better or how the results could have been more satisfactorily interpreted.

Many experiments, even under the most careful management, fail. They may fail through accidents or because technical difficulties were not foreseen. Plant material often refuses to grow in a predicted manner and it becomes very important to use experiments that fail as well as those that succeed to maximum advantage for teaching purposes. It is perhaps a fault in most classic practical teaching that an experiment is expected to work, whereas most research experience is that experiments commonly fail. Experience of failure can be turned to great advantage by a discussion of the causes of failure and by the consideration of the revised plans that would need to be made if the experiment were to be attempted again.

In assessing a student's performance in this type of practical it is necessary to take account of failures that are in no sense the student's responsibility, and this can perhaps best be done by allowing a student to gain high marks from an account of an experiment that did go wrong if it includes full interpretation of why it went wrong, together with a discussion of the steps that would be taken if the experiment were to be repeated. Much useful assessment of students' performance in project teaching of this sort can be based on a written account of what the next experiment would be.

Experiments in ecology suitable for undergraduates fall rather naturally into two categories: laboratory, glasshouse or field plot experiments on the one hand, and field experiments on the other. The first category may include types of study which are commonly missed in an undergraduate programme because they come neither within the field conventionally regarded as ecology nor in the field of physiology. Much 'whole-plant physiology' is perhaps best treated as part of ecological training because it is unfashionable with many plant physiologists and tends therefore to be missed out from courses of plant physiology.

III. LABORATORY EXPERIMENTS

The range of experiments that are possible for students at some stage in their degree course, and which require relatively little time and the most primitive equipment, is enormous. Experiments often have to be restricted to those that can be performed within one term with an allocation of one afternoon a week, plus odd periods spent observing and caring for the experiments. There are therefore strict limitations on the species grown, on the stages of growth observed and on the seasons in which the experiments are done. If artificial lighting and heating or primitive controlled environment systems are available, useful work can be done during all seasons of the year. The length of time available poses the most serious restriction on the range of subjects that can be studied, and obviously the ecology of germination, seedling establishment, early growth and problems of regeneration are especially suited for periods of short-term study. The following are examples of sorts of projects which have been proved to work and are likely to give interesting results; they are all suitable for the associated teaching of the principles of experimental design.

(a) *Density of sowing*
A range of densities of plants sown in pots or flats can be used to answer questions about plant plasticity, reactions to interference from neighbours (or competition) and density-dependent mortality. Many of the experiments of J.N.Black (1956–63) on subterranean clover are models for undergraduate projects and can be applied to a wide range of species, provided they are free from dormancy problems.

(b) *Mixed populations*
The growth of populations in mixture compared with their performance in pure stands offers an easy type of experimentation from which much can be learnt about the nature of interspecific effects. In some species a study of mixed populations can be done very well using vegetative units for establishing the populations; for example, very reliable regeneration can be obtained from root segments of *Rumex acetosella*. An experiment in which two species are sown, each in a pure stand and together in 50/50 proportions, all at a density sufficiently high for interference between individuals to occur, is fairly simple to set up and usually poses fascinating

problems in the interpretation of results! It also allows a whole series of operational problems to be exposed, such as the optimal arrangement of the pots or flats, the ideal density or densities to choose, the nature of the soil medium to be employed and the precautions that may have to be taken to eliminate edge effects.

(c) *Light intensity*

A very simple study of light intensity and its effects on growth of one species or a contrasted pair may be done using hessian or perforated zinc enclosures which reduce the light intensity to known proportions of the incident radiation outside the enclosure. Plants grown under a series of three or four such different light régimes may be compared by growth analysis or by simpler analyses of height and dry weight, etc. It is also relatively easy to study the growth of a range of plants under conditions of different spectral composition created by using sheets of photographic filter to enclose growing plants.

(d) *Nutrient levels*

To seedling populations of plants may be added a range of levels of nitrogen fertilizer or other nutrients or combinations. Small-seeded species tend to react to nutrient status most quickly, and the sorts of experiment done by Professor Pigott on the phosphate response of seedlings of *Urtica dioica* can be modified to simple form for class experiments using other nutrient additions or other species.

(e) *Depth of sowing*

Varied depths of sowing often expose relatively quick and interesting differences between species, particularly if species of different seed size are employed. A very simple experiment using seed of *Digitalis purpurea* can demonstrate the importance of burial in inhibiting germination, and can be linked with a comparison of populations sown in darkness and light to disentangle the effects of darkness from other effects of depth.

(f) *Germination contrasts*

Valuable experiments of ecological significance can be obtained by comparing dormancy of a group of species, ecologically or systematically related. Indeed, attempts to break the dormancy of seeds by the direct application of treatments which are aimed to mimic normal environmental experience can be ecologically very revealing.

(g) *Water-table experiments*

Studies in which soil in pots is maintained with the water table at the surface or at various depths below may be coupled with germination studies to show either the variation in performance of one species in the face of this one varied environmental factor or a difference between the response of two species (e.g. a comparison of establishment of *Ranunculus bulbosus*, *R. acris* and *R. repens* at various water tables is described by Harper & Sagar (1953)).

The various experiments described above are all suitable for individuals or pairs of students to perform. All of them involve the taking of critical decisions, for example, about what parameters of plant performance are to be measured. The most simple experiments can be ecologically revealing, and they are all capable of various sophisticated modifications depending on the stage in a student's career at which they are performed. In no case do they demand highly technical equipment, and the techniques that are employed have to be acquired or used because they are demanded by the experiment. This seems a better intellectual exercise than teaching techniques for their own sake or designing experiments with the aim of demonstrating a technique.

IV. FIELD EXPERIMENTS

The majority of experiments that can be performed in the field are long term, and as such are not suitable for project teaching. Unfortunately, it is difficult to generate the same interest and enthusiasm amongst students for an experiment which is being performed by somebody else and in which they are not personally involved. A partial solution to this difficulty lies in the design of long-term experiments which require annual or more often repeated treatment, and in which students can be made responsible for applying a treatment at the same time as they assess the results of the treatment applied on previous occasions. Long-term field experiments can then be designed in such a way that both a treatment and an observation is required once a year, and this can form the basis of 1 or 2 afternoons or days of field class. Most of the experiments described below satisfy these requirements.

(a) *Field nutrient applications*

Some of the most startling long-term field experiments have involved the application of a specific nutrient to established plant communities with consequent changes in floristic composition and/or productivity. Two classical examples are the experiments of Milton at Llety-Ifan-Hên (Milton, 1940) in which various combinations of nitrogen, phosphorus and potassium, with and without lime, were applied to upland grassland and the classic Park Grass experiment at Rothamsted which was essentially of the same form (Brenchley, 1958). These experiments involved annual applications of nutrients and annual records of the changes in population. This type of experiment usually yields some detectable results after 1 year, and a growing magnitude of response over a long period. We have used a simple experiment of this form on a series of habitats which are visited every year. Each year the class takes out a set of small bags of nutrients and these are applied to plots in a pegged area. Nutrients are applied to the same plots each year and we have in this way established a series of simple long-term experiments within areas which are visited as part of the general programme of field classes. These plots may be used as simple demonstrations of the extent to which individual nutrients are limiting in the various habitats or can be used for more detailed studies by individual students or pairs. They can usefully be combined with enclosure plots.

(b) *Deliberate introduction and removal of components from vegetation*
An interesting and instructive group of experiments can be made by the deliberate annual sowing or transplanting of species into a habitat in which they are not normally found. This is, of course, best associated with frequent revisits so that the fates of seedlings and transplants can be examined at various stages. However, even if only visited once a year, such an experiment provides a valuable talking point for discussion about the factors determining the presence, abundance or absence of a plant species.

The selective removal of components from a habitat is now made possible by the development of selective herbicides, and in grassland areas the responses of dicotyledons to the removal of Gramineae by the application of 2,2-dichloropropionic acid is often particularly startling. Such a treatment applied annually can usefully be used to obtain records of the changes in reproductive capacity of species present on the treated and untreated areas. The course of invasion of the habitat opened by removal of the grasses can be usefully done by simple mapping procedures, for example, the use of pantographs. A range of other essentially similar experiments is easily possible, for example, the removal of inflorescences from one species, such as the bluebell, within plots, to indicate the ecological consequences of deflowering.

(c) Lowering of the light intensity

Screens may be erected in the field which will lower the light intensity falling on a given area. These may be used on grasslands or on a woodland floor, but suffer from the disadvantage that they may need fairly frequent attention and encourage vandals.

(d) Fencing

Enclosure plots are particularly valuable for indicating to a body of students the magnitude of the pressures exerted by grazing on vegetation. It is often difficult to find sites in which small areas can be fenced, but where this is possible annual records of the vegetation may be made by succeeding generations of students.

(e) Deliberate creation of bare areas

Small experimental areas of vegetation may be cleared by burning or by the application of general vegetation killers such as paraquat. The stages of succession may then be followed from year to year, and, if a sufficient area is available, a treatment could be provided on a different plot each year so that comparison of regeneration over 1, 2, 3, 4, 5, etc., years could be made by students in the year in which they themselves effect a clearance. Somewhat comparable with this type of experiment is one in which holes are dug within an area of vegetation and filled with standard soil mixes, for example, John Innes compost, a pure peat, a nutrient poor sand, etc. These areas are then allowed to recolonize naturally. This type of experiment followed through successive years enables the influence of soil type on vegetation to be stressed more effectively than the more normal comparison of natural vegetation growing on a variety of naturally occurring soil types where other differences, e.g. exposure, cannot be disentangled from the differences in soil type. At Bangor we have a particular interest in the colonization of mine spoils, and we have found it a useful experiment to create tiny artificial mines by transporting contaminated soil and watching the process of colonization of the spoils. An even simpler experiment involves pots or flats filled with various sterile soil mixes which are placed in natural habitats and allowed to colonize naturally.

The experiments described above are only examples of a wide variety that can be performed. All allow for the accumulation of long-period records, but each year yields results which may stand on their own. Many of these experiments can be useful even though unreplicated and of a 'look-see' nature. It is, however, desirable that the experiments should be well designed so that an enthusiastic student willing to devote some vacation time to a detailed study can obtain useful, meaningful and statistically valid results as a reward for his energies. Many of these long-term field experiments can usefully be performed at field centres and it is delightful to see in the report from Slapton Ley that this is very much in the mind of the warden and his staff (Field Studies Council, 1966). Certainly, if experiments are to be seen as an essential part of the study of ecology, the field centres provide ideal sites for their performance. It would however, be unnecessarily defeatist to leave such experiments entirely to the field centres, even when natural habitats are difficult of access to a university department, because most of the experiments described above could usefully be performed on a corner of a university sportsground on a *Lolium perenne* turf!

V. THE DIFFICULTIES

The main problem in teaching experimental ecology is the amount of time required from members of the teaching staff. The great advantage of traditional field class teaching has been that it can, and unfortunately often does, involve a minimum of preparation. In its simplest form the con-ducted tour, degenerating into a nature ramble, is probable the easiest of all forms of practical teaching practised in university departments. Long-term field experiments may involve much extra trouble such as gaining permission from landowners and the annual provision of chemicals or other materials for the application of treatments. It therefore requires a long-term planning that may be time-consuming. This is, however, negligible compared to the time involved in running project experimenta-tion of the type described earlier in this paper. This must involve a tutorial-type relationship between members of staff and students, with time for discussion of the individual's problems at every stage in the design and performance of a project. This can be a most exhausting type of teaching, and members of staff have to be prepared to be on call not only during the periods allocated for the class, because difficulties may arise at any stage during the growth of experimental material. The burden of work is, moreover, not evenly spread through a term. It tends to be intensive at the beginning of a term when the discussion of individual projects has to be carried out with each student or pair of students separately. It may then go through a period of relative quiet while plants are growing and then a crescendo of activity produces a crescendo of demands on staff and demon-strators as results accumulate, are analysed and written up. But the rewards can be very great. In our experience there can be a marked change in student attitude from one in which the students have to be policed to attend the required set practical to one in which the porters complain that the students cannot be turned out of the laboratories at midnight. The enthusiasm generated by open-ended experiments, performed as projects, is a great reward in itself. Often, members of staff become as involved and excited about the outcome of experiments as the students themselves and a proportion of the experiments done always seems to turn out to have new, exciting and meaningful results.

VI. THE JUSTIFICATION

A training in experimentation is not just a training for those who will become research workers, who it can be argued would derive this sort of experience by reading for an M.Sc. or a Ph.D. With the increasing concern with experimentation in school syllabuses and the deep involvement of the Nuffield scheme in experimentation as a part of the teaching of science in schools, it becomes increasingly important that potential school teachers should have had experience of the sorts of experiments that can be performed simply, easily, with open ends, and yet have meaningful results. It is in the field of ecology that the undergraduate is most able to have the rich experience of asking a question to which the answer is not obvious, performing an experiment to answer this question, and writing and talking about the significance of his findings. It is perhaps the essentially primitive state of ecology that makes it so well adapted for undergraduate study.

REFERENCES

BLACK J.N. (1956–63) Various papers on the ecology of *Trifolium subterraneum*. *Aust. J. agric. Res.* 1956–63.

BRENCHLEY W.E. (revised by Katherine Warington) (1958) *The Park Grass Plots at Rothamsted* (1856–1949).

FIELD STUDIES COUNCIL (1966) *Annual Report 1964–5*, 22.

HARPER J.L. & SAGAR G.R. (1953) Some aspects of the ecology of buttercups in permanent grassland. *Proc. 1st Brit. Weed Control Conf. (Margate)* pp. 256–265.

MILTON W.E.J. (1940) The effect of manuring, grazing and cutting on the yield, botanical and chemical composition of natural hill pastures. *J. Ecol.* **28**, 326–356.

THE EXPERIMENTAL APPROACH TO ANIMAL ECOLOGY

T.R.E.SOUTHWOOD and N.WALOFF

Department of Zoology and Applied Entomology,
Imperial College, London

I. INTRODUCTION

One of the problems in the practical teaching of ecology, indeed in ecological research itself, is the time factor. The actual modes of action and roles of various factors in a natural population can usually be ascertained only after a study extending over many generations, that is in general several years. It is, of course, possible for a class to measure the magnitude of a factor, but its possible role or explanation remains a matter of speculation or is laid down by an *ex cathedra* statement of the teacher. An advantage in the experimental approach is that it enables one to demonstrate within a reasonable period of time the possibilities of population change and the potentialities of various factors. Although we would not suggest that a complete practical course in ecology should consist only of experiments, we do believe that, because of their advantage in demonstrating action in a relatively short time, experiments will play a rather large part in ecological teaching.

The central theme in our teaching of ecology is the population and the changes in the numbers of animals that constitute it. Therefore, we have brought together in this paper a series of experiments that demonstrate, firstly, the influence of habitat in causing population changes and, secondly, the potentialities of the various pathways of population change: natality, mortality and dispersal. We would not suggest that all these experiments should form the major part of an undergraduate course; some of them are taken from undergraduate courses at Imperial College, others from postgraduate courses and some are research experiments we have not yet had the opportunity to use in class. Most of these experiments could be used either at the undergraduate or postgraduate level or indeed in schools; the difference in emphasis at the different levels will be more in the extent of the analysis of the results than in the actual experimentation.

Many of the experiments can be carried out in the laboratory, but others demand ready access to the field, such as we are so fortunate to have at the

Imperial College Field Station at Silwood Park, Ascot, However, the field requirements are not extensive; in general they can be met if about a quarter of an acre of lawn or garden surrounded by larger areas of gardens or farmland can be allocated to ecological teaching. Indeed, the last general point we would like to make is that teaching of ecology, using the experimental approach, can be carried out in semi-urban and agricultural surroundings.

II. EXAMPLES OF EXPERIMENTS

1. *Some experiments to demonstrate the effect of habitat changes on populations*
The purpose of these experiments is to show how changes in the biotic habitat will affect the size of the population of different species. The fact

TABLE I. Some of the differences in numbers of animals per unit area in long and short grass plots (Southwood & van Emden, unpublished)

	Short grass	Long grass
Isopoda—*Philoscia muscorum*	16	97
Orthoptera—Acrididae	6	3
Heteroptera—*Myrmus miriformis*	17	29
Heteroptera—*Nabis ferus*	5	0
Heteroptera—*Pithanus maerkeli*	22	7
Coleoptera—Carabidae	7	17
Diptera—Sphaeroceridae	10	33
Diptera—*Oscinella*	39	11
Diptera—*Elachiptera*	3	16

that the changes are due to man's activities does not, we feel, in any way reduce the teaching value of the experiments; in fact, it rather tends to emphasize the additional point of how man's activities can alter the eco-system.

(a) *Comparison of fauna of short and long grass*
Adjacent plots, originally part of a lawn or field, are subjected to different cutting régimes, one plot being mown or clipped, the other left to grow. The fauna of the two are best compared using a suction apparatus (Johnson *et al.*, 1956; Southwood, 1966), but more simply a relative method may be

used and the class asked to search with an aspirator (or 'pooter') each plot for the same period of time. Quite striking differences will be found in numbers and specific composition (Table 1). After a while the botanical composition of the two plots will come to differ and it will often be possible to demonstrate that some of the differences in animals between the two habitats are due to their different floral composition and the feeding preferences of the animals.

The feeding preference of phytophagous animals may be tested by a single experiment, which is carried out annually by Professor O.W. Richards and one of us (N.W.) with a class of students. Four common

TABLE 2. The numbers of some insects taken in weedy and 'clean' fields of barley (Southwood & Cross, unpublished) and Brussels sprouts (J.G. Smith, unpublished)

Insect	Numbers/unit area in	
	Weedy	'Clean'
BARLEY		
Diptera	7	3
Coleoptera	11	0
Hymenoptera	33	14
Homoptera	6	4
Insect	Mean numbers/plant	
	Weedy	'Clean'
BRUSSELS SPROUTS		
Brevicoryne brassicae	144	66
Aleurodes brassicae	318	1163
Lepidopterous larvae	2	5

plants (A, B, C, D) are selected from the habitat in which the phytophagous insect is found and tubes or cages are set up with the insect and various combinations of equal areas of plants. A convenient plan is ABCD (four tubes), ABC, ABD, ACD, BCD (four each), AB, AC, AD, BC, BD, CD (four each), A, B, C, D (four each). In all, therefore, there are sixty tubes and each plant is offered forty-eight times.

In an experiment where A = *Holcus lanatus*, B = *Rumex acetosa*, C = *Plantago lanceolata*, D = *Lotus corniculatus*, the insect was the grasshopper *Chorthippus parallelus* (third-instar larvae). The tubes were left for 24 hours and the following was the scoring scale: much eating = 2, nibbling = 1, plant untouched = 0. The scores in this particular experiment were A—69, B—12, C—2, D—25.

(b) *Comparison of the fauna of clean and weedy fields*
It is relatively easy to obtain two adjacent plots of a crop. One should be kept weed-free by cultivation or herbicides and a natural growth of weeds should be allowed in the other. Comparisons may be made in two ways: either the total fauna of an area may be sampled with a suction apparatus or by fixed-time searching (as described above), or the numbers of a particular animal on the crop plant may be counted per plant, leaf or other suitable unit, depending on its density. Some typical results from 'clean' and weedy barley and Brussels sprout plots are given in Table 2. Again some of the differences will be due to the weeds being the host plants of certain species and this may be demonstrated as above.

(c) *Demonstration of the effect of ants on the development of aphid populations*
This is a rather more specific experiment, but we regard the greater size of ant-attended colonies as a 'habitat effect' as it is largely 'indirect', due to the influence of ants in protecting the aphids from their natural enemies (Banks, 1962) and only to a lesser extent due to the direct effect of the ants in stimulating the feeding of the aphids (Banks, 1958; Banks & Nixon, 1958). Furthermore, it has been shown in several tropical habitats that the invertebrate fauna of a habitat may vary greatly according to the species of ant that is dominant. Ants may be excluded from a plant or area by the use of netting or an insecticidal, grease, water or electrical barrier (Wheatley & Moezarski, 1950).

One convenient arrangement is to place potted broad bean plants with colonies of *Aphis fabae* in the region of a nest of the ant, *Lasius niger* (L.), as was done by Banks (1962). The ants are allowed free access to some of the colonies (these pots are simply stood on bricks), but are excluded from others by placing them on bricks standing in a shallow trough of water. It is important to ensure that the pots themselves are not stood in the water, otherwise the water-balance of these plants will differ from that of the others and this itself will also affect the development of the aphid population. Besides ensuring, by the artificial removal of some aphids if necessary, that the aphid colonies are about the same size at the start of the experiment, it is also necessary to introduce one or two natural enemies—ladybird (Coccinellidae) larvae or adults, hoverfly (Syrphidae) larvae—on to each plant. The differences in the populations will be apparent in a few days.

Another approach is to take naturally occurring plants, such as spear thistles (*Cirsium lanceolatum*), that are infected with aphids and ants and exclude the latter from some of the plants by a grease or resin barrier on the ground around the base of the stem and on the base of the stem itself.

2. *Some experiments to demonstrate the potential roles of different pathways of population change*

Changes in population size may be brought about through the pathways of natality, mortality or dispersal (including migration) or any combination of these. It is convenient to consider each of these in turn and demonstrate their effects and factors that may influence them.

(a) *Natality*

(i) *The influence of the size (weight) of an individual at emergence on fecundity*
The insect we have found convenient is the moth *Anagaster kühniella* (Zell.), which is easy to rear if constant-temperature rooms are available. Ten hatched larvae (twenty replicates) are placed on 2 g of wholemeal flour in small containers and a small roll of corrugated paper is placed on top of the flour to provide pupation sites. The container is closed with muslin held with a rubber band. At 25° C moths begin to emerge in 5–6 weeks. The females are weighed and paired with males in tubes. The males are then removed, as they interfere with oviposition in confined space. Each female is provided with a strip of folded black paper which serves as the oviposition site. The strip is changed daily and the number of eggs laid on it is counted under a binocular microscope; the muslin tops of the containers are also examined.

At the end of the experiment results can be analysed by simple statistical methods. Correlation coefficients and regression equations relating the weights of females at emergence with total fecundity (natality) are worked out and their significance tested.

(ii) *The influence of crowding and shortage of food in the immature stage on weight and fecundity of the adult moth*
The setting up of this experiment is as above, but instead of ten, 200 hatched larvae are introduced into the container with 2 g of flour. Generally there are fewer surviving individuals, which are smaller and lay fewer eggs. Comparison of survival in experiments (i) and (ii) introduces the idea of mortality in crowded conditions.

(b) *Mortality*

(i) *The demonstration of selectivity by arthropod predators*

The concept of the varying roles of predators in causing mortality can be introduced to students in a simple preference experiment. We usually select the prey insects and the predators from the fauna on broom (*Sarothamnus scoparius*). The prey are the eggs and first-stage larvae of the Chrysomelid beetle *Phytodecta olivacea* (Forster), the broom aphid *Acyrthosiphon spartii* (Koch) or the two species of broom Psyllids. A series of tubes may be set up with the following combinations: six *Phytodecta* eggs; six *Phytodecta* first-instar larvae; three *Phytodecta* eggs and three larvae; six aphids; three aphids and three *Phytodecta* eggs; three aphids and three larvae. Various combinations with Psyllids can also be used. A single predatory arthropod is then introduced into each tube and left for 24 hours. Amongst the predators which we use are the broom Miridae, Anthrocorid nymphs and adults, Coccinellid larvae, earwigs, predacious mites (e.g. *Anystis agilis* Banks), Salticid spiders, Phallangids, etc. The tubes are examined and the numbers of prey eaten are noted. Attention is paid as to whether a predator will take moving prey only, or whether it will attack stationary food as well (eggs) and also whether there is any selectivity of food.

We emphasize to students that these experiments are highly artificial and that a more exact demonstration of predation in the field is possible by serological techniques. In recent years the precipitin test has been widely used; briefly it depends on the interaction of the prey material in the gut of the predator with the antibodies in the blood serum of rabbits which have been inoculated with an extract of the prey (see Dempster, 1960; Richards & Waloff, 1961; Southwood, 1966). These techniques are available to the students at the Field Station and can be used to supplement the above experiment by studies on predators from their natural environment.

(ii) *The feeding behaviour of a predator at different densities of prey (i.e. the functional response)*

The idea of the functional response of predators has received much thought and experimental study by Holling (1964, 1965) in the last few years. The idea may be introduced to students by a simple experiment. At the Field Station cultures of Mantids are available and the nymphs are used as predators. The prey presented to them are *Drosophila* adults introduced in different densities. The numbers of flies eaten per unit time is noted and ideally a curve of the functional response is then drawn. Mantids are not widely available, but other predators, e.g. Phallangids, Salticid spiders or earwigs could be used as experimental material. Holling's laboratory experiment (1959) with the rate of removal of discs by a blind-folded human being can also be easily demonstrated.

The experiment on the effect of ants on aphid colonies described above could be considered here, too, the differences being largely due to the exclusion of predators by the ants.

(c) *Dispersal and migration*

It is perhaps superfluous to stress that movement is a characteristic of animals, but it is this property that adds so considerably to the complexity of studying animal populations and provides an important mechanism for the immediate self-regulation of population size.

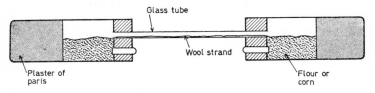

FIG. 1. Simple apparatus for investigating dispersal in a stored-products insect.

(i) *The influence of other individuals*

The influence, if any, of other individuals, i.e. of crowding, on dispersal is conveniently investigated using a stored-products beetle, e.g. *Rhizopertha dominica* (F.), and the apparatus is illustrated in Fig. 1. We have found it important to make a 'road' of strands of wool stuck inside the glass connecting tube with gum tragacanth, or similar material; otherwise the beetles can fall on their backs and may be unable to right themselves. Each chamber is partly filled with a similar quantity of flour, wheat grains or the appropriate medium and a known number of beetles are placed in one of the chambers. After about a week in a constant-temperature room the number that have left the medium and walked through the connecting tube to the other chamber is found by sorting through the medium in that chamber. Typical results for *Rhizopertha* are shown in Fig. 2. The initial densities in this case ranged from 10 to 400, but clearly this would depend on the animal and the volume of media. This apparatus could also be used to compare the amount of movement away from media, differing either in type (e.g. flour or bran) or in conditions (e.g.

various water contents) or to study the effect of numbers of other individuals of a different species on dispersal.

Emigration can also be studied experimentally using the apparatus shown in Fig. 3. This consists of a plastic bucket with wide plastic exit

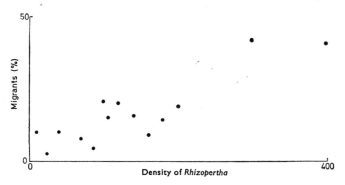

FIG. 2. The relation of dispersal to density in *Rhizopertha*, determined in the apparatus shown in Fig. 1.

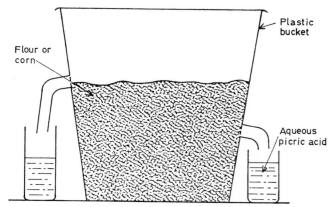

FIG. 3. A container for an artificial population of a stored-products insect allowing emigration.

tubes; a quantity of flour and a stored-products beetle are placed in the bucket and those emigrating are collected in small jars containing an aqueous solution of picric acid placed under the exit tubes. However, we designed and have used this apparatus primarily to demonstrate mark and recapture methods of population estimation in the laboratory.

(ii) *The measurement of vagility*

The vagility of an animal is its potentiality for movement; this may differ from species to species, from individual to individual, within the same individual according to age, and with the type of the habitat. It may be measured or, if desired, some of these variables assessed by releasing a number of marked individuals at a central point and collecting them subsequently in a series of traps arranged concentrically around the point of release. Some research experiments of this type have been described by Dobzhansky & Wright (1943), Nakamura *et al.* (1964) and Paris (1965); the results may simply be expressed in terms of the greatest and the mean distances travelled, or a more complex analysis may be undertaken to to determine if the population is heterogeneous with respect to rate of dispersal, if there is non-randomness in the direction of dispersal, if the rate of dispersal changes with time and which, of the available expressions, best describes the fall-off of density with distance. Details of these analyses are summarized by Southwood (1966). Paris (1965) marked woodlice, *Armadillidium*, and recaptured them under 'cryptozoa boards'. Students at Imperial College made a similar experiment using the adults of the grasshopper *Omocestus viridulus* (L.). Fifty insects (twenty-five males and twenty-five females) were marked on the pronotum with fluorescent yellow cellulose paint and released at a point marked by a stake on a south-facing slope, the northern end of which was bounded by trees. They were collected a week later and a tape measure was used to determine the distance of each specimen from the point of release (Fig. 4). Twenty-eight marked grasshoppers were recovered (twelve males, sixteen females). The average distance travelled by a male was 6.7 m; that by a female 4.3 m. It was appreciated that the distance travelled by each insect was not represented by the distance from the stake, but gave a general indication of the mobility of these grasshoppers. Many specimens were re-captured near to mounds of *Lasius flavus* (L.) which are used for basking.

(iii) *The demonstration of periodicity in movement*

An important aspect of animal movement is its occurrence in different species at different times of the diel; not only does this affect the amount of contact between species, but with small flying insects those that fly mostly near mid-day may be carried far on wind currents, whilst those that are active at dusk are likely to remain in the same locality.

Flying insects are easily sampled with sticky traps; these can be simply constructed from pieces of thick cardboard with a sheet of greaseproof paper clipped on top. A fruit-tree banding resin is then smeared on the

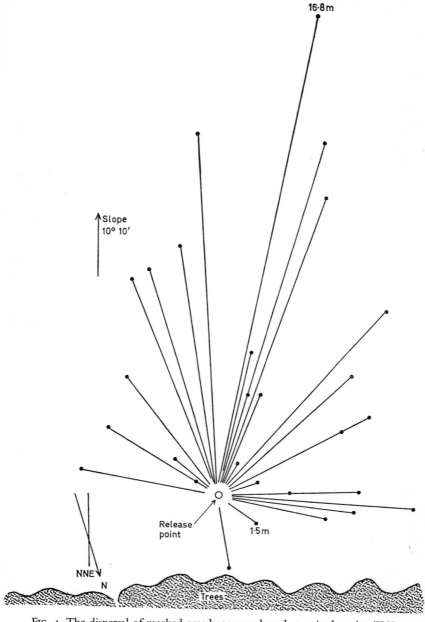

FIG. 4. The dispersal of marked grasshoppers released at a single point (V.K. Brown & C.Wall, unpublished).

greaseproof paper and this large-scale fly-paper will trap flying insects. Sticky traps can also be made from sheets of glass or pieces of perspex folded round a cylinder. A further elaboration can be introduced into the experiment by comparing the catches of glass-plate sticky traps, the

TABLE 3. Comparison of 2 hour catches of some groups by sticky traps during day and night (data from two courses at Flatford Mill Field Centre)

	Day	Night
Isopoda	0	4
Collembola—*Symphypleona*	11	4
Collembola—*Arthropleona*	0	3
Hemiptera—*Auchenorrhyncha*	45	7
Diptera—*Acalypterata*	24	1
Diptera—*Nematocera*	50	12

TABLE 4. The comparison of pitfall catches of various Carabidae

	Day			Night		
	Field	Wood	Path	Field	Wood	Path
Nebria brevicollis (Fab.)						2
Bembidion lampros (Herbst.)	4			12		
B. quadrimaculatum (L.)	2				2	
Harpalus aeneus (Fab.)				2		
Stomis pumicatus (Panz.)				1		
Pterostichus melanarius (Ill.)					2	
P. madidus (Fab.)					7	12
Calathus fuscipes (Goeze)	1					1
Abax parallelopipedus (P. et M.)					1	1
Agonum dorsale (Pont.)	2					
	Total (day) = 9			Total (night) = 43		

under-surfaces of which are painted in different colours. The sticky traps should be placed in the same position for a few hours in the middle of the day and for the same period at dusk. Some typical results are shown in Table 3.

Periodicity of movement on the surface of the ground is conveniently demonstrated by using pitfall traps—i.e. jam jars sunk into the ground until the lip is level with the surface of the soil. The greatest number of ground beetles (Carabidae) will be found in the nocturnal catch, while during the daylight hours smaller numbers of different brightly coloured species will be caught.

For example, on July 9th, 1965, traps were in operation for 4 hours in daytime and for 4 hours after sunset. A hundred yards of a footpath between two grassland areas were also examined and the results obtained by a class of first-year students are given in Table 4. Because the *Harpalus* are seed feeders, they were restricted to the field. The medium-sized predacious Carabidae were all nocturnal, e.g. *Pterostichus*, *Nebria* and *Abax*. Conditions were too cool and overcast for the active diurnal predators of the genus *Amara*, which had been collected in large numbers in the previous years. Other predominantly nocturnal animals found on the path at night were the woodlice, *Philoscia muscorum* (Scop.), *Armadillidium vulgare* (Latr.), and the millipede *Glomeris marginata* (Vill.).

The activity of the small mammals can also be examined by using Longworth traps.

III. DISCUSSION

It is suggested, not that the experimental approach to the study of animal ecology is the only one which should be presented to students, but that it forms a useful supplement to the other analytical methods. It has been pointed out by Varley (1957), in his presidential address to this Society, that frequently a simple experiment in ecology may lead to a more rapid understanding of a complex ecological situation, and we have frequently found this in attempting to convey some basic concepts in ecology to students. For example, artificial alterations in grassland habitats (i.e. by cutting down the plants in one area and leaving a near-by site untouched) provides a useful guide to the choice of habitats by some of the species. Simple experiments help to understand some of the ideas underlying natality, predation or dispersal. It should be remembered, however, that ecology is a difficult subject to teach; the best experiments and the better ecological teaching programmes are usually the by-products of many years of field research by the members of staff or by other ecologists, the most successful demonstrations being the products of the teacher's own research. In other words, the most inspiring part of the course in one university or college may be dull in another. The diversity of approach is in itself a measure of the enormity of this subject and is an important stimulus to the progress of ecology.

ACKNOWLEDGMENTS

Several of the experiments described here have been developed in conjunction with Professor O.W.Richards; to him and to other colleagues and students, past and present, who have made valuable suggestions and allowed us to quote from their results, we are most grateful.

REFERENCES

BANKS C.J. (1958) Effects of the ant, *Lasius niger* (L.), on the behaviour and reproduction of the black bean aphid, *Aphis fabae* Scop. *Bull. ent. Res.* **49**, 701–713.

BANKS C.J. (1962) Effects of the ant *Lasius niger* (L.) on insects preying on small populations of *Aphis fabae* Scop. on bean plants. *Ann. appl. Biol.* **50**, 669–679.

BANKS C.J. & NIXON H.L. (1958) Effects of the ant, *Lasius niger* (L.), on the feeding and excretion of the bean aphid, *Aphis fabae* Scop. *J. exp. Biol.* **35**, 703–711.

DEMPSTER J.P. (1960) A quantitative study of the predators on the eggs and larvae of the broom beetle, *Phytodecta olivacea* (Forster), using the precipitin test. *J. Anim. Ecol.* **29**, 149–167.

DOBZHANSKY J. & WRIGHT S. (1943) Genetics of natural populations. Dispersion rates in *Drosophila pseudoobscura. Genetics, Princeton,* **28**, 304–340.

HOLLING C.S. (1959) Some characteristics of simple types of predation and parasitism. *Can. Ent.* **91**, 385–398.

HOLLING C.S. (1964) The analysis of complex population processes. *Can. Ent.* **96**, 335–347.

HOLLING C.S. (1965) The functional response of predators to prey density and its role in mimicry and population regulation. *Mem. ent. Soc. Canada,* **45**, 1–60.

JOHNSON C.G., SOUTHWOOD T.R.E. & ENTWISTLE H.M. (1957) A new method of extracting arthropods and molluscs from grassland and herbage with a suction apparatus. *Bull. ent. Res.* **48**, 211–218.

NAKAMURA K., ITO Y., MIYASHITA K. & TAKAI A. (1964) Dispersal of adult grasshoppers, *Mecostethus magister,* under the field condition. *Res. Popul. Ecol.* **6**, 67–78.

PARIS O.H. (1965) The vagility of P^{32} labelled isopods in grassland. *Ecology,* **46**, 635–648.

RICHARDS O.W. & WALOFF N. (1961) A study of a natural population of *Phytodecta olivacea* (Forster) (Coleoptera, Chrysomelidae) *Phil. Trans. R. Soc.* **B 244**, 205–257.

SOUTHWOOD T.R.E. (1966) *Ecological Methods, with Particular Reference to the Study of Insect Populations.* Methuen, London.

VARLEY G.C. (1957) Ecology as an experimental science. *J. Anim. Ecol.* **26**, 251–261.

WHEATLEY G.A. & MOCZARSKI S.Z. (1950) An insect barrier utilizing high frequency current. *Nature, Lond.* **165**, 766–767.

THE TEACHING OF QUANTITATIVE METHODS
IN PLANT ECOLOGY

P. GREIG-SMITH

Department of Botany
University College of North Wales, Bangor

I. INTRODUCTION

Unfortunately many undergraduates arrive at the university regarding ecology as of marginal importance, requiring no great intellectual effort and, indeed, as being scarcely scientific. The difficulty is not that they know nothing of the subject but that they have acquired a set of out-of-date and ill-digested ideas. One cannot, therefore, assume any previous knowledge; but this has the advantage of allowing quantitative concepts to be introduced from the start.

A difficulty in introducing quantitative approaches is the near innumeracy of some undergraduates reading biology. Though some elementary mathematical facility is needed in various branches of biology it appears that many sixth-formers are still mistakenly advised that mathematics is not required for biology. It may be hoped that the introduction of some statistical tests into texts designed for school use (e.g. Ashby, 1961) will help to correct this impression.

Many students have thus not only an erroneous idea of ecology but a genuine fear of even the simplest mathematical techniques. To correct the former we must rely on the quality of our teaching to raise enthusiasm. The problem of innumeracy is not so intractable as might appear. Though a small proportion of students appear to be genuinely incapable of achieving even the very modest mathematical competence required for an initial understanding of quantitative plant ecology, the majority, once they see the relevance of doing so, are willing and able to make the necessary effort.

There is ample room for experiment in ways of introducing plant ecology to undergraduates as an essentially quantitative study. What follows represents an individual viewpoint and is concerned particularly with quantitative approaches to descriptive and analytical ecology.

II. MATHEMATICAL BACKGROUND

A quantitative approach to plant ecology need not involve, at the elementary level, the use of statistical analysis, but it is not possible to get far without it. It can be assumed that most biologists will attend a course in statistical analysis, but some aspects of statistics require special emphasis in relation to quantitative ecology and it is clearly more satisfactory if these can be appropriately treated in the general statistics course.

The Poisson distribution, which is of rather limited importance in biology generally, is fundamental to considerations of the spatial distribution of individuals, and deserves more emphasis than it often receives. More important, because they are treated very briefly or even ignored in many text-books for biologists, is some consideration of the principles of sampling, which students appear to find difficulty in grasping. Thus, students tend to suggest random sampling in all circumstances, although systematic sampling, in spite of the statistical limitations it imposes, has evident practical advantages and is obligatory in some cases (Greig-Smith, 1964). Even a single lecture devoted to sampling can do much to provide a basis for sound practice in the field.

A more difficult problem is raised by the multivariate techniques increasingly being used in the classification and ordination of vegetation. Here an understanding of the procedures used requires a much fuller statistical course than can normally be provided or is, indeed, within the capacity of most biological students; a point will necessarily be reached where the average student must be content with understanding what a procedure of analysis does, without fully understanding how it does it.

III. THE PLACE OF QUANTITATIVE METHODS IN AN ECOLOGY COURSE

There are two alternative treatments of quantitative methods; they may be dealt with in an independent course of lectures, or they may be partially or completely integrated into a general course on ecology. If it is accepted that ecology has now reached the quantitative stage, there can be little doubt that quantitative work should be included at the appropriate places in the general teaching of ecology. Some aspects of ecology, such as energy and nutrient flow through the ecosystem, can scarcely be treated other than quantitatively and there is no good reason why topics such as classification and community structure, where discussion in purely qualitative terms is possible, should be treated differently. Indeed, there are evident disadvantages in doing so. For example, a student is much better placed to assess the Zurich–Montpellier approach to classification if it is discussed in the same context as Williams & Lambert's (1959, 1960) quantitative classification. Conversely, the effect of the different weightings of species importance used in different quantitative procedures, a problem only now receiving much attention, is likely to be appreciated more readily if the more obvious weightings of the older approaches to classification are discussed at the same time. The importance of integrating quantitative work into the general ecology course seems obvious but it is not yet universally accepted.

The need to introduce quantitative concepts into practical work from the earliest stages is, if anything, greater. Time available for field work is limited; to use it in superficial and unorganized inspection of vegetation is extremely wasteful. Real understanding will come only from intensive work on a limited range of vegetation and only after time has been given to such intensive work can profit be gained from more extensive field classes.

The traditional practice is the converse of that just put forward; students are first shown a wide range of vegetation types and broad correlations with environment are pointed out. Only then, if at all, is attention turned to more detailed study of particular types. This approach, which sprang, I believe, from a praiseworthy attempt to combine field work in ecology and taxonomy, results in inefficient treatment of both subjects. The ecologist certainly needs to be familiar with the species represented in the vegetation with which he is working, but, especially for quantitative work, ability to recognize the more abundant species in all stages of development is more important than the field recognition of all species, useful though this is, and the more academic aspects of taxonomy are irrelevant. Taxonomy perhaps suffers less, though it is arguable that the attention drawn to habitat features in dual-purpose field work is a hindrance to the inculcation of sound taxonomic principles.

IV. FIELD WORK

There are three principal groups of quantitative techniques that need to be introduced in an undergraduate course. These are concerned respectively with classification and ordination, community structure and correlation with environment. Basic to all of them is an understanding of the various possible measures of species representation in vegetation. In Britain it is useful to introduce into field work two absolute measures, density and cover, and the only important non-absolute measure, frequency. Other measures may be discussed in lectures, but only these three are likely to be used in undergraduate exercises. In other parts of the world a different selection may be made: in the humid tropics, for example, density, basal area and canopy might be more suitable (Greig-Smith, 1965).

Perhaps because of the vague definitions of the different measures given in many elementary text-books, students have difficulty in grasping that different measures reflect different aspects of the representation of a species in a community. Unless this point is clarified, difficulties will arise in later work and it is therefore worth spending the first one or two field periods on comparison of the measures. Vegetation should be chosen that includes relatively few species but a range of growth forms. At Bangor, the ground layer, containing ten to fifteen species, of an open *Quercus petraea* woodland on a hillside has proved suitable. Each group of three or four students marks out a small area, about 4 m square, for study. Before making quantitative estimates they list the species present in what they consider from inspection to be their order of importance as constituents of the vegetation. Comparison of this order with subsequent quantitative estimates emphasizes the need for a quantitative approach, which some students are at first reluctant to accept. Each group then determines, for each species present in its area, density, cover by a suitable number of single-point quadrats, and frequency with two different sizes of quadrat.

A second period is devoted to making comparable estimates on an adjacent area of open hillside which has many species in common with the first area. The students are then asked to consider (1) possible sources of error and practical difficulties in the techniques used, (2) how far different measures place species in the same order of importance, and (3) how far the apparent difference in representation of a species in the two areas is affected by the measure used. It is hardly necessary to add that these exercises must be properly written up, with a discussion of the results, if the student is to benefit. I regard these two periods of field work as the foundation of all later quantitative work in the undergraduate course.

Even such simple exercises illustrate one of the real difficulties in teaching quantitative ecology—the time that work in the field takes. For instance, if sufficient data to be worth examining are to be obtained in a half-day field period it is impractical to use any satisfactory procedure of randomizing samples. The unsatisfactory method of 'throwing at random' has to be used along with an explanation of why it is unsatisfactory.

Basic work on the measures of species representation can usefully be supplemented by other introductory exercises that can be completed in a half-day period. Recording by several measures along a transect crossing an obvious vegetation boundary not only provides further practice in comparing different measures but introduces the problem of the delineation of the boundaries of a stand of vegetation. The concept of pattern, or spatial arrangement of species within the community, can be introduced by using isonome diagrams (Pidgeon & Ashby, 1942); although isonomes provide only a very insensitive method of detecting and analysing pattern, if applied to vegetation with intense enough pattern they serve to convey the basic concept of pattern and the need for systematic sampling in the investigation of spatial relationships. Likewise, the idea of association between species, so important in later exercises on communities, can be introduced quite simply; data for the representation of pairs of species in a series of quadrats can be displayed either graphically (for quantitative data) or in a contingency table (for presence and absence data).

The field work suggested so far is designed to avoid the use of statistical analysis. It is preferable to establish at least some of the basic ideas of quantitative ecology before introducing statistical analysis, which is to many students a troublesome complication.

After introductory work of this type it is, I believe, useful to hold an intensive vacation course during which the students can concentrate their whole attention on field work for a period long enough for some development of ideas and understanding. If the students, divided into groups of three or four, are assigned suitable projects, they can be led into investigations along the three principal lines mentioned earlier. For a number of years Bangor students have been taken to Malham Tarn Field Centre for this part of the course and such projects as variation within limestone grassland and the detailed distribution of particular species have proved suitable.

The three lines of investigation present different problems of teaching. The most intractable are the problems of classification and ordination. With the introduction of objective techniques, classification and ordination have become valuable tools in ecological investigation rather than debatable interpretations of the results of investigations. It is thus essential that students should be introduced to their use. Unfortunately, all the more satisfactory techniques involve heavy computation. This raises no difficulty at the research level, where the processing of data can readily be handled by a computer, but if students' data are processed for them by computer, only the keenest are likely to make the effort necessary to understand the operations being carried out. It seems preferable to allow them to use less efficient procedures which can be carried out without the help of a computer.

M

Using a bench electric calculating machine it has proved feasible to prepare an ordination of a small number (ten to twenty) of stands by Bray & Curtis's (1957) technique during the evenings of a week's field course. Ten to twenty stands are as many as are likely to be recorded in the time available, and are enough to allow examination of the distribution of species and environmental factors on the resulting ordination. This technique, however, has serious limitations. Provided a reasonable number of species is involved it is possible to analyse the data satisfactorily in terms of species presence alone (cf. Lambert & Dale, 1964; Orloci, 1966). It then becomes feasible to use geometric distance as a measure of interstand distance instead of Bray & Curtis's much less satisfactory coefficient (Orloci, 1966). Using Orloci's perpendicular axis construction on the resulting matrix of interstand distances, a reasonably satisfactory technique of ordination is available, which students can be expected to understand and to use under field class conditions. The more advanced techniques, having the double disadvantage of requiring the use of a computer and involving more complex analysis, are not suitable for student practical work.

Techniques of classification are more difficult to apply on a field course. The best classificatory procedure at present available is Williams & Lambert's (1959, 1960) association-analysis. This, though presenting no great difficulties of understanding, is prohibitively time-consuming by hand computation and the data must be put on one side for subsequent analysis by computer. Opinions will vary as to how satisfactory this is; I believe it to be important that a student should have his results analysed and interpreted, at least in outline, by the conclusion of a field course.

Pattern analysis, the analysis of spatial distribution of species within the community (Greig-Smith, 1961), presents no practical difficulties. The analytical technique is a straightforward analysis of variance, the principles of which are fairly readily grasped by students once they have had some introduction to statistical analysis. Lack of time often prevents the gathering of sufficient data for confident interpretation, but this is a difficulty with student field work in general.

The third main approach, the correlation of vegetation and species with environment, presents many problems, but these are concerned with the determination of environmental factors rather than with specifically quantitative techniques of analysis, and thus lie outside the present discussion. Normally, and certainly at undergraduate level, correlation between vegetation and environment can be examined satisfactorily by plotting environmental data on the framework of a phytosociological classification or ordination. Species correlation with environment can initially be examined graphically; this may be followed by linear regression or correlation as appropriate.

V. LABORATORY WORK

Laboratory work is no substitute for field work in the teaching of quantitative plant ecology, but it can be a useful supplement to it. Once students have experienced the problems of sampling in the field, work with artificial 'communities' can be a useful aid to their understanding of these problems. For example, the effect of quadrat size on the accuracy of an estimate of density, or the greater efficiency of single points over frames of linked points in cover determination, can be brought home more clearly in an artificial 'community' than in actual vegetation. There are no difficulties of identification, no risk of overlooking individuals, no uncertainty as to whether an individual should be included in a sample or not; attention is concentrated on the methodological questions under consideration. Moreover, the gathering of data takes less time and is unaffected by the vagaries of the weather!

Artificial 'communities' have also proved valuable in demonstrating the meaning of pattern and the efficiency of the techniques used in detecting and analysing it. A 'community' can be set up in which the pattern is evident on inspection but is of relatively low intensity, a situation not often found in the field. Detection of this pattern and comparison of the patterns of different 'species' by the appropriate techniques brings home to students the efficacy and sensitivity of these techniques. In theory, such demonstration should not be necessary but we have to accept that many students are unaccustomed and often reluctant to think in more abstract terms.

Elaborate equipment has been designed for this type of work (see, for example, Schultz, Gibbens & Debano, 1961), but such elaboration seems an unnecessary luxury. Metal discs, painted in different colours to represent different species and arranged on a table or floor, have proved perfectly satisfactory. It is useful to stick them down (e.g. with glycerine jelly) to prevent their being moved in the course of sampling.

REFERENCES

ASHBY M. (1961) Introduction to Plant Ecology. Macmillan, London.
BRAY J.R. & CURTIS J.T. (1957) An ordination of the upland forest communities of southern Wisconsin. Ecol. Monogr. 27, 325–349.

LAMBERT J.M. & DALE M.B. (1964) The use of statistics in ecology. *Adv. ecol. Res.* **2**, 59–99.

GREIG-SMITH P. (1961) Data on pattern within plant communities. I. The analysis of pattern. *J. Ecol.* **49**, 695–702.

GREIG-SMITH P. (1964) *Quantitative Plant Ecology*, 2nd edn. Butterworth, London.

GREIG-SMITH P. (1965) Notes on the quantitative description of humid tropical forest. *Symposium on Ecological Research in Humid Tropics Vegetation.* pp. 227–34. Government of Sarawak and UNESCO Science Co-operation Office for South-east Asia, Djakarta.

ORLOCI L. (1966) Geometric models in ecology. I. The theory and application of some ordination methods. *J. Ecol.* **54**, 193–215.

PIDGEON I.M. & ASHBY E. (1942) A new quantitative method of analysis of plant communities. *Aust. J. Sci.* **5**, 19–21.

SCHULTZ A.M., GIBBENS R.P. & DEBANO L. (1961) Artificial populations for teaching and testing range techniques. *J. Range Mgmt.* **14**, 236–242.

WILLIAMS W.T. & LAMBERT J.M. (1959) Multivariate methods in plant ecology. I, Association-analysis in plant communities. *J. Ecol.* **47**, 83–101.

WILLIAMS W.T. & LAMBERT J.M. (1960) Multivariate methods in plant ecology. II. The use of an electronic digital computer for association-analysis. *J. Ecol.* **48**, 689–710.

INTRODUCING STUDENTS TO THE CONCEPTS
OF POPULATION DYNAMICS

M. H. WILLIAMSON

Department of Biology, University of York

The most obvious feature of populations is that they increase when circumstances are favourable. So one of the first points to get clear in studying population dynamics is the way in which this increase can be described and quantified. For a population in which all the individuals are essentially the same this is easy; we write $dN/dt = rN$, where N is the population size, t is time and r is the rate of increase of population. This can be integrated to give $N_t = N_o\,e^{rt}$ which is an exponentially increasing curve which comes out as a straight line when N is plotted logarithmically and t arithmetically. r can be described as the 'intrinsic rate of natural increase of the population'. Defining it in this way means that it includes both birth-rate and death-rate, and this is not entirely satisfactory. Births and deaths are after all quite distinct biological phenomena.

What happens when there are different classes of individuals in the population? Both the theory given above and the answer to this question are given in text-books. These tell you that the proportions of individuals in different classes will settle down to a constant value and that when this has happened the population will increase exponentially at a rate given by the intrinsic rate of natural increase and that the intrinsic rate of natural increase can itself be found by solving the equation $\int e^{-rx}l_x m_x dx = 1$. This brings me to the main point that I want to make: it is not reasonable to expect students, particularly biological students, to understand this equation. The theory of integral equations is very definitely a part of advanced mathematics. It is not, for instance, mentioned in such works as National Physical Laboratory (1961) or Nicolson (1961). At the same time it is obvious that, as the intrinsic rate of natural increase comes right at the beginning of the description of an increasing population, some way must be found of getting the students to understand the concept and its consequences. This can be done by the use of matrix algebra and numerical examples.

Matrix algebra might itself be thought to be an advanced mathematical topic. However, it is quite simple to understand and it is also starting to find a place in school syllabuses. A modern practising ecologist will probably have to know how to use a computer and to do this efficiently he will have to understand matrix algebra. The use of matrices to describe increasing populations was thought of independently by Lewis (1942) and Leslie (1945). They listed the numbers of individuals in different age-classes as a column of numbers—as a column vector. The numbers at

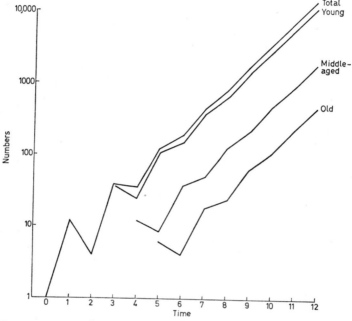

FIG. 1. Exponential population growth under the operation of matrix (1).

one time are changed into the numbers next time by multiplying this vector by a square matrix. This is shown most easily by an example

$$\begin{bmatrix} 0 & 0 & f_2 & f_3 \\ p_0 & 0 & 0 & 0 \\ 0 & p_1 & 0 & 0 \\ 0 & 0 & p_2 & 0 \end{bmatrix} \begin{bmatrix} n_0 \\ n_1 \\ n_2 \\ n_3 \end{bmatrix} \rightarrow \begin{bmatrix} f_2 n_2 + f_3 n_3 \\ p_0 n_0 \\ p_1 n_1 \\ p_2 n_2 \end{bmatrix}$$

From this it can be seen that the element of the matrix in row i and column j takes the jth element of the vector and puts it into the ith position, multiplying it by the value of the matrix element. For population dynamics this means that there must be a line of elements in the matrix immediately below the main diagonal. These shift the elements of the vector down one at each transition, representing the increase in age. There are also elements in the first row of the matrix; these take numbers low down in the vector and bring them back to the first element and so represent reproduction, the formation of new-born individuals. Provided one uses reasonably small matrices and vectors the repeated multiplication of the vectors by the matrix is a job that can be done with pencil and paper, although a calculating machine is helpful.

One can set up a population system in matrix form and ask the class to continue multiplying an arbitrary age-distribution by the matrix. They will rapidly find out for themselves that the vector settles down to stable proportions and that the rate of increase from one time to the next becomes constant. Mathematically, the population vector approximates to the first latent vector of the matrix and the increase from one time to the next is given by the dominant latent root of the matrix. An example of this is shown in Fig. 1, and refers to the 3×3 matrix:

$$\begin{bmatrix} 0 & 9 & 12 \\ \frac{1}{3} & 0 & 0 \\ 0 & \frac{1}{2} & 0 \end{bmatrix} \qquad (1)$$

The initial vector is

$$\begin{bmatrix} 0 \\ 0 \\ 1 \end{bmatrix}$$

meaning that there were no individuals in the two younger age-classes and just one reproducing adult at the start of the experiment. The elements of the matrix say that the chance of a young individual surviving to be middle-aged is one-third and the chances of a middle-aged individual surviving to old age is one-half, and that for each middle-aged individual observed at the time 0 there will be 9 young ones at the time 1 and to each old-age individual there will be 12 young ones. It is clear from Fig. 1 that there are damped oscillations in the total numbers and the numbers of each of the three classes, and that all three classes are soon increasing at the same steady rate. Because of this the proportion of each to the others remains constant. This is all that is needed to show that there is a stable age distribution and that there is a definite rate of increase, λ, which is 2. The population doubles in each time interval. The intrinsic rate of increase is given by $\log_e \lambda$, which is the slope of the lines expressed in suitable units. The fact that the intrinsic rate is approached by damped oscillations is another part of the theory easily demonstrated this way.

When presenting a concept one should also consider its limitations.

The intrinsic rate of natural increase was invented in the first place in order to compare different human populations. The difficulty here was that when there were appreciably different age-distributions the crude birth-rates and death-rates were misleading. In extending the concept to populations of other species one comes up against the problem of what death-rate should be measured. In practice, experimenters have tried to reduce the death-rate as much as possible in the hope of coming to some inevitable, genetically determined, death-rate. It seems unlikely that most experiments are so well performed that the death-rate could not be further reduced, but quite apart from this it is not easy to see that this experiment-ally determined death-rate has much relevance in the study of natural populations. Its inclusion in the statistic λ reduces the validity of that statistic.

Another question we can ask about the statistic is—does it contain nearly all the information we need to know to describe the behaviour of a growing population? The answer regrettably is that it does not. An illustration of this is given in Fig. 2. Here we have another population whose rate of growth is determined by the matrix:

$$\begin{bmatrix} 0 & 3 & 36 \\ \frac{1}{3} & 0 & 0 \\ 0 & \frac{1}{2} & 0 \end{bmatrix} \tag{2}$$

The death-rates in matrix (2) are the same as those in matrix (1), so that the validity of death-rates can be ignored in this comparison. In both systems, the old-aged individuals leave more offspring than the middle-aged ones, but the difference in reproductive rates is much larger in matrix (2). So, comparing the two matrices, there is a higher middle-aged fecundity in matrix (1) ($9 > 3$), and a higher old-aged fecundity in matrix (2) ($36 > 12$).

The population increase produced by matrix (2) is subject to more violent oscillations, and these have not been damped out in the time shown in Fig. 2. Nevertheless, the intrinsic rate of natural increase, and the stable age-distribution, is the same for both matrices. That is, $\lambda = 2$ for both of them, and the stable age-distribution is

$$\begin{bmatrix} 24 \\ 4 \\ 1 \end{bmatrix}$$

for both. Taking the rate of increase as the only statistic needed would be equivalent to saying that these two populations behaved in the same way.

Some might want to go into more algebra here. The stability depends on the ratio of the moduli of the first and second routes: this is 2.00 for matrix (1), and 1.15 ($=2/\sqrt{3}$) for matrix (2). For that matter, the fact that there is a real positive dominant latent root, and that there is no other of larger modulus, is stated by the Frobenius–Perron theorem, which says that this will be so for all non-negative matrices. Few biologists will

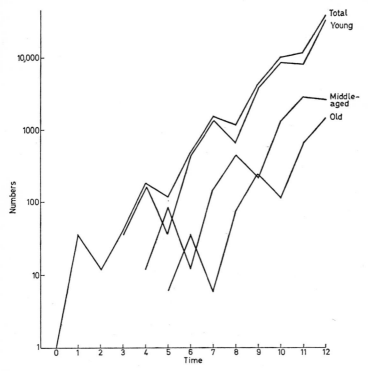

FIG. 2. Exponential population growth under the operation of matrix (2).

be interested in such points, and the biological realities of the situation can be made clear by the examples I have already given, and by another approach.

It is a natural extension of what has been done so far, to study the effects of various systems of exploitation on these theoretical populations, and this is discussed below. Other extensions are also possible. Density dependence can be brought in, and one can show, as Leslie (1948) first did, that the final age-distribution differs depending on whether one controls the birth-rate or the death-rate. It is quite simple to produce oscillations. If the element $\frac{1}{3}$ is changed to $\frac{1}{100}$ every time the population size (or indeed any section of the population) exceeds an arbitrary number, strong stable fluctuations result. It is not so easy to study interactions between species, but competition can be imitated by running two populations in parallel and making the elements of both matrices functions of the numbers

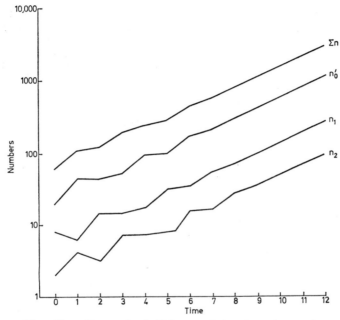

FIG. 3. The effect of harvesting half the population, but taking only young individuals. Births and normal deaths are given by matrix (1). Σn = total population, n_0' = the number of young after harvesting, n_1 = the number of middle-aged individuals, n_2 = the number of old individuals.

of the two species. This implies a definition like that of Odum (1959) or Williamson (1957), which incidentally is the only type of definition that covers competition by mutual cannibalism as in *Tribolium* (Landahl, 1955). One can also use matrices in population genetics (Williamson, 1959, 1960) but this is too big a topic to pursue here.

The rate at which a population can be harvested is an obvious point to consider when talking about the intrinsic rates of natural increase. If the population can double in each time interval, will it be held steady if half of it is harvested each time? Does it have to be in any particular age-distribution for this, and can half the population be taken in any arbitrary way over the age-classes? These questions can be answered quite easily by direct trial. For instance, if one takes half of each age-class as it stands at any time, the population will soon settle to constant numbers distributed in the stable age-distribution. This result holds for both matrices (1) and (2) and for any arbitrary initial age-structure.

Other methods of harvesting can be used to bring out the differences between matrices (1) and (2). Consider what happens if half the population is taken, but this half consists entirely of young. There is an analogy here with the harvesting of Pribilof fur seals. The results of this, working with matrix (1) and starting with the stable age-distribution, are shown in Fig. 3. The population settles down to a new rate of increase and a new age-distribution, reaching these through damped oscillations. The increase is in fact 38 per cent per time interval, which is perhaps unexpectedly large for a process that some people would have expected to stabilize the population. This system of harvesting can also be represented in matrix form:

$$\begin{bmatrix} \frac{1}{2} & -\frac{1}{2} & -\frac{1}{2} \\ 0 & 1 & 0 \\ 0 & 0 & 1 \end{bmatrix} \begin{bmatrix} n_0 \\ n_1 \\ n_2 \end{bmatrix} \rightarrow \begin{bmatrix} n_0 - \frac{1}{2}\left(n_0 + n_1 + n_2\right) \\ n_1 \\ n_2 \end{bmatrix}$$

The same system of harvesting applied to matrix (2) gives a similar result, but the increase is now 48 per cent per time, a difference that could be important in practice. To look at this another way: what proportion of the population should be taken from the young to produce a steady state? The answer is 73 per cent from matrix (1), 80 per cent from matrix (2). These figures are quite far apart, and are both a long way from 50 per cent, which is the only numerical answer to the question that one could give simply from a knowledge that $\lambda = 2$.

What, then, should we tell our students about intrinsic rate of natural increase? My own view is that we should introduce it through the matrix notation and say that it is the single most useful statistic to be got from the information in the matrix, but that all the information in the matrix is biologically interesting and we can only get a complete picture of the population by considering all of it.

ACKNOWLEDGMENTS

These examples were first used in the Department of Zoology, Edinburgh, and I am indebted to the students who worked with them. I would like to thank Miss N.Spektorov and Dr J.D.Currey for their comments.

REFERENCES

LANDAHL H.D. (1955) A mathematical model for the temporal pattern of a population structure, with particular reference to the flour beetle. *Bull. Math. Biophys.* **17**, 63–77, 131–140.

LESLIE P.H. (1945) On the use of matrices in certain population mathematics. *Biometrika*, **33**, 183–212.

LESLIE P.H. (1948) Some further notes on the use of matrices in population mathematics. *Biometrika*, **35**, 213–245.

LEWIS E.G. (1942) On the generation and growth of a population. *Sankhya*, **6**, 93–96.

NATIONAL PHYSICAL LABORATORY (1961) *Modern Computing Methods*, 2nd edn. HMSO, London.

NICOLSON M.M. (1961) *Fundamentals and Techniques of Mathematics for Scientists*. Longmans, London.

ODUM E.P. (1959) *Fundamentals of Ecology*, 2nd edn. Saunders, Philadelphia.

WILLIAMSON M.H. (1957) An elementary theory of interspecific competition. *Nature, Lond.* **180**, 422–425.

WILLIAMSON M.H. (1959) Some extensions of the use of matrices in population theory. *Bull. Math. Biophys.* **21**, 13–17.

WILLIAMSON M.H. (1960) On the polymorphism of the moth *Panaxia dominula* (L.). *Heredity*, **15**, 139–151.

SECTION IV
THE TEACHING OF ECOLOGY
IN OTHER COUNTRIES

SOME APPROACHES TO THE TEACHING OF ECOLOGY IN AMERICA

H. A. MOONEY

Department of Botany, University of California, Los Angeles

I should like to talk about the teaching of ecology in the United States with emphasis on examples best known to me and hence about plant ecology at my home institution, the University of California at Los Angeles (UCLA). I will proceed from the very specific and then talk in less detail about certain aspects of ecology teaching in other places in California and then in the country as a whole.

I. ECOLOGY AT LOS ANGELES

The approach to the teaching of plant ecology taken at my campus has to be considered in context. UCLA is a very large university, particularly strong in the liberal arts and at present lacking colleges of forestry and agriculture. The campus is located in the midst of a megalopolis but surrounded by a region of highly diverse topography, climate and vegetation.

A. *Introductory courses*

Introductory plant ecology, for the past few years at least, has been given in two separate courses, both of which are combined with an introduction to plant systematics. One of these courses is for non-biology majors and the other is for majors. The non-major course is simply called field botany and concerns itself with the local flora and vegetation.

Being centred in an urban area, working within the traditional 3-hour laboratory for ecological field exercises is often not possible. Most of the ecological field work must be done at weekends. The types of exercises depend on the level of the class. For example, in the field botany class the field trips are primarily an introduction to the local vegetation. During one weekend trip the class is brought to a near-by mountain range, the San Jacinto Mountains, and introduced to such diverse vegetation types as desert, chaparral, woodland, montane and subalpine forests.

This trip exemplifies the virtually unlimited vegetation types that can be visited by a field class on a weekend most of the year.

The combined systematics-ecology course for majors is a recent innovation. In redesigning our undergraduate major, a core curriculum was established so that all students would receive introductory material in all of the basic biological areas. Certain traditional areas were combined to make this possible in the prescribed time; for example, we now give single courses in anatomy and morphology as well as systematics and ecology. The systematics and ecology course has proven to be quite successful. We do not attempt to teach all of ecology or all of systematics in this course but concentrate on overlapping study areas. A detailed consideration of the population is our focal point. We discuss the genetics, evolution, adaptations, establishment, maintenance and distribution of populations.

In this course we have a series of field trips. One of the first trips is to an area of diverse topography located in an ecotone of two major vegetation types: the lower edge of a montane forest and the upper elevational extreme of the shrubby chaparral. Within this area we instrument rather heavily a small valley which has chaparral on the south-facing slope and forest on the north. For a 24 hour period we measure profiles of temperature, wind, humidity, and in addition we make measurements of radiation and evaporation. An elevational gradient of about 1000 ft is also instrumented for temperature and wind direction. Readings of non-recording instruments are made at hourly intervals by the class. Previous to the field exercise, laboratory classes introduce the students to the operating principles and procedures of the instruments.

The synthesis of the mass of data accumulated in this 24 hour period is an arduous task. It is, however, quite worth while for gaining an understanding of the spatial and temporal variations in the physical environment and equally as important in understanding the interaction of the various environmental components. On one occasion we utilized recording instruments for a certain portion of this exercise; however, the data derived in this manner were not nearly as meaningful to the students as were the data they collected the hard way, every hour.

Density distribution of the vegetation components is sampled along the now-quantified environment gradient. This exercise is, then, an introduction to vegetation sampling as well as an introduction to plants and environmental relationships.

This small valley subjected to intensive study has a vegetation anomaly. There is a finger of shrubby vegetation on the otherwise forested north-facing slope. The composition of this anomalous vegetation is like that of the south slope. We spend several hours developing an understanding of the dynamics of this pattern. During the course of the exercise we look closely at the age-class distribution of the neighbouring tree population, learn how to cross-date increment cores and establish the time of two important past environmental events, a severe drought and a fire. With these pieces of information we hypothesize how the anomaly was established and how it is maintained.

By this time, late in the weekend, the students have learned a little of the environment, present and past, and have opened their eyes somewhat to vegetation patterning. We then take a look at another past environmental event—the effects of a disastrous flash flood adjacent to the study area. These latter two exercises illustrate another attribute of southern California which makes ecology teaching rather easy. It is not only a land of environmental contrasts but it is a land of recurring environmental catastrophes—fires, droughts and floods. These catastrophes are responsible for moulding the vegetation into sharp patterns as well as providing an evolutionary stimulus which promotes diversity.

A second type of weekend trip we take is to an area completely new to the instructors as well as the students. California is endowed with many areas of complex geology and topography and hence vegetation types. In arid regions the influence of geological substrate on the vegetation is particularly profound. We visit such a complex area with the objective of first sorting out the vegetation patterns and then deriving a unified hypothesis to explain them.

For example, last year we studied a rather small, topographically complex, area which at first look had an inexplicable patterning of physiognomic types ranging from forests, woodlands and grasslands to chaparral. Before the weekend was over we managed to produce an environmental model which accounted for all the patterns and included the effects of lapse rates, slope exposure, inversions, substrate type and fire. The dramatic shifts in physiognomy make it easy to see and learn of the influence of the environment on vegetation patterning. The study of the gross patterns exhibited by shifting physiognomic types is a good introduction to the more subtle plant population patterns studied in exercises and in the advanced classes.

By the end of the course students are acquainted with concepts of evolution as well as ecology. A final weekend trip includes a study of the habitats of populations of two species and of their hybrids. Previous indoor laboratories have introduced the students to analysis of variation and recognition of hybrid characters in these taxa. This final trip then puts together what they have learned about the total biology and ecology of plant populations.

B. *Advanced courses*

Subsequent to the introductory systematics and ecology course, students may elect advanced courses in either of these subject areas. In the advancd ecology course the subject-matter is covered in discussion periods where we consider basic concepts of ecology. In each of these we try to cover a classic paper where an idea or viewpoint was first expounded as well as the most recent review in the field. The laboratory portion of the course emphasizes independent, rather than group, projects as in the introductory course. The independent problems are usually experimental in nature. At the conclusion of the semester we have a presentation of the results in the format of a scientific meeting. Group projects are also undertaken if special interests are expressed or special opportunities arise. For example, this past semester, because of the interests of a visiting professor, Dr S.R.J. Woodell of Oxford, we undertook a problem in patterning of desert shrubs. In an intensive weekend the class sampled the species patterns, calculated the data on the site, and then endeavoured to explain the distribution types found. The exercise proved very worth while since we found a variety of distribution types which were explained by on-the-spot observation.

In the advanced course, in addition to special problems, we try to make at least one extended trip to an area very different from the local vegetation and past experience of the students, and we undertake independent or group projects depending on the opportunities. These trips provide a little adventure as well as broadening the students' basic experience and hence interpretive capacity.

C. *Training of graduates*

Since up to the present time at UCLA we have not had any graduate courses in plant ecology, the formal training of graduate students is handled in a variety of ways such as seminars and other group activities. Our seminars cover ecological theory as well as practice. The general format now being used is to have a meeting or so to discuss what is known about a particular topic, what we as a group could contribute new, and how we could go about doing this. Then we have a weekend trip to carry out these objectives. A final meeting is then held on this topic to collate and discuss our data. In a seminar now in progress we are studying desert plants. Two weeks ago we undertook a comparative study in the field of the water relations of a desert tree, shrub and herb. We measured for a diurnal period the micro-environment of the transpiring surfaces of these plants, their transpiration rates, stomatal movements and internal water balance. Earlier in the semester we investigated regional patterning of *Larrea* in relation to mean precipitation (a balloon with camera ascent was used in this exercise), and herb and shrub association patterns. Before the semester is over, we will investigate field yield versus density of some desert annuals. These are creative seminars and make up for the absence of formal courses where ecological techniques are covered.

As an outgrowth of our joint undergraduate courses in systematics and ecology, this past fall we had a combined seminar with the systematists on a topic of interest to both groups—island phenomena. This seminar concluded with an expedition to study an island problem.

Graduate students of plant ecology at UCLA are working on a variety of problems from entirely field problems on the one extreme to entirely laboratory on the other, and in environments from timberline to the deserts and the coastal bluffs. It has been a tradition that we all help one another in the actual data gathering for these projects so that we all learn of the techniques and problems involved. Furthermore, in this way, problems that would usually be too ambitious for an individual can still be executed, such as those involving large amounts of equipment in remote areas or large numbers of samples or observations.

A certain number of students have usually been involved in my own research programme in the White Mountains which is some distance from the campus. However, even those that are not directly involved spend some time in the research area becoming acquainted with the programme.

So, because of the variety of activities in progress by all of us, students in plant ecology manage to attain a fairly broad training despite the lack of graduate courses in plant ecology and in other applied plant ecological areas like forestry, agronomy, etc. The outstanding programmes in animal ecology at UCLA also add considerable depth to the training possibilities of students in plant ecology.

D. *Imminent changes in course structure*
The entire curriculum on our campus is in the process of changing due to a conversion from the semester to the quarter system. Several changes will be made in the programme I have just outlined. For example, we will soon have an introductory ecology course given jointly by the zoology and botany departments rather than separate courses in each. This combined course will follow a three-quarter general biology course given jointly by these departments (plus bacteriology) and would precede advanced courses in either plant or animal ecology.

There is a general trend in the United States of offering fewer specialized courses at the undergraduate level in favour of building a strong and broad general science foundation. Professional concentration is thus postponed to graduate school. As an example of this trend, and as an introduction to ecology elsewhere in California, I would like to outline the biology curriculum at the University of California at Irvine.

II. ECOLOGY AT IRVINE

The Irvine campus is a very recent addition to the University of California. Its Division of Biological Sciences is structured into four departments: molecular and cell biology, organismic biology, population and environmental biology, and psychobiology. The Division is the basic unit concerned with undergraduate training. The four departments provide the staff for this programme as well as determine the nature of the graduate training.

The undergraduate biology programme at Irvine is briefly as follows (required science courses given only): The freshman year includes inorganic chemistry and calculus. The second, or sophomore, year is devoted to an introduction to biology, organic chemistry and physics. The third and fourth years are filled with a six quarter sequence (the 'core') covering introductory courses in all the four departmental areas. A student interested in ecology would elect in addition to the core courses, advanced undergraduate courses ('satellite' courses), for example, marine ecology.

The advantages of this system are many for both the student and the administration: (1) There is only one basic course for any given subject area. In many schools introductory ecological material may be given in several different courses, e.g. in general ecology, animal ecology, plant ecology, evolution and systematics; in habitat-oriented courses such as marine ecology and limnology; and in organism-oriented courses like forestry, ornithology, mammalogy and entomology, etc. (2) The level of integration approach permits concentration on unifying biological principles rather than on a survey of biological diversity. (3) All students in biology are thoroughly grounded in all of the basic areas before graduation.

There are obvious difficulties with this system. Transfers from other colleges are hard to fit into the course flow. Also, the core course could tend to be extremely large and to be conducted by a committee with all the attendant disadvantages.

Cornell University in New York recently reorganized into a biology division with departments and sections similar to that of Irvine.

III. THE NATURAL LAND AND WATER RESERVE SYSTEM

Another highly significant recent development in the University of California related to the teaching of ecology is the establishment of a Natural Land and Water Reserve System. The goal of this system is to preserve for teaching and research purposes representatives of diverse types of terrain and forms of life throughout California. This is no small order considering the topographic and biological diversity of the state. Land areas of three types are included within the system:

1. Land (or water) used chiefly for teaching, especially for undergraduates, within 15–30 minutes' driving time from a UC campus (there are nine campuses). When the system is completed each campus will have several reserves representing diverse types of terrain and serving different fields of study (ecology, geography, geology, anthropology).

2. Selected, larger pieces of land that are shared by several campuses for use as field camps.

3. Special reserves, often remote, that preserve some unique biological, geological, or archaeological feature. These are primarily research units. The successful completion of this system should bring stability to field teaching within the University. Further, long-term experimental programmes can be pursued with some confidence of fruitful completion.

There are many indications that the future development of teaching and research programmes in plant ecology in California is going to be meteoric. This could hardly have been predicted even a few years ago when a plant ecologist was a fairly scarce commodity in the state.

IV. ECOLOGY ELSEWHERE IN THE UNITED STATES

With my remaining time I would like to say something, in very general terms, about teaching of plant ecology in other parts of the United States.

The teaching of plant ecology up the present has been strongly directed by a relatively few people and institutions. A particularly prominent lineage has been the one initiated by H.C.Cowles at the University of Chicago, perpetuated by W.C.Cooper at the University of Minnesota and proliferated by several of Cooper's students into a number of contemporary teaching centres such as those led by Oosting and Billings at Duke, Buell at Rutgers, Daubenmire at Washington State, and Marr at the University of Colorado. Other universities that have been prominent in producing graduates in plant ecology in the recent past are those at Wisconsin, Chicago, Illinois, Texas and Emory University. The Ph.D. production in plant ecology at Duke University, the most prominent contemporary centre, up to the present time has been forty-two.

There is at present a strong interest in developing additional teaching programmes in ecology throughout the country, and, no doubt, new centres will arise. At present there is a critical shortage of people to fill all of the available teaching positions.

The whole complexion of ecology teaching in the United States is in a process of gradual change. The fairly recent infusion of federal support to teaching at all levels from secondary schools, through to post-doctoral training, has opened new opportunities not previously available to ecology students. Such diverse activities as text-book revisions, undergraduate research participation programmes, graduate fellowships and assistantships, advance science seminars and field station maintenance are among the types of programmes that the government supports. Dr John Cantlon of the National Science Foundation estimates that his agency alone expends approximately two and a half million dollars annually for graduate training in environmental biology.

V. THE EVOLUTION OF THE SUPERPROGRAMME

In conclusion, I would like to speak briefly of one probable future trend in the teaching of ecology in the United States—the evolution of the superprogramme. As specialized knowledge proliferates and disciplines splinter, the task of providing a well-rounded ecology programme becomes increasingly more difficult. Further, as the interactions between the social and natural sciences become ever greater, the need for an even broader training of ecologists than previously provided will be necessary. To meet this need new programmes are arising which cut across traditional departmental boundaries. Examples of these are a Natural Resource programme at the University of Michigan combining studies in economics, ecology, conservation and regional planning; a Regional Planning programme at the University of Pennsylvania staffed by a plant ecologist, a resource economist, a geologist-hydrologist and a regional planner; and an interdepartmental programme at the University of Tennessee which includes staff members in botany, zoology, geology, economics, mathematics, forestry and crop sciences.

As always, and as everywhere, the success of these programmes is most dependent not only on the basic intellectual framework upon which they are built, but on the enthusiasm and inspiration of the teachers involved.

ACKNOWLEDGMENTS

I am grateful to the following people for providing information which, although it may not have appeared directly in this paper, helped considerably in its formulation: Drs J.Cantlon, M.Levine, G.Woodwell, J.Marr, L.Bliss, A.Reid, A.Boughey, E.Kormandy. Drs S.Woodell and W.Billings kindly reviewed the manuscript and offered valuable suggestions. I express my appreciation especially to the National Science Foundation for providing a travel grant.

THE TEACHING OF ECOLOGY ON THE CONTINENT, WITH SPECIAL REFERENCE TO THE NETHERLANDS

L. VLIJM

Department of Zoology, Free University, Amsterdam, the Netherlands

I. INTRODUCTION

In this survey, which is not an easy one to make, I shall try to cover several aspects of the teaching of ecology. As to the teaching of ecology on the Continent, I must confine myself to the university level, especially in Germany and France, but I feel that even then there will be many short-comings.

It is evident that the teaching of ecology is rooted in the history of ecological research and the development of an ecological way of thinking. Therefore it will be necessary to follow up some lines in the development of continental ecology in the past, which have resulted in the way ecology is taught now.

This is an ambitious programme for such a short contribution. It is quite obvious that a selection had to be made in the vast field which has to be surveyed. More will be said about animal ecology than about plant ecology. This does not mean a depreciation of the latter; it merely reflects certain limitations in the author's knowledge and experience.

II. SOME LINES IN THE DEVELOPMENT OF ECOLOGY

In most disciplines, research has to be developed and problems attacked by various investigators before the theory of the discipline has been advanced to such an extent that it can be taught. This seems to be contrary to the views of some other investigators. For instance, Kontkanen (1950) states: 'In such a scientific discipline—in the initial stages of research—theory and practice often diverge greatly, with theory forging ahead and striving after a unifying synthesis, while practical application struggles with the practical difficulties that arise in the course of research.' We will see that theory and theory are not always the same. That, I presume, is the cause of the disagreement.

Before a theory (in my sense) of a discipline can be developed, there must be some agreement about the concepts which are basic in the discipline. Perhaps in the last few years we have arrived at the stage in which there is increasing agreement about these concepts. However, even now, the use of the same word (e.g. 'biotope', 'habitat', 'niche', 'community') is not always a guarantee for a mutual understanding.

As the roots of the research of today, of the concepts used now—and they seem to be rather important for the teaching of ecology now and in the future—can be traced back into the end of the last century, some knowledge of the history of ecology is necessary. The following is my interpretation of the course of this history.

A. The history and development of plant ecology

As a zoologist it is difficult for me to see some lines in the history of plant ecology. It is not an easy task and only the main points can be discussed. Most people agree that the study of plant ecology has developed from the discipline of plant geography. From an overall knowledge of the relations between plant-cover and climate, an effort was made to study in more detail the relationships between plants and their environment. I think it is quite understandable that the first steps in this direction were found in Western Europe, as here the density of botanists was highest, and differences in climate—given the rather small countries—far less than in other areas. This may have influenced the search for detail, and the investigations in rather small areas, which sometimes have been said to be characteristic of at least some countries of the Continent.

Though ecology as a term was first used by Haeckel, the birth of ecology as a modern discipline is usually dated back to 1877, when Karl Möbius gave a description of an oyster bed, calling it a biocenosis, or rather, community. I think this concept of 'community' was a prescientific one. Also Dahl, the successor of Möbius at Kiel, used the term in a way unlike that in which it is used today with our modern knowledge. A marked advance in ecological thinking was made by Elton (1927), when he first used the concept 'niche', because this concept provided an entry to the *characteristics* of the community. This is now dealt with by the branch of ecology known as 'production biology'.

This concept 'community'—used by Möbius for an entity consisting of both plants and animals—was narrowed by Dahl (1908) to zoöcenosis, and separated from the phytocenosis, the plant community. Perhaps even at this time there was some difference in the attitude of botanists and zoologists? From the aforementioned plant geography, a basis was laid down for the discipline of 'plant sociology', which forms part of the field of plant ecology. The use of *socii* (relatives) is very revealing. The same term can be found in the concept of plant association, sub-association, etc. Certain relationships between plants are hypothesized on the basis that sometimes the same species are found together in several localities. I think plant sociology, after being started, was rather strongly influenced by the techniques which were developed to describe vegetation. In this respect the French–Swiss school under the direction of Braun-Blanquet (1921, 1928), and the Swedish school under the direction of Du Rietz (1921), have to be mentioned. Dominance and fidelity are the two criteria which are used.

The associations which were described are designated by some investigators as real entities, which have a mode of life in their own right and not only in respect of the species which they contain. However, the underlying causes of the occurrence of such associations were only understood to a very limited extent. Some investigators even seemed not to be interested in the fate of the species and the individual plants, but concerned only with that of the association as a whole. From this basis, and accentuated by the techniques used, plant sociology developed into a more or less static description of plant communities. The dynamic aspect in the associations could be found only in the seral situations, with sets of species following one another in time towards a climax vegetation, which could only show changes after long periods.

Plant sociology, in its origin and aims, has to be seen as an effort to study synecological problems, but in plants alone. It studies the phytocenosis. Many research workers in this field seem to agree that zoologists have to consider plants and vegetation-cover, but at the same time are in danger of overlooking the need for a botanist to be aware of the effects of animals on the plants they study.

It is interesting that, in the first period, the autecological approach to plants was to be found only in plant physiology. I think that this was due to the fact that the complexity of the interrelations of all the environmental factors together was the stumbling-block which forced investigators to isolate single factors in a known laboratory environment, ensuring that the effects of this factor alone were analysed.

Though the first steps towards an autecological way of thinking— i.e. towards a study of the physico-chemical factors of the environment in relation to one, or a few, species—were made at a rather early date (Lundegårdh, 1925), most of the investigations in plant ecology were concerned with plant sociology, and it is doubtful if this has changed on the

Continent. I think the influence of Lundegårdh has been much greater in British plant ecology.

Interesting phenomena are found in plant sociology, and an enormous body of data has been gathered, but it looks at times as if the discipline is coming to a dead end, in which the description is the final goal in itself. There are, however, opportunities to escape this deadlock, if an experimental approach can be induced. It is possible to think not only in respect of problems in production biology, but also in an experimental approach to competition.

B. *The history and development of animal ecology*

As mentioned earlier, Möbius's concept of 'biocenosis' or 'community' can be designated the beginning of the study of animal as well as plant ecology. Dahl (1908) used the concept in the field of terrestrial ecology, at the same time narrowing it to zoöcenosis (animal community). The study of animal communities made a less good start than that of plant communities. This was partly due to the fact that problems were dealt with as if animals were similar organisms to plants, without regard to possible movement or change. Serious difficulties arose also from the far greater number of animals in any area to be studied, and from the gaps in systematic knowledge in a great number of animal groups.

Such studies as were made were the work of specialists, who covered the animals known to them but left all other animals out of account. However, the framework of the research can be immediately compared with that in plant sociology. Good examples of this kind of research can be found in the work of Petersen (1914) on marine bottom communities, which was a later, but still unenlightened, contribution (Verwey, pers. comm.) In terrestrial ecology, the same type of approach can be seen, for instance in Kontkanen (1950). I could have mentioned several other, even more outstanding, authors, but I have selected the name of Kontkanen because he has realized the shortcomings of this approach.

When studies, like those mentioned above, are not directed towards the investigation of particular animal species, I feel they come to the same dead end as was indicated for plant sociology. In this field, also, a vast body of data is in our hands, waiting for the person who knows along which lines it has to be worked out.

This type of research at the same time has developed into a description of the phenology of a great number of animal species. Most species are periodic in one or more seasons and sometimes vicariance of species can be observed. There is some dynamic aspect—in the same way one can find it in plant sociology—in the cyclic sequence of species in an area.

In general, another difference between the plant and animal ecologist can be observed. As was said before, the plant sociologist has an opportunity to describe the plant community as a more or less static unit. The animal ecologist—usually being a specialist—is always confronted with the animals which move, especially at the time he is trying to pick them up. This has caused specialists, concentrating on a group of animals which they could identify usually even in the field, to make efforts to know more about these species: How do they live, what do they eat, by which animals are they preyed upon?

This, perhaps, could be the reason that autecological research on animals had a better start than on plants. This autecological approach, as far as I can see, developed from dealing with the complexities of communities, with so many species of animals. Because of the practical difficulties in animal synecology, investigators were forced to concentrate on the relations of a *few* species with the environment. On the other hand, I believe that autecological studies were stimulated by the fact that animals move; there seems to be a need to concentrate more and more on the active behaviour of animals.

It is obvious that an autecological approach can begin from several standpoints, e.g. from morphology, physiology or ethology. Sometimes they are found together in one paper. They all, however, have originated as far as I can see at a later stage. This is quite clearly the case for the physiological and ethological approaches, which only developed as separate branches after the start of comparative physiology and ethology in the 'thirties.

It is quite clear that synecology and autecology can be seen as two ways of thinking about the same problems. All who have written about these branches agree on that point. In short, one can state that synecology has the tendency to know nothing about all things, whereas autecology tries to know all things about nothing.

It seems to be of great importance that both will gain knowledge, interpretable for the other branch. This could be the only way which leads to an understanding of the relations between plants, animals and environment.

C. *The attempts at a synthesis of plant and animal ecology on the Continent*
It was stated above that the separation of animal and plant ecology, as is even found now for the greater part of the Continent, existed from the

very beginning of ecology. It must be said that the notion of a general
ecology was always in the background, though not operating. The approach to a general ecology clearly has been made by Thienemann (1931,
1939), one of the founders of hydrobiology. It seems of interest that the
concept of an ecosystem can be more easily developed from the research
of some pond, or some ditch, than from the far more complex terrestrial
entities.

There seems to me another more important reason why the concepts of
general ecology, in the sense of the holo-ecosystem, have not been developed to a greater extent. These concepts are possibly recognized merely
from a philosophical background. The 'Holism' of Smuts, I think, can
be found at the base in the continental way of thinking about ecosystems.
Some mystic elements can also be traced in it, in Thienemann as well as
more clearly in, for instance, Friederichs (1927, 1943): 'So gelangt man
auf dem Wege der Ökologie zur totalen Weltschau, zur Schau einer
Welt in der alles zu allem in Beziehung steht, alles auf alles direkt oder
indirekt wirkt und in der alles gleichzeitig in Bewegung und Verände-
rung ist. . . . Die Entstehung einer Wissenschaft von der Natur kündigt
sich an'; and elsewhere: 'Erst die Einsicht in die absolute Zusammenge-
hörigkeit von Lebensstätte und Lebenserfüllung, von "Blut" und "Boden"
gibt den Begriffspaar Lebensgemeinschaft und Lebensraum seinen tiefsten
Sinn.'

This 'philosophy of the harmony of spheres' was, quite understandably,
fiercely fought, for example, by Bodenheimer (1958), who remarks:
'German ecologists have compared the supraorganismic hypothesis of the
bio-communities to listening to "the harmony of spheres". . . . It is
obvious that no scientific method can arrive at a perception of the
symphony of spheres. It is in this sense, and in this sense only "that we
would gladly accept the accusation of being a non-musical person,
unable to perceive the music of nature's conception".'

I think there is no need to say that most investigators on the Continent
were afraid to work in such a general ecology.

D. *Another approach to general ecology*
There has been, however, another way round to general ecology,
meant as the synthesis of plant and animal ecology, through production
biology. I think on the Continent awakenings in the direction of problems
in production biology were coming especially from the applied branches
of ecology: agriculture, forestry, and fishery and game research. These,
however, were branches of an anthropocentric general ecology, and this

seems, in the present conditions, an important point to make. It seems to me that production biology in America also had impulses from the purely scientific approach, e.g. in the work of Lindeman (1942). The point is that production biology, the research of the use of energy in a community, seems to have had a very good start. The situation in the Western countries (including the U.S.A.) in these respects seems to be quite equal to the present situation in Eastern Europe. Sometimes, however, nature seems to be narrowed now to the nature for man, to man-made nature. In the philosophy of Huxley (1957) and Teilhard de Chardin (1955), a direct connection with this way of thinking can be observed.

E. *The mosaic pattern of ecology*
I have tried to show some of the lines which can be drawn from the past to the present situation of ecology. Other lines could have been followed. The start of population genetics and the mathematical approach in biology have had a marked effect upon ecological research. We will not follow up these lines.

The effect of all we have seen can be called a mosaic pattern. In the field of ecology many research centres, each working along its own lines, are found. The techniques to be used for the description of this mosaic pattern have not yet been developed. It is even more difficult to show keypoints in this structure. If this picture is right for ecological research, it will also serve for the teaching of ecology.

II. THE TEACHING OF ECOLOGY IN THE NETHERLANDS

The first point I want to make is that most of the leading Dutch ecologists (presumably the situation on the Continent is the same) have learnt ecology by their own efforts. The main cause, I think, can be found in the rather late incorporation of the teaching of ecology in university courses. Until some years ago no definite schools existed.

The first institute, in which a continuous ecological research programme was developed, was that of the Dutch Zoological Society at Den Helder, which, under the direction of Verwey, has, since 1932, carried out investigations in the Dutch Waddensea. It is now named the Netherlands Institute of Sea Research. It offers an opportunity for students of all universities to study marine biology (the head of the biological division is Dr. Groot, the head of the hydrographical division is Professor Postma). Within a few years it will be established in a new building, on the island Texel. Many zoologists in the Netherlands had their first contact with ecological research in this laboratory. The influence of Dr Verwey in this respect has been very important.

A. *Distribution ecology*

From the very beginning investigations in the Institute of Sea Research were directed into distribution ecology. The requirements of animals occurring in the Dutch Waddensea, as to bottom structure, water level, salinity and temperature were studied. Attention was paid especially to physiological and ethological ecology. Verwey mentioned (pers. comm.) that originally he expected to find biological interrelations between species to be of primary importance as causes for the distribution of these animals. When, however, one disregards the *numbers* of animals, the reaction of the organisms to the physico-chemical factors is most important, and biological factors are secondary.

It seems to me that this is the case in all approaches concerning ecological distribution. A specialist, knowing his organisms, can predict their occurrence even in an area he did not visit before.

At the universities, ecological research on distribution can be found in Leiden (Kuenen). The same approach has been made in our group at the Free University at Amsterdam.

B. *Population ecology*

Population ecology in our country has been started by the late L.Tinbergen (Groningen) since 1950. Partly in collaboration with Kluyver he investigated great tits and their prey. At present Klomp (Wageningen) has continued this type of research, concentrating now upon the regulation of the number of animals (caterpillars) by predators (tits) and parasites. At Groningen population ecology persisted mainly as population genetics (Wolda). Also at Leiden (K.Bakker) research can be found in this branch.

In population ecology attention is given mainly to biological interactions, whereas the study of abiotic factors mostly has receded to a secondary level. In all cases it is quite obvious that the food acts as the most important limiting factor; sometimes numbers are controlled by predators.

The difference indicated earlier between population and distribution ecology, though not a basic one, frequently can be met in discussions between research workers of the two groups.

C. *Plant ecology*

Plant ecology in the Netherlands is mostly incorporated (in the form of plant sociology) in plant systematics. Among others, the research in the universities of Utrecht (Lanjouw), Amsterdam (Meeuse) and Nijmegen (Stoffels) should be mentioned. Another form of plant ecology—comparable with distribution ecology—can be found at the University of Groningen (D.Bakker); the approach here can be compared to that of Harper (Bangor). Some years ago a start was made by the Free University at Amsterdam (Kuilman).

D. *Institutes outside of the universities*
Apart from the ecological centres at the universities, several others can be found. It is not possible to give a complete account of all these centres and the research which is done. Some, however, are mentioned below.

The Ecological Institute (Kluyver) can be found at Arnhem. It is composed of two subdivisions: one, under the direction of Kluyver, is mainly engaged in the study of problems in the distribution of animals, e.g. the dispersal of animals in the newly built polders in the late IJselmeer district. The botanical division (Adriani) at Oost-Voorne, carries out autecological studies on plants.

At Arnhem the ITBON, the institute for applied ecology (Voute), can be found. It consists of several research groups, e.g. one concentrating on terrestrial bottom communities and litter-decay (van der Drift) and one on game research (Eygenraam).

Fishery research is done at the RIVO at IJmuiden (Korringa). The institute dealing with nature research (RIVON, Mörzer-Bruins) should also be mentioned. It consists of two divisions, one working on animals in nature reserves (Mörzer Bruins), the other on plants (Westhoff). The investigations are primarily to make an inventory of plants and animals in nature reserves, and methods to preserve them are studied. The institute collaborates to a great extent with the Government and with the Society for Nature Conservation. Mörzer Bruins also lectures at Wageningen about problems concerning the conservation of nature.

In several smaller institutes other ecological studies are in progress, but it would take too much space to cover them all.

E. *Teaching techniques*
At present about 1500 students in biology are registered in the universities. The last few years the annual intake has increased (1962—230; 1963—250; 1964—325; 1965—375). Usually these students will gain some insight in ecological problems during their first or second year's lectures. In some universities, however, separate lectures are given on ecology, giving an introduction into the subject, whereas during later years of the study

o

specific topics will be dealt with. In all cases, as was said before, animal and plant ecology will be taught by separate lecturers. The situation in near-by countries seems to be the same (Delamare-Debouteville, 1965; Braun, pers. comm.).

Practical courses were rarely given until recently, but a change can be detected. In some universities practical courses, partly in the field, partly in the laboratory, have started, or will start, in a few years. These include ecological techniques as well as the description of habitats. In general, it can be said that interest in ecology is increasing.

Both in lectures and in the field, I believe one should concentrate on the most important key—observation. To perform critical experiments with any animal, observation over a long period is necessary. Only then can you descend to the level of the animal itself, so that the questions you ask are simple enough to be answered by their reactions.

On the other hand, it needs all the abilities of man, and even more, to develop a vision of the whole of ecology. Research in ecology is not easy— but far more difficult is the teaching of ecology.

ACKNOWLEDGMENTS

The author wishes to thank Dr J.Verwey and Professor D.J.Kuenen for stimulating discussions about the teaching of ecology. However, he alone takes responsibility for what has been said. Mr H.Cook, M.S.A., and Dr J.M.Lambert (Southampton) were so kind as to give advice about the English text.

REFERENCES

BODENHEIMER F.S. (1958) *Animal Ecology To-day.* Junk, Den Haag.
BRAUN-BLANQUET J. (1921) Prinzipien einer Systematik der Pflanzengesellschaften auf floristischer Grundlage. *Jahrb. St. Gall. Naturw. Ges.* **57,** 305–351.
BRAUN-BLANQUET J. (1928) *Pflanzensoziologie.* Biol. Studienbücher 7, Berlin.
DAHL F. (1908) Grundsätze und Grundbegriffe der biozönotische. Forschung. *Zool. Anz.* **33,** 349–353.
DELAMARE-DEBOUTEVILLE (1965) Les équilibres des faunes et des flores. *Revue Avenirs,* Les carrières de la recherche Scientifique, Févr.–Mars.
DU RIETZ G.E. (1921) *Zur methodologische Grundlage der Pflanzensoziologie,* Thesis, Uppsala.
ELTON C. (1927) *Animal Ecology.* Sidgwick & Jackson, London.
FRIEDERICHS K. (1927) Grundsätzliches uber die Lebenseinheiten höherer Ordnung und den ökologischen Einheitsfaktor. *Die Naturw.* **15,** 153–186.
FRIEDERICHS K. (1943) Uber den Begriff 'Unwelt' in der Biologie. *Acta Biotheor.* **7,** 147–162.

HUXLEY J. (1957) *Religion without Revelation*. Harper & Row, New York.

KONTKANEN P. (1950) Quantitative and seasonal studies on the leaf hopper fauna of the field stratum on open areas in north Karelia. *Ann. Zool. Soc. Vanamo*, **13**, 1–91.

LINDEMAN R.L. (1942) The trophic-dynamic aspect of ecology. *Ecol.* **23**, 399–418.

LUNDEGÅRDH H. (1953) *Klima und Boden*, 4e Aufl. Gustav Fischer, Jena.

MÖBIUS K. (1877) *Die Auster und die Austernwirtschaft*. Parey, Berlin.

PETERSEN C.G.J. (1914) The animal communities of the seabottom and their importance for marine zoogeography. *Rep. Dan. Biol. St.* **21**, 1–68.

TEILHARD DE CHARDIN P. (1965) *Le Phénomène humaine*. Du Seuil, Paris.

THIENEMANN A. (1931) Der Produktionsbegriff in der Biologie. *Arch. f. Hydrobiol.* **22**, 216–222.

THIENEMANN A. (1939) Grundzüge einer allgemeinen Ökologie. *Arch. f. Hydrobiol.* **35**, 267–285.

ECOLOGY TEACHING IN TROPICAL AND ARID COUNTRIES

L.F.H.MERTON

Botany Department, University of Sheffield

I. INTRODUCTION

The title of my paper is 'Ecology teaching in tropical and arid countries'. In fact I shall confine myself to the arid and semi-arid subtropics and tropics and to the humid tropics, of which I have had personal experience. Moreover, most of my comments are derived from a consideration of the situation in the Old World rather than the new. Here the teaching of ecology is mostly at university level and is predominantly in English or to a lesser extent in French, the teaching of ecology in schools uncommon and largely confined to those countries in which the British system of sixth-form teaching is in operation and English language text-books are widely used. I shall scarcely mention Australia. If at times I appear to generalize too widely, it is because the parts of the world I shall consider are both large and very varied and few specific statements can be made to which there are no exceptions.

II. THE GENERAL SETTING

The two regions which I am going to cover have this in common, that they include vast areas in which the local cultures are at a low level of technological, and particularly industrial, development and a high proportion of the inhabitants are engaged in subsistence farming. In many areas the rate of population increase is explosive, and in those countries which have recently attained independence from colonial rule populist governments have been concerned to provide additional land for cultivation by peasant farmers. Whether the emphasis is principally on large-scale schemes involving a high capital expenditure, as in the great irrigation schemes of the more arid lands, or on the planned resettlement of areas hitherto unavailable for small-scale peasant agriculture either for political reasons, as in the Kenya Highlands, or as a result of better communications and increasing government control in backward and sparsely settled regions, there is also a widespread local and unplanned expansion into unoccupied land. This increasing pressure on the natural vegetation, whether little or much altered from its original state, is rapidly reducing its extent and the alterations of the environment which result from settlement have created new problems, both agricultural and political. These may be exacerbated by the introduction of agricultural machinery which enables a greatly increased rate of alteration of the habitat. The ploughing of steppe in central Turkey in order to increase the area of land under cereals for export, a part of the agricultural policy of the late Menderes Government, allowed 1 year of good grain harvests. Subsequently, in a region of erratic rainfall, dustbowl conditions developed over wide areas. The destructive effects of increasing cattle grazing in central Africa are well known. In central Asia, the Sudan and elsewhere, irrigation schemes in arid areas have created suitable habitats for the rapid multiplication of indigenous species of grasshopper and other insects to the level at which they have become serious pests (Uvarov, 1962). In Iran the restriction of movement of tribes practising transhumance from winter grazing in the plains and foothills to summer pastures in the mountains and their settlement in the lowlands have affected the incidence of human disease and have resulted in drastic overgrazing, an increase of arable land and an increased rate of loss of fuel and soil.

I stress this situation because it is the setting in which the teaching of ecology in underdeveloped countries must proceed. We may read the reports of visiting ecologists who have visited these areas, we may know of the great and praiseworthy work of FAO and UNESCO in tackling their problems, but we sometimes forget the almost complete and universal ignorance, not only of the principles of ecology, but of any causative relationship whatever between the actions of the agricultural population and the resulting changes in the land. Soil erosion is nowadays recognized and defined by the farmers of the American Mid-West (though it has not been so for long); it is not at all by the villagers of Syria or the Celebes.

III. REQUIREMENTS AND FACILITIES

Most of the centres of tertiary education in the countries I am speaking of are of very recent origin: in the ex-colonial territories the vast majority were founded shortly before independence or immediately afterwards. The higher echelons of technical departments of government were largely recruited from overseas; independence has had two consequences in this field: the rapid loss of experienced expatriates, often before any adequate local replacements were available, and the coming to power of people who had other political and social aims in view and who were committed to programmes involving changes in social organization and land-use far more rapid and far-reaching than any colonial power would have dared to introduce in recent years. The more enlightened of these governments are conscious that with their limited resources, both in money and in manpower, research in institutes of further education and in government research stations must be primarily in applied fields. This is particularly true in agriculture.

In countries where settlement is expanding planned land-use is essential. The relevance of ecological research to such planning is clear—and teaching is the prelude to research. It is essential that the future graduate staff of technical departments should have some ecological training, since by its nature ecology is synthetic and should give an understanding of fundamental processes in nature which will foster in a worker in an applied field an appreciation of the aims and relevance of other disciplines. All too often in the past, and all too often in the present, foresters and agriculturalists have been bitterly opposed. In Turkey, until recently, the development of improved pastures and the development of livestock were the concern of two distinct departments, which scarcely at all co-operated.

But technical departments are generally regarded as adjuncts of the administration. The Science graduate, if he is clever enough, enters a technical department. It is the Arts graduate who enters the administration and has the power to make decisions which profoundly affect land-use and all the consequences of land-use, sometimes against the advice of his technical advisers.

It is essential, therefore, that a general knowledge of ecological principles should not be confined to Honours graduates in the biological sciences but should be regarded as an essential qualification for a recruit to the administrative service. Moreover, as in England, the majority of graduates become schoolteachers and in the villages have the power to open the eyes of the future farmers and graziers to the interdependence of man and animals and vegetation. Legislation aimed at the conservation of natural resources is useless unless it is effective and laws are only obeyed if there is an understanding of their relevance.

I should like to see, therefore, a course in ecology as a necessary requirement for any degree or teacher's certificate in such countries: a course in simple terms and concerned primarily with Man and his relation to the land, conceived as a part of the general intellectual background of any educated person. Breadth of understanding of the interaction of Man and his environment are quite as important as depth in countries where a few qualified men must make decisions which affect the development of natural resources and the livelihood of so many. Such a course must be an integrated one, resting on the foundations of geography, climate and social organization.

To return to the first main consequence of political change which I mentioned earlier: the loss of expatriate technical personnel. Many of these had a wide experience of local vegetation, soils and land-use extending over many years. Partly because the best of such men were often concerned with the day-to-day minutiae of administrative work, partly out of dilatoriness or diffidence, the information they possessed was seldom adequately recorded, or if recorded not published to the scientific community at large. Anyone who has travelled in such countries knows how important and illuminating reports may be hidden away, unvalued, in the archives accumulated by the superseded régime.

It is in this situation that the teaching ecologist must work and it is in teaching institutions that a high proportion of the modern generation of expatriate biologists is employed. Small though the total number of expatriate ecologists is they are frequently the only ecologists on the staff, and it is with them that I am principally concerned today.

A university teacher may be on permanent appointment, but even so few stay long. Increasingly the tendency is for the recruitment of short-term appointees, often on secondment. Such a seconded scientist must usually learn *ab initio* the detailed nature of his region, the names and characteristics of the plants and animals with which he has to deal and about which he must teach, and the agricultural traditions and social organization which determine the older patterns of land-use. He must rely upon texts which are miserably few, often inadequate and rarely suitable for direct teaching. How few text-books of elementary botany deal in any but the most general way with tropical examples! One can use a British elementary mathematical text-book in Singapore but not easily a biological one.

The teacher himself has four main sources of information other than his own observations. First there are the classic accounts of early travellers and biogeographers such as Wallace and Schimper, still full of stimulating and informative material. Even now one must go back to Handel-Mazetti for a description of some parts of the Middle East. There are the great taxonomic works, which provide the basis for ecology, the reports of government departments (those on forestry are particularly useful) and, finally, there are recent research papers and the reports of symposia. The coverage here varies greatly. Of outstanding value are the reports of the specialized agencies of the United Nations, in particular FAO and UNESCO.

But over great areas up-to-date information may be scanty and disjointed, floras difficult to use or even to obtain and local accounts nonexistent. Even where they do exist they may be unsuitable for teaching. An increased flow of research papers is, of course, needed but what are needed even more are regional, compilative studies for teaching purposes. These may be concerned with selected phenomena or with the biology of selected groups of plants, as is Holltum's admirable little book *Plant Life in Malaya* (Holltum, 1954), which has the unusual merit of examining tropical vegetation from the viewpoint of the tropics rather than that of the temperate regions, or they may be concerned with the general ecology of a region—as Hopkin's recent book *Forest and Savannah* (Hopkins, 1965), written for Nigeria but pertinent to much of West Africa. Such texts as those by Odum, Greig-Smith and Kershaw are widely used but need local supplementation; on the other hand the works of Heinrich Walter, whose first volume of *The Vegetation of the Earth*, deals with the tropics and subtropics (Walter, 1964), though valuable for the teacher, suffer from the disadvantage, as does much of the best work from Indonesia, of being in German, which is less widely understood in these countries where English is already a second language, than in Western Europe.

The teaching ecologist, therefore, must publish what he can, even if the gaps in his knowledge are considerable, and must bear in mind that clarity of style and lucidity of exposition is even more important than usual since he is writing for students to whom English is a foreign language.

I have mentioned some of the characteristics that the humid and arid tropics have in common. In considering the teaching of ecology in more detail in the sections which follow, I must deal with them separately, pointing out some of those features which offer good opportunities for the teaching of fundamental ecological principles. In practice, most teaching in these countries is descriptive and analytical rather than experimental. It is still to a large extent classificatory. In very few institutions is there any integration of zoological and botanical ecology and this usually where the coast is within accessible distance, in courses of marine biology. Modern methods of community analysis are being widely introduced but a consideration of energy-flow and nutrient-cycling has so far been largely confined to theory—although the advent of the International Biological Programme has stimulated a number of ecologists into exploring the feasibility of introducing an investigation of productivity into field courses.

Among the examples of topics which lend themselves to teaching, which I shall give later, I have included both examples which I or others have used and suggestions for projects which I have myself studied sufficiently to know that they could be handled by a class. I have included nothing which I do not know is feasible.

IV. ARID AND SEMI-ARID REGIONS

Arid and semi-arid regions are characterized by variable rainfall and open vegetation. In the absence of irrigation the more arid portions are comparatively sparsely inhabited and often by nomads or peoples practising transhumance. These people rely upon free grazing herds or flocks for much of their food and clothing and even shelter. Man and animals may be a highly integrated symbiotic unit. Centuries or millennia of grazing and the extraction of woody plants for fuel has resulted in the extreme degradation of the vegetation; in the savannah belt of central Africa fire is universally used to clear litter and stimulate regrowth of palatable fodder before the onset of seasonal rains, and shifting cultivation is widespread. Plant communities are composed of relatively few species, highly adapted to an arid environment and long-continued biotic pressure.

In such situations studies on the biological mechanisms whereby species survive or avoid the unfavourable season, on successional changes resulting from protection from fire or grazing, the phenomena involved in germination and establishment of seedlings and the importance of micro-climate, in which topography plays an important role, are all fruitful and capable of subdivision into teaching exercises. Areas enclosed and protected from fire and grazing may show astonishingly rapid changes in specific composition and vegetational structure and the frequency and timing of burning may markedly affect regeneration, as Trapnell, for example, has shown in West Africa (Trapnell, 1959). Relict stands of trees, sometimes preserved for religious reasons, may give valuable information on the nature and distribution of woodland, which, near its limit of growth in arid regions, may disappear without a trace over wide areas. The autecology of desert species involves a study of water relations, the examination of root-systems and the factors that influence both the survival of seedlings, which must tap sufficient resources in their first season of growth to enable them to survive a subsequent drought and, related to this, the spacing of adult perennials. Mechanisms such as those discovered by Went in his work on germination inhibitors in the seeds of desert annuals and the production of toxic exudates by roots or litter are probably widespread. The fruits of annual species of *Medicago* contain something under a dozen seeds which germinate singly, sometimes producing three or more successive plants from a single pod in as many years, though if the seeds are extracted they have a high rate of simultaneous germination; many such legumes in which the unit of seed dispersal is an indehiscent pod or an inflorescence, as in some *Trifolium* species, show the same phenomenon. The seeds of many annual grasses of the Middle East, such as *Stipa capensis*, will only germinate below a certain temperature, and so on.

Topography is an important determinant of vegetation: by affecting the flow and concentration of water and through aspect. In arid climates a high proportion of the radiation reaching the ground surface is direct insolation, unscattered by any cloud or tree cover, and therefore markedly directional. Catenary systems can be worked out in relation to the depth of the water table and varying soil character: such systems are a striking feature throughout the semi-arid regions. A study of microtopography in relation to the germination of annual grasses is particularly instructive, especially as trampling by animals in much-grazed regions is as important a determinant of vegetation as is the removal of their foliage. Moreover, micro-relief of the order of 1–2 in. may, by concentrating the leaching effect of rainfall, determine whether, for instance, the surface vegetation is of annual herbs and grasses or deep-rooted halophytic perennials. Here the cycling of salt by the halophyte is a phenomenon readily studied in student exercises.

Arid and semi-arid regions offer excellent opportunities for the study of animal populations in relation to vegetation and especially for the study of insects because all parts of the vegetation of most habitats are accessible and comparatively simple sampling techniques can be used. The study of insect population dynamics in relation to seasonal climatic variation and to protection from fire or grazing again has both theoretical value in teaching and applied value in agronomy.

Much steppe and savannah appears to be a mosaic between rather sharply defined communities and here modern statistical techniques for the analysis of vegetation may be interestingly applied. The spacing of *Artemisia herba-alba* bushes in *Artemisia* steppe in the Middle East appears, on visual examination, to be closely related to topography: on level ground it appears astonishingly regular, but Greig-Smith and Chadwick have recently shown that in semi-desert *Acacia–Capparis* scrub in the Sudan pattern analysis does not support the conclusions from visual examination of a regularity of spacing imposed by competition for water (Greig-Smith & Chadwick, 1965). Very little is known about the productivity of natural vegetation of semi-arid regions and how this is related to grazing practice and much of our information is from North America and Australia.

The use of aerial photographs in surveying vegetation, not normally considered an undergraduate exercise, could profitably be introduced here. The value of such mapping should not be underestimated since, apart from being a prelude to an examination of the causes of the observed distribution, records of changes in distribution over a period of years are of prime importance.

The difficulties that face the teaching ecologist in such a situation derive from the fact that all vegetation is secondary. Only in favoured situations as, say, the University of East Africa at Nairobi are a wide range of habitats and vegetation types accessible. Moreover, detailed ecological knowledge is very scanty in many areas.

V. THE HUMID TROPICS

In separating the humid tropics from the arid and semi-arid subtropics I am, of course, aware of the enormous variations in climate, flora and fauna and vegetational structure which can be found between them. But I want, very briefly, to consider the difficulties and opportunities which await a teaching ecologist in the other extreme of the range I am considering, in the humid tropics and, particularly, in tropical rain forest. First, the difficulties: the richness of floristic composition, the necessity for learning to distinguish species from bark and leaves, where the first branch may be 150 ft up, in some places the difficulty of access. The structure and pattern of the forest are so complex that students (and teacher perhaps) are bewildered. Single dominants are rare and there are no sharp discontinuities in vegetation clearly related to environmental features. It may be truly impossible to see the wood for the trees. Thus, in order to find vegetation floristically poor enough and with species readily enough identified, one must go to secondary or seral communities. Here, too, it is possible more easily to demonstrate the relationship between soil texture and aeration, the height of the water table and vegetation and to study changes with time. Thus, in the University of Malaya, student field excursions included visits to mangrove forests where the primary colonization of mud and a succession of dominants associated with increasing distance from the sea and decreasing salinity of flood-water could be seen. On the east coast of

Malaya sand-dune complexes of varying age allowed the demonstration of soil development and successional changes with time and statistical methods of vegetational analysis could be introduced in low-growing vegetation. Here, too, the soils were unusual, well-developed podsols with iron pan being developed on the older dunes.

Within the forest itself the situation is different. Only the floor of the forest is readily accessible, yet high above one's head the trees, lianes and epiphytes produce new flushes of leaves, flower and fruit and a specialized fauna of insects live. Almost all the diurnal species of mammal frequent the tree-tops. Thus, to ignore them is to ignore a large and important part of the ecosystem. A tree-top platform, therefore, from which the behaviour of monkeys, the feeding of birds and the flowering of plants can be studied is worth much trouble and expense. But most of the time must be spent below.

Apart from straightforward dissertation on what is observed during a walk through the forest, what can be practically accomplished in student exercises? In the first place autecological studies on the rate of growth of forest plants, both species of the canopy and of the forest floor, on how long a single leaf remains alive, on seedling establishment can readily be done and may lead to a study of the physiology of shade tolerance. The phenology of flowering and fruiting offers a wide field for observation in which the occurrence of inherent rhythms, divorced from seasonal climatic variations, can be demonstrated. There are very few even tentative estimates of biomass, productivity and nutrient content of primary rain forest. This is hardly a teaching exercise but observations on the quantity and nature of leaf fall and on the rapidity of the decomposition systems can be. How important is the role of termites in the breakdown of plant material? Little is known of root systems or of the relative importance of mycorrhiza. Again, why do species of the primary forest not regrow immediately after the forest has been felled? Are the reasons for their exclusion the obvious ones? Such a simple experiment as the collection of surface soil from a variety of situations and the identification of the seedlings which can be grown from it has shown that seeds of species of secondary vegetation may be present deep in the primary forest. In a situation where trees may grow 6–10 ft in a year and there is no season in which they do not grow, competition between tree species may readily be studied experimentally.

Rodents can be trapped and marked for recapture and amphibia readily caught by torchlight at night, an exercise which can be amusing with a student party. Bryophytes are uncommon in lowland forest except on leaves and sapling twigs. On older leaves astonishingly complex communities can form on a single leaf, on which lichens, liverworts and species of *Trentepohlia* may harbour a population of rotifers, nematodes and numerous flagellates. Here is an opportunity to study the development of a microcosm and the increase of specific content with time.

The structure, behaviour and ecological relationships of the plants of the humid tropics offer such a wide choice for the study of biological phenomena that the problem is one of selection. A single day in tropical rain forest suggests more topics for study than are needed for half a dozen Honours courses. One could construct a biological course based on the figs alone, with their varied life-form, ecology and phenology and their obligate insect pollinators.

One of the delights of teaching biology in the tropics is that living and growing plants and animals are always available for study, and it makes it easier to remind students throughout their course that the material they are studying is from living organisms which have a place in a natural ecosystem. Few students in Malaya had ever been in the forest which covered the greater part of their country before they came to the university and yet it is essential for biologists throughout the world that they become aware of the richness of their biological inheritance. For the teacher, the teaching of ecology in the tropics and subtropics is not only of absorbing interest but has a social relevance which it is difficult to underestimate.

REFERENCES

GREIG-SMITH P. & CHADWICK M.J. (1965) Data on pattern within plant communities. III. *Acacia–Capparis* semi-desert scrub in the Sudan. *J. Ecol.* **53,** 465–474.
HOLLTUM R.E. (1954) *Plant Life in Malaya.* Longmans, Green, London.
HOPKINS B. (1965) *Forest and Savanna.* Heinemann, London.
TRAPNELL C.G. (1959) Ecological results of woodland burning experiments in Northern Rhodesia. *J. Ecol.* **47,** 129–168.
UVAROV B.P. (1962) Developments of arid lands and its ecological effects on their insect fauna. *The Problems of the Arid Zone: Proc. Paris* (1960) *Symposium,* pp. 235–248. UNESCO, Paris (Arid Zone Research, 18).
WALTER H. (1964) *Die Vegetation der Erde in ökologischer Betrachtung* Bd. 1. *Die tropischen Zonen,* 2nd ed. Gustav Fischer, Jena.

SECTION V
GENERAL ORGANIZATION OF FACILITIES

GENERAL ORGANIZATION OF FIELD STUDIES

Tom Pritchard

Education Advisory Section, Nature Conservancy

I. INTRODUCTION

Although field studies are now a fairly well-established feature in formal education, one can hardly say that they benefit from any overall administration or much official guidance and encouragement. In this country we are not surprised by this state of affairs. We have become accustomed to live with a situation in which the future of new educational achievements is determined by whether they are sustained by a band of enthusiasts long enough for 'the big machine' to prepare itself to take them over. But the big machine will not assimilate field studies until it understands what they mean in educational terms. Objectives in field studies at different educational levels have then to be defined and policies formulated. It is futile to talk of policy without recognition that financial resources must be found. We have heard that the Nuffield scheme, for instance, will cost a great deal of money to implement. We also know that the Field Studies Council, however anxious to break new ground and provide more facilities, is badly held up by financial shortages. Until these fundamental steps of defining objectives, formulating policy and earmarking financial resources have been taken, it is difficult to talk about organization.

Until 2 years ago, there was practically no indication that those in the field studies movement were going to organize themselves. Neither was there any indication that anyone else was going to do it for them. Field studies have emerged over the years in a haphazard way, partly from the amateur naturalist movement, partly as a product of the conservation movement and partly as a result of advances in the field sciences, especially ecology. They are, in turn, conducted either as a pleasurable pastime, or as a basis for preparing people to behave properly towards the countryside, or as a serious scientific discipline. These studies are nowadays encountered at all levels of formal education from primary school to university, and beyond in adult education. They have spread from formal education into the realms of public education, mainly through the actions of the conservationists. Indeed, they have recently played a part in the training of middle management executives in the electricity supply industry and of members of the land-linked professions.

II. INVESTIGATIONS INTO THE PRESENT PATTERN OF
FIELD STUDIES

Before 1963 no one knew very much about the amount of field studies
undertaken in the educational institutions or about the form of these
studies. We were seriously concerned in the Nature Conservancy about the
absence of data and of any kind of assessments, however subjective. We
were concerned because the quality and extent of these studies would
inevitably govern the number and competence of potential recruits into
ecological research and conservation. We were also concerned because
field studies could influence the degree of public understanding of
environmental problems, and thus of conservation, which we could
anticipate for the future. With these points in mind, the Conservancy set
up in 1960, under the chairmanship of its Director-General, Max Nichol-
son, a Study Group on Education and Field Biology. That Study Group
was composed of twenty-three members from educational institutions, the
Field Studies Council, museums and other bodies providing facilities or
instruction in the field sciences, the BBC and Independent Television,
and Her Majesty's Inspectorate, as well as a Director of Education. They
set out to explore the position. It took them 2½ years of hard work,
gathering information by questionnaire and other survey methods,
conducting research, reviewing literature and audio-visual aids and discuss-
ing the formidable problems they encountered with a large number of
experts in this country and overseas. They set out their findings in a
report called *Science Out of Doors*, which was published by Longmans in
May 1963.

It became pretty clear early on during these investigations that, regardless
of what organizational pattern was eventually developed, field studies
pose two basic groups of problems of ways and means.

A. *Methodological problems*
The first group of problems relates to methods of teaching in the open air
as opposed to the more customary methods developed in the classroom and
laboratory. In this group we come across a multitude of other educational
issues, such as determining what to teach at different levels and thus of
designing syllabuses; deciding how to integrate preparatory indoor work
with what is done in the field and subsequently; designing fair and reasonable examinations; remodelling timetables; and so on. Most of these issues
are, and should continue to be, the responsibility of teachers, examiners
and educational administrators.

B. *The demand for facilities*

The second group of problems is very different in nature. These relate to finding and securing facilities for field studies, such as educational nature reserves, other teaching sites, residential and non-residential field centres, field museums and mobile units. Also in this group of problems lie those of providing specialist supporting services, from various societies, trusts, museums, and government bodies such as the Nature Conservancy, as well as developing the use of radio and television and other audio-visual aids.

Today we can say that there are people who know a great deal about one or more of these problems. But it will take a team of master minds to combine potential solutions to isolated problems in such a way as to create an organism which one could regard as a rational framework for conducting field studies effectively and economically under all circumstances. The difficulty is partly one of communication between specialists and teachers. It is partly one of a disinclination to bring to bear the principles and methods of science to rationalize a multi-factorial situation. It also partly stems from an absence of a sense of urgency and from our reluctance to apply cost-benefit analysis to education processes. I would couple to this last remark what I personally regard as one of the most serious defects in our education system in so far as field studies are concerned. That is the virtual absence of communication between those who teach on different rungs of the educational ladder. We have not until very recently made any serious attempts to ensure continuity in field studies through the various stages of education so that boys and girls can at each level absorb what can best be learnt at that stage on the basis of what has been rightly learnt at the stage before. Heavy odds have confronted the parent who requires for his child a continuous and progressive education about living things and their environment from primary to university level. It is encouraging to hear that this situation is to be put right in the Nuffield scheme.

What we have, then, is a complex, highly flexible education system which offers a great deal of scope for individual teachers to take their pupils or students into the field. The number of enthusiastic teachers who take advantage of this situation is growing rapidly. Thus their demands for facilities are being felt acutely by those organizations which ought to be in a position to provide what is required. Teachers want land, water, residential accommodation, specialist advice and so on. Until recently, official educational bodies have not been able to do much to meet these requirements. The leaders of field parties have had to use their own initiative and do the best they could to an extent often far beyond what might reasonably be expected of them. Some of the demand has been met by the Field Studies Council, the Youth Hostels Association and other bodies, most of them voluntary and non-profit-making organizations. However, their total contribution in terms of student numbers has been only a small one. In other respects, particularly in setting an example of how to undertake field work under varying circumstances, some of these bodies, principally the Field Studies Council, have played a vital role. It is only recently that local authorities have themselves made substantial additions to facilities, mainly in the form of field centres.

Science Out of Doors does, of course, contain a lot of detail about the facilities available and the use made of them. That report cannot be regarded as a complete assessment of the situation, but it is the only reference we have. Although it is already getting out of date, some of the information it contains still serves as a valuable guide for finding ways and means of providing more effective support for field studies and especially as a signpost for more intensive investigations of various problems.

III. POSSIBILITIES FOR PROGRESS

Some useful progress has been made between 1963 and 1966. In 1965 there were two large conferences, one at Keele run by the Conservancy and the other in London run by the Field Studies Council. The Keele conference considered the educational implications of the Countryside in 1970 conference held in 1963. Even though it had a strong flavour of conservation, it dealt in depth with means of finding facilities in the countryside for education. Lord Bowden, then Minister of State for Education, gave an encouraging impetus to the conference in his opening address. His was the first public statement by a Minister dealing with the role of field studies in education.

The conference arranged by the Field Studies Council dealt more fully with co-ordination of effort among those who run residential centres in the countryside. This was specially important as a means of bringing together those who have had long experience of running field centres and those Local Education Authorities who are now seeking to provide similar services.

These conferences created an improved climate for collaboration, and many follow-up tasks are now being tackled. Such tasks, and others which were created by the Study Group on Education and Field Biology, are really of two kinds.

A. *Collaboration between organizations*

First, there are those which are designed to consolidate the collaboration already achieved between different organizations. Machinery for inter-communication is being developed. There are even signs that some teachers' guides, text-books and other literature on field studies are being prepared. I hope the British Ecological Society and the Field Studies Council will take a leading role in these developments. Demands are also being made for a national body to promote advisory services, to improve communication between the large number of bodies concerned with field studies, to encourage further investigations and to act as a spokesman in official circles. It seems likely that this body will take the form of a Committee on Environmental Education modelled in some respects along the lines of the Study Group on Education and Field Biology, but with a much wider representation from educational, scientific and administrative circles. Obviously, there are innumerable tasks which ought to be tackled soon. One that always seems to stand out is the important job of collating all the experience and knowledge we already possess. There have been brilliant achievements in field studies by individuals, but all too often the only people who get to know about them are the students who have benefited. I wonder how many teachers are aware, for instance, of Arnold Darlington's techniques for overcoming a total absence of open country which were described earlier in this volume. Why is it that the new techniques which various universities are trying out so often remain unknown to many others? Surely this is the sort of problem that can be solved fairly easily. Even if the machinery designed to cope with communication turns out to be expensive, I hardly think that it will cost more to maintain than the country is already paying because some have to learn from scratch techniques which are already in use elsewhere. This is an old problem, I know. It applies all over the place. It is an awful indictment that it has been allowed to persist for so long.

One of the finest features of our unorganized education system is that it has offered for so long excellent opportunities for experiment. But no advantage is to be gained if the results of these experiments are to be allowed to remain in obscurity because we cannot be bothered to publicize them in the most suitable way.

B. *Improvement of methods and facilities*

The second group of tasks is concerned with further research and surveys. If we are to replace the present *laissez-faire* way of conducting field studies we must find out more about how to do this in an effective and economical way. Field studies are changing rapidly in their character, as papers in this volume have already shown. Although we can adapt our existing resources to cope with many of these changes, we must recognize that entirely new situations are presenting themselves. The sort of questions that come to mind are, for instance:

(i) How far can teachers usefully be supplemented by visiting specialists and by such services as radio and television?

(ii) What is the potential usefulness of neighbouring, small and artificial— as distinct from remote, larger and more natural—educational nature reserves?

(iii) How important is security of tenure over land and water used for field work?

(iv) What may be the role of day centres?

(v) Can field studies programmes be devised which take full account of factors such as seasonal changes and the need for continuity between courses at successive levels?

(iv) How far is it educationally desirable to have links with the applied biology in farming, forestry and conservation?

A start has already been made in the examination of factors such as I have mentioned. We have already heard of the Nuffield contribution and of the American BSCS, which lie mainly in the educational sector rather than the facilities sector. We can add to these the work of Dr Elizabeth Perrott at Keele, sponsored by the Nature Conservancy, on techniques of using nature reserves and other teaching areas.

A number of the projects which fall rather more into the facilities sector are also well under way. The Education Advisory Section of the Conservancy, established in April 1964, has put a substantial amount of its limited resources into initiating and taking part in a programme of operational research, including:

(i) the selection, development and management of teaching sites in urban areas and methods of relating their use with that of more distant, rural sites;

(ii) the development of day centres and associated teaching sites near urban areas, as at Alvecote Pools and Ainsdale Sand Dunes;

(iii) the development of a provincial museum, at Leicester, as the main centre for field studies for the county and city;

(iv) the incorporation of educational sites into the master plan of the New Town at Dawley.

Such projects are designed as pilot schemes to examine a whole group of characteristic factors at a time. Thus we are hoping to obtain coverage not only of technical land and water management problems, but also of tactical issues and those relating to land acquisition, finance, administration and the requirements of educational users. It is hoped that over the next few years a number of blueprints can be prepared as examples of how to tackle a range of situations up and down the country.

IV. CONCLUSION

Although much more is desired, I feel that we have made a reasonable start in this country on educational research relating to field studies. Already the sums being spent, although small, are quite a reasonable proportion of the annual investment in educational research in recent years. Education in Britain currently has a turnover of about £1000 million a year, and the cost to the country is about 5 per cent of the gross national product. Yet this immense investment has not until very recently concerned itself at all with improvement in its own processes. As recently as 1963, the total spent on educational research was a paltry 0.0001 per cent of the total expenditure on education. It is a little more now, but it still does not bear comparison with industries like the engineering or chemical industries which sometimes spend up to 15 per cent of their turnover on research. It is a depressing thought that in 1963 the amount spent on educational research was equivalent to that spent on research by the glue industry or by the whitewash industry.

Where does the blame lie? It is always easy to castigate ministers and civil servants, but I would like to conclude by daring to suggest that at least some of the blame lies with the educationalists themselves. Are our priorities right when it comes to choosing research topics? Are departments of education in universities always justified in promoting projects on past educational achievements while neglecting cryingly urgent projects on science education? Are such departments receiving encouragement from the science departments to initiate projects, either independently or in collaboration with lecturers in science? What is being done in the training colleges? And what of the teacher's own role in research? What support does he require? Is his problem one of isolation? Is it financial? How much use is made of such resources as exist, such as the Royal Society's fund for scientific research by teachers in schools?

Over the last few years I have tried to look very critically at the tactics of making progress, and one thing has become quite clear: the initiative must come from those engaged in the practice of teaching. It is no use passing the buck. We must also break down isolationism by every means possible. The present symposium, I am sure, has contributed substantially towards doing just that. There is a great wealth of experience and knowledge to be passed around. Such dissemination of knowledge must be a continuing process running hand in hand with the many other tasks which must be completed before we can achieve a national organization for field studies.

THE ROLE OF FIELD CENTRES IN
ECOLOGICAL TEACHING

Field Studies Council, Preston Montford Field Centre, Shrewsbury

I. INTRODUCTION

This paper is not primarily concerned with the content and methodology of courses run at field centres. In these respects, as in many others, there is too much variation from one centre to another for such generalizations to be useful. Furthermore, the ecological teaching at most FSC centres is undergoing rapid change in response to the current development of new ideas and approaches in the subject as a whole. Behind my title lie a number of implicit questions; not only the obvious one: 'What are field centres for?', but also: 'Of what kinds are they and how are they run? Do they meet the present demand on their services, both in quantity and quality? Are they being used in the best possible ways? And in basic educational terms, are they really necessary?'

Ecology is not the only branch of biology to which field data are relevant, but it in fact draws a greater proportion of its primary information from studies in the field. It is still a highly empirical discipline, if indeed discipline is the right word. This lack of a formal theoretical framework, and the great complexity of the material and the relationships with which it is concerned, make the subject difficult to teach. It does not lend itself readily to classroom or laboratory treatment unless the students can draw mentally on experience and examples which they have encountered at first hand.

The majority of schools (and of higher institutions for that matter) are situated in urban areas. This does not necessarily deprive them of material for local field studies, but it usually makes for a lack of ecological variety and of security for repetitive observation and experimental work. Furthermore, it is seldom easy for a school biology teacher to convert even a double practical period into a field excursion, much less to extract a full class for half a day from an overfull programme of competing school activities.

If field studies are admitted to be a desirable part of biology teaching, and if such acute difficulties are met with in seeking holes in the school timetable and sites in the neighbourhood, then the inevitable solution must be to take or send pupils elsewhere and for longer periods. The teacher who arrives at this fairly momentous decision must then decide where to take them, how to organize their field studies and how to pay for the exercise. He needs a residential base from which to operate in 'good teaching country' (whatever that may mean); at least minimal facilities, including indoor working space, together with books and simple apparatus; security of access to the chosen teaching ground; and a fund of local background information and technical advice on which he can draw. All this assumes that the teacher feels competent to lead his own class in the field and is free to do so. The evidence suggests that the majority of teachers actually prefer to send their pupils away to be taught by somebody else, whom they expect—rightly or wrongly—to give better value than they could themselves.

This is what field centres are for, and perhaps I can best illustrate their functions in practical terms by running briefly over the recent history of the Field Studies Council and kindred organizations.

II. THE FIELD STUDIES COUNCIL

The Council for the Promotion of Field Studies (which later changed to its present title) was founded in 1943 and had opened its first four field centres by the end of 1947. Later centres have been acquired at intervals in response to the growing demand for places, and by the end of the present year they will total eight. Field centres were first envisaged primarily as residential establishments providing accommodation and modest technical facilities for amateur naturalists and university field classes. The admission of school parties on courses organized by the wardens and staff of the field centres led to a change in the whole conception of their purpose, and has been largely responsible for the successful development of the Council's work over the past 21 years.

The field centres have been chosen partly for the suitability of their premises, but mainly for the richness and variety of the geographical and ecological features of the areas in which they lie. At the present time about 25 per cent of the visitors to all the field centres are sixth-form biology students and a further 10 per cent biologists from training colleges and universities, out of a total intake of nearly 12,000 per annum on residential courses mostly of 1 week's duration. The majority of the school pupils are attending courses run by the staff of the centres, but a significant and slowly increasing proportion operate independently under the guidance of their own staff.

Each centre is staffed on the academic side by a warden and two or three assistants, all graduates whose qualifications between them cover the principal fields of teaching. With an intake of fifty to sixty students on residential courses every week for 8 months of the year, the academic staff at each centre find their time largely taken up by routine field teaching duties. Nevertheless, they are encouraged to engage in research on topics more or less closely related to their teaching work. The results of such research are published from time to time in the Council's own Journal, *Field Studies*, which also takes papers relevant to the centre's working areas from outside contributors.

The individual centres are more or less autonomous in the planning of their programmes, in devising the subject-content and curriculum of their courses, and in the enrolment of visitors. The courses are run in every week between the beginning of March and the end of October, programmes with a calendar of organized courses being issued each November for the following season. Apart from the routine sixth-form courses in geography and biology and less frequent ones in other subjects at the same level, each centre includes a number of more advanced and specialized courses (sometimes run with the help of outside tutors); increasing attention is being paid to the provision of courses in field methods for teachers.

The Field Studies Council is independent financially and administratively, and meets practically all its running and capital costs out of the fees paid by visitors. Annual grants are received from the majority of universities, but these are offset by a rebate in the fees paid by university visitors. Nevertheless, the Council is still indirectly grant-aided in that most school pupils and teachers attending the centres are eligible for some financial assistance from their Local Education Authorities.

At the present time the Council occupies a special position among the organizations which run field study centres, by virtue of its longer experience, its highly qualified teaching staff with their opportunities for original research, and its close links with universities and research institutions. The Council's independence, moreover, has made it possible to act on a fundamental conviction that teaching in the field must not be tied to any formal academic syllabus, but should be free to draw both its data and its synthesis from the whole landscape.

A generation of biology teachers has grown up with experience of the Council's centres at the student stage, and many teachers with or without this experience are now taking advantage of courses specially run for them at these centres in order to help them to run field courses themselves. Through this 'multiplier effect', and also through the technical knowledge it can put at the disposal of those other bodies wishing to establish field centres, the Field Studies Council is now in a position to exert an educational influence far beyond the thousands of students who actually visit its centres annually.

III. OTHER ORGANIZATIONS

Dr Pritchard has dealt in his paper with the general organization of field studies, including the important role of the Education Advisory Section of the Nature Conservancy. I need therefore deal only briefly with the provision of facilities by other bodies, concentrating on those whose functions are closest to the Field Studies Council. The Scottish Field Studies Association is essentially similar in conception and purpose, though at present it only operates one full-time field centre and is a comparatively young organization.

Another recently formed organization is Bio-Probe, and this differs from all the others in running well-equipped mobile units which can be set up at any one of a great variety of suitable localities where access and good teaching ground are assured. In many ways the work of Bio-Probe is complementary to that of centres run by the Field Studies Council, for while the former has the advantage of a much wider choice of area to work in, the latter are in a position to accumulate much larger funds of detailed local knowledge and to carry out continuous long-term experiments on their own land.

At least twenty-five Local Education Authorities now operate one or more residential centres for pupils from their own schools and, while some of these (e.g. those in Northumberland) come close to the FSC standard, the great majority are primarily conceived as bases for outdoor recreational pursuits; field studies are then a secondary function and few of these centres employ staff with technical qualifications of the appropriate kind. At most LEA centres the intake is in practice largely restricted to pupils from schools under the administering authority, though about half of them are actually located in areas well beyond the bounds of the county or county borough concerned.

Intake is similarly restricted, of course, at most of the field stations run by university departments and a few colleges and schools. These serve a very important educational function, but there is relatively little propagation of new methods and ideas from one institution to another. This limitation does not apply to research institutions like those run by the Freshwater Biological Association and the Marine Biological Association, but in terms of student intake these bodies naturally make no more than a marginal contribution.

A number of Youth Hostels are specially equipped to provide facilities but no teaching assistance for visiting field parties.

IV. ADEQUACY AND EFFECTIVENESS OF THE SERVICE AND ITS USE

It is all too clear that the places available for pupils requiring field study courses (especially those at FSC centres) are far short of the current demand, and that the demand itself is only a fraction of what it should be if all biology students were encouraged to do some field work. There is no immediate or easy solution to this problem; just as ecology is the Cinderella of the biological family, so field studies are still widely regarded in educational circles as a luxury of dubious value. As long as this official attitude persists, field centres and kindred establishments will lie in a stagnant backwater far from the turbulent and invigorating mainstream of education where all the limited supply of financial oxygen is borne.

Admitting that the service is inadequate in quantitative terms, can better claims be made for its quality? Here, of course, I can speak only for the field centres run by the Field Studies Council, and in particular for my own at Preston Montford. A field centre is a better place from which to do field work than, say, a guest house, because it is specifically run and equipped for this purpose; nevertheless, we are still not in a position to provide full sets of reference books, microscopes and field equipment for visiting parties, many of whom have to bring some gear of their own.

This situation is improving by degrees, but to put it right would require an injection of capital far beyond the current resources of an unsubsidized private organization.

Those who choose to take jobs at field centres do so for a variety of reasons, including the attraction of a healthy outdoor life, the opportunities to study nature and the landscape at first hand, the satisfaction of imparting information and enthusiasm to others without the restrictive walls of the classroom and the syllabus, and the chance to contribute to the aims of conservation. For those who share this outlook I can think of no more stimulating and rewarding career; but the job tends to attract those who by temperament and talent are naturalists rather than experimental scientists. It is quite proper that field centres should be staffed by such people, but this characteristic coupled with academic isolation makes it doubly difficult for the centres to keep pace with the current trend in ecology towards an increasingly quantitative, functional and experimental treatment. Like all other teachers, our staff (from wardens down) are in urgent need of in-service training. We already enjoy this to some extent through our opportunities to have courses run by experts from other institutions, but I believe that our relatively high rate of turnover of staff might well be stemmed by improving the opportunities for sabbatical leave and refresher training.

The low ratio of resident staff to visiting students and the consequently large proportion of time spent in actual teaching duties aggravate both the training problem and the parallel one of finding enough time for research and for planning modifications to routine courses.

I have been candid about what I see as the main defects in the present service. In spite of these, I am convinced that the continuous opportunities our staff have for meeting and overcoming the special problems of teaching ecology in the field put them in an excellent position to pioneer new approaches and methods, which several of them are already doing.

I shall now be equally candid about shortcomings in the use of the facilities provided by field centres. The majority of parties operating independently from our centres, including those from universities, still follow an old-fashioned, pedestrian and descriptive approach to field studies which grows year by year more remote from the current advances and changing attitudes in other branches of the subject. We learn an enormous amount from the exceptions to this generalization, and it is a pity that much of their improved methodology goes unrecorded.

The approach I have just criticized reflects a still widespread attitude that ecological field work is in some way separate and 'different' from the rest of biological teaching, rather than being an integral part of it. I am frequently depressed to find this same mistaken outlook among the teachers who send unaccompanied parties of students on our own courses. All too often these students have been given only the vaguest idea of why they are coming on the course, have received no preparation for it (in spite of leaflets indicating what the course will be about) and do not expect to get any help when they return to school in linking their short field course with the content of their curricular studies.

Lest I be thought harsh to the point of arrogance, I must make it clear that I do not consider biology teachers wholly or even mainly to blame for this state of affairs. Few teachers have been given more than the briefest acquaintance with field teaching methods in their training. The syllabus under most examination boards pays lip-service to the value of field work, but fails to make it clear how this should relate to the main themes of the subject. Such schemes as the Nuffield Biology Project give some hope for a breakthrough on this problem, but we are still a long way from making field work and ecological experiments as integral a part of the teaching programme as laboratory practicals are. There is a grave lack of good ecological text-books and practical handbooks. Those university departments and other institutions which are forging new research techniques and new field teaching methods have until recently done little to propagate their discoveries in a form in which teachers can adopt them. And finally the field centres themselves are all too inclined to underline their independence both by ignoring the requirements of the A-level syllabus and by keeping their hard-won experience in field teaching techniques very much to themselves.

V. CONCLUSIONS

In spite of my criticisms, I hope I have made it clear that field centres are a necessity in biological education: they serve as miniature field research stations, located in ecologically interesting areas and staffed all the year round; they serve as repositories for local field data and as clearing-houses for the various research activities going on in their districts; they have a part to play in the forging of new field teaching techniques and their transmission to other teachers; they undertake the training of teachers as well as students in field methods and in specialized branches of the field sciences; they can help to co-ordinate a great variety of local field activities, including those of other kinds of environmental centres (e.g. LEA centres); they provide an opportunity for the expansion of the pupil's environmental horizons beyond the surroundings of his home and school; their service includes the intangible but real benefits to be enjoyed while learning in a residential community, and the cross-fertilization of ideas between people working in different disciplines but sharing a common interest in field problems; and they can promote the teaching of conservation not as an abstract concept but through practical examples and through a deeper understanding of the environment.

What is needed now is more money, better training and more co-ordination of effort in the promotion of ecological field studies. The money will not come easily, but the other points can be dealt with almost immediately. Field centres can compensate to some extent for their failure to provide enough places for pupils by putting on more training courses for teachers in field teaching methods, and they should be enabled to draw more widely on university staff to help with the direction of such courses. Provision should also be made for more frequent and more effective interchange of ideas and discussion of problems between people in the various professions concerned. I would hope to see in due course more university research students based at field centres for their field work, more school teachers released to help with the running of field courses, and more opportunity for field centre staff to be seconded temporarily to schools and even university departments. The initiative taken by the British Ecological Society in organizing this symposium is an encouraging pointer to improved co-ordination of effort in the future.

SECTION VI
VOCATIONAL ASPECTS

POSTGRADUATE INSTRUCTIONAL COURSES IN ECOLOGY

C.H.GIMINGHAM and J.B.KENWORTHY
Department of Botany, University of Aberdeen

G.M.DUNNET and H.MILNE
Department of Natural History, University of Aberdeen

I. INTRODUCTION

This paper will be concerned with the recent development of 1 year postgraduate courses in ecology in British universities. It is not intended to discuss the familiar system of postgraduate research studentships, by means of which financial provision is made for graduates starting full-time research under supervision, thereby normally qualifying for Ph.D. degrees in about 3 years, or for M.Sc. degrees 'by research' in shorter periods. This system is deeply ingrained in British universities, and through it many of our distinguished plant and animal ecologists have successfully started their research careers in Departments of Botany, Zoology, or more recently Biology, up and down the country.

However, courses of instruction of an ecological character, leading to M.Sc. degrees 'by examination', are now offered in several universities. Since, so far as we are aware, no British university possesses a Department of Ecology (although Edinburgh's Department of Forestry and Natural Resources is beginning to approach this) the provision of this further training usually involves a co-operative effort by several existing departments. First in the field was University College, London, where from 1960 a 1 year instructional course has been available, qualifying in the past for a Diploma in Conservation and now for an M.Sc. in Conservation (the diploma being retained for candidates ineligible for the degree). Undoubtedly, as far as Britain is concerned, this has been the pioneer in the field of postgraduate ecological teaching. Not until the current academic year (1965–66) has it been followed by courses in other universities: the first of these to be announced was an M.Sc. course in Ecology at Aberdeen University, while both Durham University and the University College of North Wales, Bangor, are also offering courses in similar terms, all these being 12 month courses with the degree awarded on the basis of examination.

II. THE NEED FOR POSTGRADUATE INSTRUCTIONAL COURSES IN ECOLOGY

Openings for graduates looking towards careers in ecological science are beginning to increase in number, but they are by no means all alike in the type of qualifications and outlook they demand. On the one hand, the requirement may be for persons whose training has gone deeply into theory and technique in a limited field. These graduates will be expected to tackle specific fundamental or applied research either on their own or as members of teams in which differing specialisms contribute to the solution of complex problems. On the other, a very wide ecological knowledge and grasp of principles in breadth rather than depth may be appropriate for those seeking employment as administrative or planning officers concerned with problems of land use, conservation, etc. For these, familiarity with all aspects of the subject, as well as with numerous ancillary sciences, is desirable. It may be argued that training for the former group should go deeply into modern research in the candidate's chosen specialism, whereas for the latter, it should have a broader sweep. Alternatively, some combination may be sought, bearing in mind that the research ecologist may find himself virtually alone and perforce a 'jack of all trades'. This situation may be as true in some university departments as it is, for example, in applied research in certain developing countries. Moreover, it is probably the case that specialized research will be more effective if backed up by a broad ecological outlook.

Apart from their elementary scientific background, most potential ecologists graduating from British universities have received what is, in effect, a relatively specialized training contained in Honours courses in either or both of Zoology or Botany. They may be well equipped in certain aspects of either plant or animal ecology, but less frequently have they had the opportunity of becoming fully conversant with both fields, or with important areas of study demanding an integrated view of the living components of the ecosystem. While exceptions to this pattern are developing in certain universities and will be discussed briefly later in this paper, it is against a background of contrast between the qualifications which may be desirable for at least some ecologists, and those which most graduates actually possess, that a need has been felt for what are in essence vocational courses for intending ecologists. In view of what has been said, it is hardly surprising that the courses so far offered differ rather fundamentally in their aims and attitudes. (Here we speak with first-hand knowledge of the Aberdeen course only, and our comments on the others derive from the published prospectuses and outlines of curricula, supplemented by very helpful discussions and correspondence with members of the staffs concerned.) While in all cases an attempt is made to increase the ecological background and experience of the students by the incorporation of both plant and animal ecology, it is probably true to say that the emphasis in Bangor and Durham is rather on specialist training, whereas in University College London, and Aberdeen the orientation is more towards a 'broadening' curriculum. For example, it appears that in the two former universities, instruction is very largely provided by the biological departments, and during some part of the year, students may specialize in selected options or concentrate on research projects. In this way, they should become particularly well qualified for research in certain specific branches of ecology. By comparison, in UCL and Aberdeen, certain other departments are involved, including Geography (in both), Soil Science, Forestry, and Statistics (in Aberdeen). Students are expected to attend all the courses offered, which aim to balance their appreciation of the botanical and zoological components of ecology and to build in some information and experience of techniques not always available in undergraduate curricula in a biological science.

However, there remains what is probably a basic difference in attitude between the UCL and Aberdeen courses, in that the former is (to quote from the UCL circular) 'essentially a training in the application of physical geography and ecology to problems of land use and management of natural resources'. It is, therefore, a course in which the ecological outlook is brought to bear on practical problems and is not basically a course in ecology *per se*. The concept of the Aberdeen course is to broaden the outlook of students to the whole field of modern ecology, and in this connection an appreciation of the ways in which the ancillary subjects mentioned above impinge upon ecological research is regarded as most important.

The fact that several different types of postgraduate courses are now available may be taken as an indication that university ecologists, at least, regard a training along one or other of these lines as of value. Undoubtedly, there is also a demand for it among graduates. During the 6 years in which the UCL course has been running, there have been 222 applications from which forty-four candidates were selected; while in 1965, at Aberdeen, there were thirty-nine applicants for about five places. These figures probably give an exaggerated impression of demand, since numerous applicants on successfully securing some other appointment withdrew their names. None the less, they represent a substantial and widespread interest, although it remains the usual practice among the best qualified to seek a post or to become a Ph.D. student at the end of a 3 or 4 year first-degree course. On the whole, acceptance of places in M.Sc. courses has been resorted to only if the other avenues of advancement are closed.

The academic attainment expected of entrants thus raises some problems. Universities will not normally accept qualifications lower than Second Class Honours degrees for entry to a postgraduate degree course, unless special circumstances obtain, such as considerable relevent experience since graduation. Aberdeen, for example, taking the view that, while openings remain few but important, the best scientists should be attracted to them, normally expects a First or Upper Second Class Honours degree from its applicants for the M.Sc. course in Ecology, although this is not an absolutely rigid requirement. Whether or not it is realistic, in view of the fact that holders of these degrees normally have access to Ph.D. scholarships, etc., remains to be seen. The demands at UCL are less strict in that a Second Class at any level is acceptable. This may be in keeping with the slightly different aims and orientation of the course, although in practice a majority of candidates embarking on the course enter with First or Upper Second Class Honours degrees. There is general agreement that these courses, and through them recruitment to vitally important posts in applied ecology, should never become an escape route for the less competent.

III. THE CURRICULUM

The provision of this kind of additional training has recently been much advocated by government and grant-awarding bodies, although, in contrast to the U.S.A., in this country the trend has been slow to acquire popularity. It has resulted in the formulation of a large number of short postgraduate courses in subjects representing either some specialized part of a normal undergraduate course (such as 'Crystallography') taken up in greater detail, or else a sphere of study spanning the interests of several of our traditional departments (such as 'Crop Protection', 'Biophysics', etc.). It is to the latter category that courses in ecology generally belong.

The curricula of the several M.Sc. courses in ecology will naturally reflect the research interests of the departments concerned, particularly where specialization is encouraged. But in all cases there is bound to be an element of ecological theory and extensive provision for the practice of ecological techniques, both in the laboratory and field. Students whose previous experience has been rather exclusively botanical or zoological are generally advised that they are expected to become equally proficient in plant and animal ecology and should take the opportunity of working up whichever is the least familiar. A further general feature of all the curricula is that they aim to achieve what cannot readily be achieved in the normal undergraduate curricula. This is to say that those aspects of ecology are emphasized in which account is taken both of the plant and animal components of the ecosystem, and particular attention paid to spheres in which current research is most vigorous.

Beyond these common characteristics lie the inherent differences between the courses, deriving from distinctive concepts of aims and objectives. Bangor and Durham each list a series of special subjects, from which some may be chosen for detailed study or project work. In Bangor these are: (a) statistical ecology, (b) population ecology of animals and plants, (c) world vegetation types with emphasis on the tropics, (d) micro-climatology, (e) ecological genetics, (f) crop ecology, (g) ecology of freshwater and marine organisms; while in Durham, the list is as follows: (1) physiological ecology of plants, (2) physiological ecology of animals, (3) phytosociology and genecology, (4) conservation and applied ecology, (5) freshwater ecology and water supplies, (6) ecological aspects of applied entomology (of which three are chosen for the second part of the course).

Both lists include certain options stressing the applied aspects of ecology, but these constitute the central theme of the UCL course, in which discussions on the theory and practice of conservation, land utilization, etc., have a prominent place. A further difference between UCL and the other centres is that applicants with certain backgrounds other than purely biological are acceptable. Elsewhere, the aim is to take biologists* and offer them additional training in ecological theory and technique. At UCL, on the other hand, the aim is to include, in addition to biologists, a number of geographers, geologists, civil engineers, even economists and planners, and to superimpose an appreciation of ecological principles desirable for careers such as regional planning, landscape architecture, and some aspects of conservation, national park management, etc. The curriculum must therefore provide some of the fundamental biology and ecology necessary for the proper appreciation of ecological principles, at an elementary level which may sometimes seem out of keeping with a postgraduate course. This is a problem inherent in the aims and attitudes of

* In Aberdeen, for example, it is stipulated that candidates whose Honours course was not biological (e.g. Geography, Geology) will be accepted only if a biological subject has also been studied to a relatively advanced level, or if in some way considerable familiarity with biology can be shown.

a degree expressly related to conservation or other specific applications of ecology. It does not arise to the same extent in courses designed primarily as advanced tuition in the science of ecology, which are in a position to restrict their intake to candidates who, in one form or another, are already biologists.

Although Aberdeen shares with UCL a wide-ranging curriculum, the aim here is to equip the potential research ecologist with an appreciation of theoretical and technical advances in ecology and a number of ancillary sciences. The importance of the latter in the training of ecologists is emphasized, and perhaps a unique feature of the course is the advantage taken of a nucleus of teachers and research workers in topics such as soil science, ecological statistics, geomorphology, climatology, micro-meteorology, forestry and land use. Their contributions, in the main designed specifically for the M.Sc. in Ecology, provide a varied but co-ordinated approach to the subject when integrated with those of the experimental, analytical and descriptive ecologists. As British universities are at present organized, such a wide variety of studies can hardly be embraced by a single department or even one school of studies. Hence, courses of the type outlined are most effectively mounted in those universities in which a number of established departments contain members whose work is relevant and who are prepared to collaborate in this way. Where, as in Aberdeen, members of research institutes such as the Macaulay Institute for Soil Research and the Scottish Department of Agriculture and Fisheries Marine Laboratory can also be brought in to the teaching scheme, this is of the greatest value. Graduates can in these ways be provided with a training in ecological research which has seldom before been possible, as well as a realization of the impact which a broadly based ecological outlook can have upon practical problems of management. Perhaps this will be less directly suitable for those eventually finding their place as administrative or planning ecologists, but none the less they too should be the better able to appreciate and apply the results of detailed research.

There is one other aspect of the curriculum on which different standpoints have been adopted. This concerns the merits of devoting a substantial proportion of the time to investigational projects. As a valuable introduction to the procedure of planning and carrying out an independent inquiry, such projects often form part of undergraduate as well as postgraduate courses. They stimulate interest and enthusiasm, provide a means of assessing problem-solving ability, and give the student useful experience of techniques of field research, forcing him to come to grips with sampling procedures, methods of analysis and presentation of data, etc. They figure in the schemes of work set out for the UCL, Bangor and Durham courses. Besides the independent investigations, group projects are arranged as part of the UCL course, to which each student contributes from the standpoint of his own special interest. On the other hand, in a short course, research projects may lead to a disproportionate amount of time spent on a very limited topic. Further, in the case of ecology, there may be a tendency for the projects to concentrate upon the survey-type of work (and occasionally to become little more than descriptions of an area with species lists or a series of natural history observations). In this way, a wrong impression may be created of ecological research, since vegetational, environmental, and some experimental studies may require accumulation of data throughout a complete cycle of seasonal variations or over considerable periods of time, and are less amenable to project work. For these reasons, individual dissertations are not required at present in the Aberdeen course, although much of the practical instruction will take the form of limited investigations, wherever possible relating to long-term research, while field reports, including critical assessments of field classes and visits to research establishments, are required.

IV. IS THIS THE BEST WAY TO TRAIN ECOLOGISTS?

The opportunities for indulging an interest in ecology are evidently becoming much increased. Perhaps the opportunities for professing it are not increasing at the same rate, although there are more research studentships available and an ecological background is increasingly recognized as desirable, for example, among teachers. There is every reason why postgraduate courses may serve both these vocations. Equally, we may hope that there will be more openings for ecologists in local government, conservation, river boards, game boards, highland development and the like, at home and overseas, for it is our contention that an ecological approach to these activities is vitally important.

However, this very diversity presents problems in training ecologists. Does the future of ecology lie primarily in teams of specialists, each contributing their own individual approach to a broad problem? Or shall we require a body of ecologists equipped to deal with extensive, regional problems without necessarily a very detailed technical experience in any particular branch of research? Probably both kinds will be required, and up the the present insufficient attention has been given to matching the type of training provided to the types of career available to ecologists. With special courses few in number, the tendency has been to adopt one particular approach but to arrange a curriculum in the hope that it will be more or less suitable for whatever openings in the ecological field may arise from time to time. For example, to quote again from the UCL prospectus, which describes a course primarily orientated towards posts in conservation: 'It has also proved valuable as a preliminary training in research methods with especial emphasis on the field sciences.' In fact, nearly 50 per cent of those completing the course have entered employment involving research or teaching or both, but clearly it does not necessarily follow that they have received the most appropriate training for these careers.

Coming, as it does, towards the end of a symposium devoted to consideration of the best ways of teaching ecology, this paper must emphasize the necessity of seriously thinking out the role of postgraduate courses in the whole scheme of biological education in universities. The opportunities available in a postgraduate year devoted entirely to ecology are very attractive and much can be achieved, particularly in regard to field work and visits to places at which research can be seen in progress and discussed. But in view of the great differences among our universities in the attitudes of biological departments to the teaching of ecology, no clearly envisaged relationship exists between our postgraduate courses and what has gone before.

The problem is further complicated by the development of a new structure in certain Schools of Biology, in which much of the traditional detail of systematic botany and zoology has been removed from first-year undergraduate courses, and emphasis is laid rather on general biological principles. From this broad foundation, separation takes place into streams which cut across traditional frontiers, and one such stream may be devoted to ecology. This type of system is, for example, emerging at Edinburgh where, after a first-year course common to all biology students, those who have ecological interests may proceed, not to Departments of Botany or Zoology, but to one of the options offered by the Department of Forestry and Natural Resources. Here they may take either a course in general ecology or one with direct application to natural resource management. They will thus receive as undergraduates an education with objectives similar to those of the postgraduate courses we have been considering, and may perhaps proceed straight to posts requiring this type of qualification. A similar pattern is being planned within Biology Departments or Schools of Biological Studies in certain other universities.

This may be regarded as a system in which instruction is broad at first, gradually becoming narrower as it proceeds. In this scheme there is, perhaps, no place for the kind of course discussed in this paper, much of the contents of which are probably incorporated into the first-degree work. On completion of this, the narrowing process will often continue as a graduate settles down in a post or starts research for a Ph.D. It is still necessary, however, to ask whether this is going to be the best way of training ecologists. The problem is whether the omission of a traditional detailed background of courses in botany or zoology will prove a serious lack. Where it is absent, there may be difficulties in the way of super-imposing anything more than a superficial appreciation of what ecology is about; but the Edinburgh experiment and developments elsewhere will be watched with interest.

Against this, it may be claimed that a better procedure is to allow our undergraduates to grow up as biologists, even as botanists or zoologists, becoming deeply immersed in these subjects and thoroughly familiar with their content (including ecological aspects), and then to superimpose upon this firm foundation a wider approach to ecology. This does not imply that ecology is inappropriate in undergraduate courses; on the contrary, it should clearly take its place among the chief branches of whatever biological subject is studied at each level of instruction, bearing a particularly important relationship to the teaching of physiology. How-ever, in this system the potential ecologist shares with other biologists a limited, but very thorough, foundation usually in one biological subject only. The 1 year postgraduate course then provides an opportunity for 'topping up' and broadening the candidates' understanding of ecology, as well as offering valuable additional experience in the spheres of soil science, geography, agriculture, forestry, genetics, meteorology, statistics etc., before the return to a more limited field of research or other employ-ment. This topping-up procedure may be related expressly to certain administrative applications of ecological science, such as conservation and land management, but it is then unlikely to serve well as a foundation for research, even research concerned with problems of conservation and management. The alternative is to organize a scheme of training intended to be of value for those aiming at ecological research. To return, in conclusion, to our own case, it is our objective to fill this latter role, and we feel that at present the best avenue to this goal is through a thorough grounding in one or more of the biological subjects (in which ecological teaching has played its part as one of several branches). We hope, then, to provide a useful further equipment for ecologists, in the form of ideas and techniques. But again, is this the best way?

ECOLOGY AND ENVIRONMENTAL DESIGN

J. R. HERBERT*

Generation Design Department, Central Electricity Generating Board

I. INTRODUCTION

In the title of this paper, the key word is 'Environment', which not only stands between the two subjects of the phrase, but also supplies the vital concept which the two disciplines share in common. For it is the study of the environment which is the concern of both ecologists and designers, however much this may have been overlooked in this present age of cultural specialization. It is the author's hope that this paper may help to clear away many misconceptions and misunderstandings which obstruct and obscure discussion between these two groups of people, by emphasizing the common ground between their two fields of intellectual activity and by explaining the differences in their operational approaches to the environment. In following this line of inquiry, we must inevitably concentrate most attention on the role of the designer, not only because this will be relatively unfamiliar to the reader, but also because it may help to arouse interest in a 'market' for the results of ecological teaching and research.

These aims define a task of such formidable dimensions that it would be a rash man who would engage in it without prior reconnaissance. Fortunately, the route has already been plotted by the pioneer work of Patrick Geddes in the first quarter of this century, though unfortunately since his death more than 30 years ago his conceptual framework has been often ignored in favour of his more applied work. Nevertheless, it was this distinguished biologist who provided the theoretical foundation for present-day town and country planning by recognizing the organic and evolutionary characteristics of cities and regions. His application of scientific method also extended to other aspects of social organization, and it is encouraging to our present inquiry to note how closely he related science to design in his conceptual organization grid 'The notation of life'.

II. MAN AND ENVIRONMENT

We must recognize that we are naturally homocentric in our conception of the environment because of our participation in human society. However, we can appreciate that in the last few millennia Man has

* Present position: Partner, Land Use Consultants

established such a commanding role in relation to this planet, that he has come to dominate its terrestrial, and to a lesser extent its aquatic, habitats. We can say without exaggeration, that of all species, Man has the greatest ability to transform his environment. The fact that this symposium has been held is proof that he also has the unique ability, if he chooses, to reflect upon what he is doing.

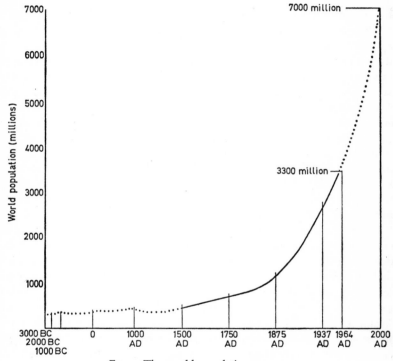

FIG. 1. The world population curve.

This power of environmental dominance has, until very recently, been restricted both in extent and effect. Its development has been dependent on two intimately connected phenomena of dynamic nature—the ability to use natural resources, and the increase of human population. The close relationship between these two aspects may be exemplified by considering the British population under different levels of technology. The hunting/gathering economy of Mesolithic times supported, at most, a few thousand individuals in the same area and with the same latent resources which now serve (in part) to support some 52 million.

The growth of the utilization of natural resources, in its triple aspects of food technology, power technology and materials technology, has been admirably surveyed by Jope (1965). This account needs, of course, to be supplemented by a consideration of the development in social ideas and institutions such as is provided by Mumford (1934, 1944). The parallel numerical development of Man may be summarized by reference to Figs. 1 and 2, which also conveniently bring out the degree of development

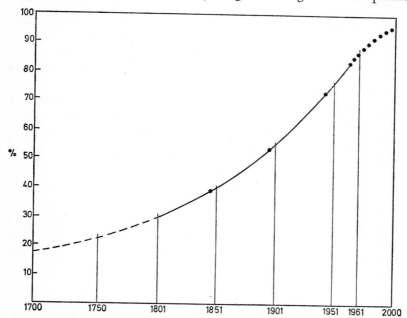

FIG. 2. Urbanization in England and Wales, A.D. 1700–2000. The graph shows the percentage of the population living in urban communities, i.e. those with a population over 5000 in 1700, over 10,000 in 1851, and over 20,000 in 1961.

of urban ways of living that these goals and techniques have made possible. Incidentally, it is worthy of comment that in Britain we are still at the top of the league table in the matter of indices of urbanization. More of our population are inhabitants of the 'Built Environment' than in any other country, even though this still accounts for no more than 10 per cent of the land area. (Perhaps, therefore, we should regard this country as being the prototype for the urban society towards which the rest of mankind appears destined to develop. Consideration of the environmental conditions experienced in London may perhaps deter the commission of similar errors in the hundreds of new cities which must develop throughout the world during the remainder of this century.)

The process of cultural change has inevitably been paralleled by physical changes as Man has modified his surroundings; the climax forest has given place to city or to farmland. In Britain, the consequences have often been extremely rewarding, both in terms of sustained yield and of beautiful landscapes, and of diversification of habitat. Those aspects have been well surveyed by Lowenthal & Prince (1964), but on the opposite side of the ledger must be entered numerous examples of habitat destruction, both rural (Darling, 1955) and urban (Mumford, 1938). The biological aspects of such man-made devastation have been well examined both by the British Ecological Society, and by the International Union for the Conservation of Nature and Natural Resources (IUCN, 1957).

In examining the processes of modification of the landscape pattern at the first 'Countryside in 1970' Conference' (Herbert, 1964), the author drew attention to the three categories of effect that human intervention in the environment produces. Under conditions of long-settled, humanized environments such as north-west Europe, it is now rare for habitat destruction to be deliberately contrived, since the land resource is now so restricted in relation to human requirements. (This situation will of course soon be attained in other areas, such as North America, where land is still underrated as a resource). It is the *unintentional* and *haphazard* consequences which are the main problem in the European and specifically British contexts, due to the failure of traditional systems of land tenure and management to deal adequately with the environmental consequences of the technological mass society.

It is upon this general situation that we are required to reflect, bearing in mind Holford's dictum that '. . . adequate space is a natural good' applies to all species, not solely to Man. The outcome of such reflection must be to define policies for action and operational techniques for implementing them. Knowing must become the spring-board for doing, which in turn must be based on systematic and rational techniques for evaluating the range of choice—in short, upon design.

III. THE NATURE OF DESIGN

A. *The sequence of activities*

For the reasons stated above, before discussion of this topic can begin, it is necessary to clear away a number of widespread misconceptions, and establish some common ground from which to proceed. By derivation, the word 'DESIGN' is associated with the verb 'to designate' (Latin: designare = to set apart) and implies *selection* in relation to a purpose. But design covers more than the simple act of choosing; it implies a logical *sequence* of choices—a network of decisions—relating desired ends to available resources. It therefore describes a systematic intellectual process based upon criteria for selecting from a number of alternatives. The establishment of these criteria falls within the field of aesthetics, i.e. the branch of the science of ethics related to the perception of the beautiful or pleasing. As Archer (1964a) has shown, the form of 'case-law' logic applicable to these inquiries differs from the numerical logic of physical science, but is no less rigorous in its application; moreover, much of the basic data concerning human preference has been obtained by the biologist or social scientist (Vernon, 1962), and at the level of *descriptive aesthetics* can be handled in terms of numerical concepts. Morever, in many parts of this area of intellectual activity, the qualities of experience, judgment and intuition remain just as valuable as they are within other fields of scientific inquiry.

To turn now from the philosophical basis of design to its application in practice, we must consider the essential elements of the designer's task. He is required to identify a preferred solution to a *problem*, which in turn is defined by the physical and social constraints that are present. The starting-point for the process is dissatisfaction with existing environmental patterns which leads to a demand for change; the designer is therefore commissioned by the patron (who may perhaps also be the user) to create a new artifact to stabilize the environment at a new level.

The prior formulation of a prescription or model is therefore the essence of design activity. The aspect of user satisfaction is not, however, restricted to the narrow operational purpose of the artifact. Its employment will in turn affect the senses of the operator (or occupant, if a building or adapted space) through such factors as noise, smell, feel, etc., and thus influence his psychological state. This is particularly true of the appearance of the object, which is inherent in its physical form, irrespective of whether the designer's terms of reference covered questions of visual quality. The objective of design activity must therefore be an appropriate standard of achievement in all these respects, expressed as a fully integrated unity. Design is therefore the purposeful seeking after the most appropriate reconciliation of all the constraints involved.

In carrying out this activity, the designer is following an orderly sequence of activities (Fig. 3) which is constant whatever the nature of the artifact to be produced. Of the phases indicated, by far the most important

R

is the 'creative phase' which is central to the whole process (Archer, 1964b). This is the so-called 'creative step' which synthetizes the components of the system into a new and original order which *after* completion, is seen to be apt—the 'Quality of Inevitability' which is the hall-mark of successful designs. However, two more processes must be carried out before the designer's task is complete. Firstly, he must develop his solution to prove its validity and practicability, which he does by making analogues or models. These can take a variety of forms (Fig. 4), depending on the size,

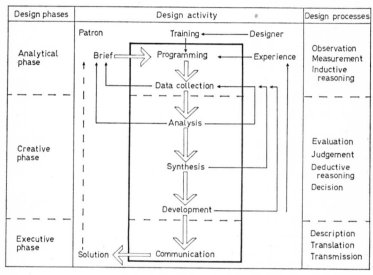

FIG. 3. The sequence of activities in design.

complexity and production run of the artifact; thus for a short-life consumer product, such as a chair, the most effective check may be the construction and testing of a prototype, which would clearly be impracticable in the case of an expensive 'one-off' design such as an ocean liner or nuclear reactor. Thereafter, the designer must communicate his solution as being the most fitting answer to the problem originally posed. The final process is that of *feed-back* of operational results, both via the designer and the user which completes the loop and enables the experience obtained to be recycled.

B. *The design of human environment*
As has been stated above, the stimulus for any design activity is the desire for change, and the first phase is concerned with analysis of the existing

situation and of the operative constraints. We are all well aware that the environment is in a constant state of change, and ecologists are accustomed to investigating complex and dynamic situations among biological communities. Moreover, in the theories of energy-flow and nutrient cycling, they have powerful conceptual guide lines to direct their inquiries. However, it is only very recently, under the influence of ideas borrowed from the fields of operational research and cybernetics—both of which acknowledge a considerable debt to biology—that environmental designers have started to evolve a theory of change in the man-made environment. In

	TYPE OF ANALOGUE		EXAMPLES	
Most. abstract	Symbolic logic		Boolean alegbra Mathematical models	Best for testing
	Verbal expression		Evocative words Definitive statements Patent specifications	
	Graphic expression	Diagrams	Flow diagrams Circuit diagrams Vector diagrams	
		Sketches	Evocative sketches Definitive sketches	
		Formal drawings	Perspective Renderings Scale drawings	
	Simple models		Block models Space models Scale models	
	Working analogues		Electrical analogues Rigs Photoelastic models	
Most concrete	Prototype		Full size mock-up for user testing	Best for communication

FIG. 4. Designer's analogues (after Archer, 1964).

fact two of the most seminal suggestions (McLoughlin, 1965; Alexander, 1966) were published only at the end of last year.

Following this approach, we may regard the human environment as a dynamic network of interlinked systems. Some of these systems are natural—the physical and geographical bases for life on this planet. Some are biological—the ecosystem concept familar to ecologists and now beginning to spread more widely. Yet others are social—the demographic and cultural influences on human behaviour; while the final group, Holford's 'Built Environment', comprises the physical systems which Man has constructed for his use and enjoyment. The essence of this emerging schema is that all these components are in dynamic interaction, and that change in one has widespread repercussions upon the others. Thus, for the first time, we are beginning to be dimly aware of a general theory upon which to consider change in the human environment.

Closely allied to this is the attempt to discover more meaningful categories for the components of the 'Built Environment', since the inadequacy of the conventional everyday descriptions is becoming increasingly apparent. Following one approach, his system of 'Ekistics', Doxiadis has postulated thirteen structural systems (summarized in Doxiadis, 1959); while Alexander, having analysed an Indian village community in terms of 141 human requirements, has identified twelve structural components (Alexander, 1963). McLoughlin (1965) has discussed changes in human environment in terms of four aspects—developmental, locational, behavioural and systemic change—though these categories may well need revision. Thus, it may be argued that recent advances in the fields of the life sciences, human sciences, and social sciences are now beginning to produce an intellectual ferment amongst the environmental designers, a ferment which can only be beneficial in reopening closed questions and querying ancient dogmas and assumptions.

Now it is time to turn our attention more closely to those groups of people that have so far hidden under the umbrella label of 'environmental designers'. Who are they, what do they do, and how do they do it?

They are contained in four of the professional groups whose development characterizes the post-Newtonian period of social specialization; these are, in chronological order of seniority, Civil Engineers (1818), Architects (1834), Town and Country Planners (1914), and Landscape Architects (1929). (The dates in each case refer to the foundation date of the professional body in this country.) They are linked in two respects: they share the common basic discipline of design, and they are concerned with the use of land in their activities. The former attribute means that they practise an art, based to varying degrees upon technology; the latter, they share with those bodies controlling and managing land and with whom they are sometimes grouped under the rather clumsy title of 'Land-linked professions'. Let us now take each in turn for a closer examination.

1. *Civil Engineers*. There are some 20,000 chartered civil engineers whose *métier* is aptly described in the words of their foundation charter as controlling 'the Great Sources of Power in Nature'. Their concern is with the design of structures—which may range from a radio mast, through a highway, to a dam—and is primarily technical rather than social in its direction. Their training draws heavily upon the earth sciences and upon materials technology, and lays most stress upon the more abstract ana-

logues as means of communication; perhaps, for this reason, they often display a rather low level of visual consciousness.

2. *Architects*. There are approximately 19,000 qualified architects, which gives them a higher ratio to the population than in most other countries. They are essentially concerned with the design of interior spaces adapted for human use, ranging in scale from the single room to a complex of several buildings together with the space about them. There is therefore inevitably a considerable social content on their work which is being strongly emphasized at present; at the same time, rapid developments in building methods are placing a premium on knowledge of developing materials technology. Architects' training concentrates on graphic and model analogues and this emphasis on visual matters may sometimes degenerate into 'styling'—the attempt to impose an idiosyncratic form upon the design.

3. *Landscape Architects*. This profession differs markedly from the previous two, both in numbers and in range of operation. There are only some 250 fully qualified members of the Institute of Landscape Architects, who take for their field of activity the design of exterior spaces adapted for human use. These may range in size from a terrace garden to a regional park system, but inevitably lean heavily upon the modification of climate–soil–plant systems. This activity may be described as the considered visual expression of ecological relationships which are adapted for social purposes; it therefore draws on the biological as well as the social sciences, though it is relatively weak in technology due to the latter's patchy development in these areas of knowledge.

4. *Town and Country Planning*. Like landscape architecture, this profession is relatively small with some 3000 qualified members, and is expanding rapidly also. When we consider its scope, however, it becomes apparent that it differs in one major respect from the other three; as Professor Page observed in his closing address to the 1962 Conference on Design Methods: '. . . the planner himself cannot control the detailed physical design [of environments]. Essentially what he is doing in this situation is providing a strategic framework within which other people can operate in detail'. The planner's concern is with the changing pattern of human requirements for land and its resources, in which situation he attempts to predict and anticipate the extent and direction of change, so that he can lay down guidelines for what has been called the 'main structure' of environments. In so far as it is possible to express these factors quantitatively and in terms of distribution, the profession draws heavily upon the social sciences and upon geography, and finds its main

design analogues in the rather abstract forms of reports, statistical tables and maps. However, there has been increasing recognition in recent years that more subtle and qualitative concepts are necessary. As has been noted above, the evolution of more refined concepts of environment could well lead to considerable changes in the practice of town and country planning.

In concluding this section, there are two general points that must be made about the design process; they are both rather obvious, but not yet sufficiently recognized. The first is that all design activity is a dialogue between two parties—the patron and the designer of his choice. The former must choose wisely, and also frame his questions with care and precision; the latter must examine a wide range of solutions before arriving at an answer which is not only apt for the situation, but must satisfy his design. Only if all these conditions are fulfilled can a really high level of patron achievement be reached, and since, in the case of the environment, the patron is ourselves, either individually or in our collective guise as the community or one of its social organizations, the ultimate responsibility must fall on our shoulders.

The second point is that since design activity involves choice it is a decision-making, executive activity. These choices may involve many people in their consequences, and are always concerned with money and with time—which is often a synonym for money. The order of magnitude of these decisions is evidenced by the example of a major power station, where £70–80 million is required to be invested over some 5 years in accordance with a predetermined programme, and where delays in commissioning new generating plant can run up charges of tens of thousands of pounds per day. The moral of this is that decisions have to be taken in time, whether or not the full information is available; anticipation is the only safeguard against error, since knowledge after the event must be paid for dearly.

C. *Interdisciplinary influence and collaboration*

All that has been said above leads to one fundamental and essential conclusion—that ecologists and designers must both realize that they share a common bond in the study of the environment. It must surely be obvious that understanding of the processes of environmental systems is the foundation from which policies for the guidance of change must spring. In the face of the pressures of population growth and technological development which confront us, ecologists and designers must hang together, if they are not to hang separately, condemned by a society under pressure to solve today's problems at the expense of tomorrow's needs. Mankind has to learn ways of regulating its activities so that they do not damage the habitats in which it co-exists with other species. The concepts of 'ecology' and of 'design' begin to indicate pointers towards this goal; if ecologists and designers can learn how to work effectively together, their influence upon society will be correspondingly strengthened. Both groups must, however, commence by recognizing the validity of the other's approach and its relevance to their own field of activity.

The ecologist must accept that only through conscious pursuit of design is the environment likely to be modified—and modified it will inevitably be—in such a way as to conserve biological systems and potentials. In his turn, the environmental designer has to acknowledge the value of ecological experience in his own analysis of environmental systems. This value has been most aptly expressed in E.M.Nicholson's words: '. . . ecology has been compelled to tackle problems technically analogous to those which confront the student and forecaster of pressures and trends in human society'. To this useful operational experience must also be added valuable concepts concerning ecosystems and populations.

Moreover, in the author's contention, recent studies in the influence of environmental stress on the social behaviour of animals (Russell, 1964; Harlow & Harlow, 1965) provide analogies with human behaviour that give added meaning to Stapledon's theories of 'Human ecology'. Discussion of the 'Teaching of Ecology' must surely give thought to the potential social implications opened up in this way, but we must now examine areas of practical collaboration between ecologists and designers.

The ecologist is entitled to make first bid, by asking for a chain of suitable habitats of local, regional and national value to be set aside and safeguarded for teaching and research purposes. Only by such provision will properly trained workers and adequate data be accumulated to understand the workings of ecosystems. The planner in reply will ask for an inventory of the sites concerned and their relative importance; are they an Upper Teesdale or merely a convenient pond; do they represent a consensus of opinion from several of the biological sciences or are they of interest only to one; is the interest permanent or transient and therefore replaceable? In the case of a conflict of land-using interests, he will want to know whether any measure of the value of the site can be produced which can be weighed objectively with all the factors involved.

The landscape architect will inquire whether the value of the site can be enhanced by deliberate programmes of management, and what assistance he can offer in the way of controlling access, or in transferring

plant communities. The civil engineer will offer his assistance in providing
a range of new habitats arising from his construction works, and will ask
for a specification of the physical factors required in time to fit into his
programme.

In their turn, the environmental designers will ask for guidance on the
biological effects of their proposals—the effect upon fisheries of the
effluent from a proposed new town—what will happen if a salt-water lake
is created for hydro-electric power—can a stream be diverted without
killing an adjacent oak wood? They will produce a whole range of existing
and proposed man-made habitats, ranging from artificial lakes, through
open-cast mines, to man-made hills, and ask for ecological advice in their
construction and after-management. They will hope that some of this
can be provided by analogy with existing habitats, but if tackled persuas-
ively, may well recommend their patrons to sponsor research work.
The proviso here is that the ecologist can both be comprehensive in his
assessment, and can set out an effective case for useful applied research;
in the author's experience, this latter is a skill that is often lacking.

IV. TRAINING FOR COLLABORATION

To achieve the mutual understanding required for the above conditions,
a major reorientation of approach will be required in university teaching
of these two groups of subjects. How this will be achieved must obviously
depend upon experiment and predilection, but the objective is quite clear
—close mutual understanding between ecologist and designer. For the
latter, it would seem a basic requirement is for their particular discipline
to be taught within the concept of the environment as a network of
systems, and for them to experience ecosystems in the field. Certainly
the student of planning and of civil engineering requires a higher ecological
content in his curriculum, perhaps best achieved by setting design problems in an environmental context rather than by introducing a new subject
as such into the course.

To be presumptuous, the author would like to suggest that students of
ecology would gain greatly if some of their field work were applied to
development problems, and if greater attention were paid to man-made
habitats for teaching purpose. The use of Alvecote Pools for this purpose
seems a most excellent example to follow elsewhere.

In conclusion, the author's experience as a part-time lecturer in the
Department of Town Planning at University College London over the
last 3 years may be of interest. This Department has been developing an

environmental approach towards the training of postgraduate planners, an approach which it is hoped will also be further extended to the landscape designers very shortly. In collaboration with Dr Newbould, joint lectures and seminars on a variety of topics have been held with the conservation course in the Botany Department. The next logical step forward is for collaborative field work by students in the two departments, and this we are hoping to introduce during the next academic year. These are, as yet, short and tentative steps, but it seems probable that they are along the right road for both ecology and design.

REFERENCES

ALEXANDER C. (1962) The determination of components for an Indian village. In *Conference on Design Methods*. Pergamon, Oxford.

ALEXANDER C. (1966) A city is not a tree. *Design*, **206**, 46–55.

ARCHER L.B. (1964a) Aesthetic and logic. *Design*, **172**, 46–49.

ARCHER L.B. (1964b) The nature of design. *Design*, **174**, 70–73.

DARLING F.F. (1955) *West Highland Survey: An Essay in Human Ecology*. Oxford University Press, London.

DOXIADIS C.A. (1959) Ekistics, the science of human settlements. In *Proc. Town and Country Planning Summer School*, 1959. Town Planning Institute, London.

HARLOW M.K. & HARLOW H.F. (1965) Romulus and Rhesus. *The Listener*, February 11th, 1965.

HERBERT J.R. (1964) The changing rural landscape. In *Proc. 1st 'Countryside in 1970' Conference*. HMSO, London.

HOLFORD W. (1965) *The Built Environment—Its Creation, Motivations, and Control*. Tavistock Publications, London.

IUCN (1957) *Proc. 6th Technical Meeting, Edinburgh*, 1956. Society for the Promotion of Nature Reserves, London.

LOWENTHAL D. & PRINCE H.C. (1964) The English landscape. *Geog. Rev.* **54**, 309–346.

McLOUGHLIN J.B. (1965) Notes on the nature of physical change—towards a view of physical planning. *Jnl. T.P.I.* **51**, 397–400.

MUMFORD L. (1938) *The Culture of Cities*. Secker & Warburg, London.

MUMFORD L. (1944) *The Condition of Man*. Secker & Warburg, London.

MUMFORD L. (1947) *Technics and Civilization*. Routledge, London.

RUSSELL W.M.S. (1964) Violence, monkeys and man. *The Listener*, November 5th and 12th, 1964.

VERNON M.D. (1962) *The Psychology of Perception*. Penguin Books Ltd, Harmondsworth.

CAREER OPPORTUNITIES FOR ECOLOGISTS
IN THE DEVELOPED COUNTRIES

P. J. NEWBOULD

Botany Department, University College London

I. INTRODUCTION

The definition of an ecologist is far more difficult than the definition of ecology. Just as the percentage of ecological thought or practice in a research programme may vary from 0 to 100, so the scientists involved may range from total ecologists the whole way through to total non-ecologists. Many people doing thoroughly ecological research would be surprised to hear themselves described as ecologists.

However, the problem in this paper is to arrive at a definition which, although arbitrary, can be used consistently by different people. It was necessary to make inquiries about ecological employment from the main employing agencies, and for this purpose two categories of ecologist, *sensu stricto* and *sensu lato*, were used, and were defined as follows:

'An ecologist *sensu stricto* would have a degree in botany or zoology (more rarely forestry, agriculture, geography, geology) and research experience (often a Ph.D.) in ecology. Ecology is work centering on the study of organisms in relations to their natural environment (normally outdoors in the field). The natural environment of a weed species would include arable land, and that of a stored products pest, the stored product in question. Microbial ecology should only be included where it deals with soil microbiology (i.e. not medical or industrial microbiology). Some fundamental research in the fields of agriculture, forestry or fisheries would certainly qualify. I would be inclined to omit human ecology for which the training is normally sociology or anthropology.

'An ecologist *sensu lato* would have a degree or equivalent in any of the earth or life sciences, but need not have research experience. He would be working on a topic having some reference to organisms in a more or less natural environment. This could include, for example, geological, geomorphological or climatological research in which the role of organisms is important, or research which is primarily taxonomic, behavioural or genetical but which includes a good deal of ecology. It could also include rather more immediate or applied research on agriculture, forestry or fisheries especially where this deals with populations of plants or animals. I would be inclined to exclude those who are providing a service for ecologists, such as chemists, biochemists, statisticians, especially if they never collect their own samples or data.'

For some purposes, an even more arbitrary definition of ecologist is used, namely, membership of the British Ecological Society.

Since this paper is concerned only with *developed* countries, the statistical material is derived almost entirely from Britain, on the grounds that there is little *net* movement of ecologists between *developed* countries. Clearly there is likely to be a *net export* of ecologists from Britain to *developing* countries, but this is the subject of another paper.

II. THE EMPLOYMENT OF ECOLOGISTS

Several different techniques have been used to discover how ecologists are employed in Britain at present, and the results are set in Tables 1–6.

1. *The membership of the British Ecological Society*

The list of current addresses of the 971 members of the BES resident in the UK allows one to assign likely employment to about three-quarters of them. The data are set out in Table 1. Probably over half the members of the BES are involved in education at university or other levels. Other major categories are the Nature Conservancy and other conservation agencies (8 per cent), freshwater and marine research (together 5 per cent) and agricultural and horticultural research (5 per cent).

Comparison of this list with the *Commonwealth Universities Yearbook* (1965) suggests that about three-quarters of the university members of the BES are in fact lecturers (of any grade from Assistant Lecturer to Professor), the remainder presumably being research students or research fellows. An analysis of the numbers of BES members on the lecturing staff of twenty-seven university Botany Departments and twenty-seven university Zoology Departments is given in Table 2. Universities with Departments of Biology were omitted, as were several other universities where it was felt the figures would be difficult to obtain, or misleading for various reasons. Ecologists (BES members) represent about 25 per cent of the staff of Botany and Zoology Departments, a figure which is used in another context later. The detailed figures from these fifty-four departments show that there is no tendency for larger departments to contain more ecologists on their staff, nor for ecologists to be aggregated in their departmental distribution. In fact, the numbers of staff ecologists per department show no significant departure from a Poisson distribution and university ecologists must therefore be considered to be randomly distributed.

TABLE 1. Employment of members of The British Ecological Society (employment inferred from addresses (members resident in UK only))

		Per cent
Universities	391*	41
Other educational posts	65†	7
Nature Conservancy, etc.	80	8
Freshwater research	31	3
Marine research	24	2
Agricultural research	51	5
Museums, zoos, Kew	29	3
Pest research	18	2
Other	57	6
No information	225‡	23
Total	971	100

* Approximately 300 lecturers and ninety research students, research assistants, etc.

† Minimal estimate, see ‡.

‡ A fair proportion of these are probably school-teachers.

TABLE 2. Distribution of University lecturers in ecology

	Twenty-seven Botany Departments	Twenty-seven Zoology Departments
Ecologists	87	55
Ecologists/department	3.2	2.0
Total academic staff	282	304
Academic staff/department	10.4	11.3

2. *Nature Conservancy research students*

The subsequent fate of all those awarded Nature Conservancy research studentships, during the years 1949–65, was determined so far as possible, and is set out in Table 3. While these figures are not strictly comparable

TABLE 3. Analysis of Nature Conservancy research students, 1949–65

Total numbers
Botany   73 ⎫
Geography   13 ⎬ 161
Zoology   75 ⎭

Reject
Not enough information   8 ⎫
Died before taking a job 2 ⎬ 17
Mental breakdown   1 ⎪
Women married, no jobs   6 ⎭

Sample population remaining 144

Membership of BES

	Member	Non-member
Botany	48	16
Geography	2	10
Zoology	32	36

Higher degrees

	Ph.D. or D.Phil.	M.A. or M.Sc.	None
Botany	45	1	18
Geography	6	2	4
Zoology	44	4	20
	95	7	42*
Subsequently became university lecturers in UK	58	0	14

Summary of subsequent employment, 144 students

	Percentage of all jobs	No.	
University lecturers, UK	39.2	72	{ 7 Geography
			30 Zoology
			35 Botany

Category	%	Jobs	Subcategory		
University research UK	5.5	10			
Other teaching and lecturing	5.5	10	College of Education	3	
			Technical College	2	
			School	4	
			Field Studies Council	1	
Overseas	17.4	32	Africa	13	} 17 University lecturers
			Australia, New Zealand	8	} 14 Research
			North America	7	1 Social work
			Malaya	3	
			Galapagos	1	
			Director	1	
Nature Conservancy	14.2	26	Research	13	
			Conservation	12	
			Museums	3	
Museums, etc.	2.8	5	Kew	1	
			Zoo	1	
Ecological research	7.7	14	Marine	3	
			Freshwater	2	
			Agriculture and horticulture	9	
Married and retired	3.3	6			
Miscellaneous	4.4	8	Hydrological research	1	
			Science administration	1	
			Planning	1	
			Aerial survey	2	
			Wildfowl Trust	1	
			UKAEA	2	

183 jobs

* Overestimate; information not up to date for some, others still writing up.

with those in Table 1, it is interesting that in both cases about 40 per cent of the ecologists are in universities. The figure of 17 per cent obtaining employment overseas can be used as an indication of the likely level of export of UK born and trained ecologists (mainly *s.s.*). While not all the Nature Conservancy research students are ecologists, the fact that 43 per cent are not members of the BES suggests that not all British-trained ecologists belong to the Society. Thus the sample in Table 1 is incomplete.

TABLE 4. Employment of students from University College, London, Postgraduate Conservation Course, 1960–66

Total students 44	
7 from current course not yet fixed up	
1 failed	
leaves a sample of 36.	
36 students have had the following occupations:	
Research for a higher degree, at a university or college of technology*	12†
Nature Conservancy	7
Weed Research Organization, Forestry Commission Research, Rothamsted	3
Planning, Landscape Design, National Parks Commission	6
University or college of technology lecturers	4‡
Teaching	6
Game warden	1
Head of Uganda National Parks	1
Museum	1
Consultant engineer	1
Other	1

* Two at a college of technology.
† One in Trinidad.
‡ One in Canada.

3. *University College, London, Conservation Course*

The data on the employment of students attending this course are given in Table 4. It is felt that all these students leave the course as ecologists *s.l.* and those with a biological degree as ecologists *s.s.* Four of the thirty-six students are currently overseas, but one of these came from Uganda, with a Makerere degree, so that the net export is really three out of thirty-five (8.6 per cent). The population involved is really too small to allow any significant conclusions to be drawn.

4. *Questionnaire*

To supplement the meagre data presented above, a questionnaire was sent to some forty-seven organizations or research stations in the UK

TABLE 5. Summary of employment of, and demand for, ecologists

	Ecologists s.s.	s.l.	Total	Total as a % of 1400 (see below)	Annual turnover of existing posts	Approx. annual expansion
1. Agricultural research	56	209	265	18.8	26.8	0
2. Nature Conservancy, other conservation	71	64	135	9.6	4.7	11.7
3. Pest and veterinary research	46	15	69*	5.0	3	1.7
4. Forestry	1	(22)	23	1.6	2	0
5. Freshwater	43	24	98*	7.0	4.8	5.1
6. Marine	39	4	94*	6.7	6.1	4.8
7. Overseas survey, home-based	4	20	24	1.6	2	0.5
Total			708		49.4 (7%)	23.8 (3.4%)

Add to this:
Universities	(*c.* 400)
Other educational establishments	(*c.* 200)
Research establishments overlooked above	(*c.* 100)
Final totals	*c.* 1400

Assume the same rate of turnover (7%) — 49 — *c.* 100†

Assume the same rate of expansion (3.4%) — 23.8 — *c.* 50

Notes

Categories 1–7 based on replies to a questionnaire.

Figures in parentheses, other than percentages, represents author's guesswork.

* Total figure includes additional employees not subdivided into *s.s.* and *s.l.*

† This figure represents partly a resorting of ecologists within the existing employment pool, and partly retirement and emigration, creating vacancies for new ecologists. This could mean that as much as half this turnover figure represents additional vacancies.

thought to employ ecologists, asking them how many ecologists they currently employ, what the rate of turnover is, and whether they envisage any expansion or decline in the demand for ecologists within their

organization. The two categories of ecologist, *s.s* and *s.l.*, were defined
as in the introduction to this paper. There was a good response, including a
number of protests about these definitions, and the results are set out

TABLE 6. Numbers of ecologists in relation to total population

Resident in	Number of members of BES or Ecological Society of America	Total population	Ecologists per million population
UK	1000	50 million	20
USA	2500	150 million	17
Canada	150	15 million	10

TABLE 7. Annual production of ecologists (from the Nature Conservancy
directory of postgraduate students engaged in ecological or physiographical
studies 1964)

Subjects studied
    Plant ecology *s.s.*   90 ⎫
    Animal ecology *s.s.*   122 ⎬ 212
    Plant and animal ecology *s.l.*   34 ⎫
    Geography with ecological implications   86 ⎬ 120
    Not studying ecology at all   39
                                                           371
Allowing for some to take 4 years, plus a small failure rate, this means
    an annual output of about .60 ecologists *s.s.* ⎫
                                                    35 ecologists *s.l.* ⎬ 95
A number of graduates with no post-graduate training will become
    ecologists *s.l.* The Department of Forestry and Natural Resources,
    Edinburgh, will also produce ecologically trained graduates, say   30
Postgraduate ecology or conservation courses at Aberdeen, Bangor,
    Durham and University College, London, produce about.   25
                                                                          ──
Annual production of ecologists in the UK is therefore approximately   150

in Table 5. In a few cases it was necessary to adjust the returns in the light
of personal knowledge, and it was also necessary in some cases to convert
general statements about turnover and expansion into numerical values.
    The employment figures differ from those in Table 1 for BES members.

This is largely attributable to the fact that the questionnaire discovered many more ecologists *s.l.* employed in agricultural research, pest and veterinary research, and freshwater and marine research, i.e. in the more applied aspects of ecology. Presumably a good many of these ecologists are not members of the BES and it is hoped that the new *Journal of Applied Ecology* may stimulate them to join.

5. Ecologists in relation to total population

Table 6 suggests that developed countries have between ten and twenty ecologists per million of population. Presumably this figure is still rising and also the numbers required by developing countries should be greater than those required by developed countries. This suggests that when the world population reaches, perhaps at the turn of the century, 6000 million, there might be a global requirement for ecologists of 100,000. Interplanetary travel may increase this demand.

III. THE PRODUCTION OF ECOLOGISTS

Very tentative figures set out in Table 7 suggest that current production of ecologists is running at a minimum rate of 150 per year, and the true figure may be in excess of 200 per year.

IV. THE DEMAND FOR ECOLOGISTS

The questionnaire data in Table 5 suggest a demand for ecologists in the UK of about 100 per year. The figures suggest comparatively rapid expansion in the demand for ecologists within the Nature Conservancy and other conservation organizations, and within the fields of freshwater and marine ecology. By contrast, the agricultural research stations and organizations felt that expansion in their employment of ecologists would be negligible. This difference may be partly due to optimistic as against pessimistic forecasts. Some of the agricultural organizations were somewhat surprized at their staff being referred to as ecologists.

The Table 5 sample is clearly incomplete, and an attempt was made to compensate for this. One field of activity not considered is that of land- and resource-use planning, and landscape design. While the employment of ecologists here is currently negligible, it is likely to expand greatly within the next 10 years. Increasing emphasis on field studies at all levels of education may stimulate another requirement for ecologists. The

TABLE 8. Demand for ecologists in the UK (based on data in Table 5)

	No. ecologists
Annual expansion of existing organizations	*c.* 50
Vacancies arising from retirement or emigration, etc. (50 per cent of annual turnover figure)	*c.* 50
Employment in new spheres of ecological activity, e.g. landscape design, land reclamation, planning, etc.	(*c.* 20)
Total annual demand for ecologists in the UK	*c.* 120

TABLE 9. Posts for ecologists advertised in *Nature* (from Marsh, 1962) (data from the *Institute of Biology Journal*, July 1962)

	UK University or technical college		UK Research, advisory or industry		Total		Overseas total	
	1960	1961	1960	1961	1960	1961	1960	1961
General biology, zoology or botany (assume 25 per cent university posts, 10 per cent other, go to ecologists)	25	21	2	2	27	23	18	16
Plant or animal ecology; fisheries, hydrobiology	9	8	25	27	34	35	27	32
Agronomy, horticulture, pl. physiology, pl. nutrition, entomology (assume 50 per cent of posts are ecological)	11	11	23	25	34	36	46	56
Total ecologists	45	40	50	54	95	94	91	104
Ecologists as per cent of all biologists	21.2		20.2		20.6		30.4	

demand figures from Table 5 are summarized in Table 8, and an additional guess inserted for this sort of thing. The final total, a demand for 120 ecologists per year in the UK, is very tentative and may be regarded as a forecast covering the next 5 years. The increase in membership of the BES is running at a rate of about 100 new UK members per year.

An analysis of posts for biologists advertised in the journal *Nature* is given by Marsh (1962). Table 9 represents a summary of these data. One difficulty in interpretation is that an advertised post can represent either a new post, or turnover in an existing post. A new senior appointment might set off a chain involving as many as, say, five advertised posts in 1 year, as everyone moves up one. There is a faint indication from Table 5 that turnover in existing posts may represent twice as much as the establishment of new posts. However, turnover will also include total retirement, emigration and death, so that it might be realistic to suggest that about half the advertized posts represent new intake into the profession while the other half represent a reshuffling of existing ecologists.

I have carried out an analysis of posts advertised in *Nature* during part of the past year (26 weeks within the period 2/1/65 to 19/2/66) and the results are presented in Table 10. It was not possible to complete the analysis for the whole year and there are dangers in converting these results to an annual basis. Nor is it likely they are strictly comparable with the figures compiled by Marsh, though the increase in advertised posts is probably genuine. If 50 per cent of these advertised posts represent new intake into the profession, the demand is somewhat lower than suggested in Table 8, inferred mainly from Table 5. Not all posts are advertised in *Nature*, and some are filled without any advertisement anywhere. Lately there has been a standstill in the planned expansion of the Nature Conservancy, which is shown as a lack of advertised posts. The planned expansion figures, however, still feature in Table 5.

The comparison of my figures (Table 10) with Marsh's (Table 9) demonstrates clearly the great increase in overseas demand. The figures for 1960 and 1961 suggest a static UK demand, with an increasing overseas demand, which is about equal in magnitude to the UK demand. By 1965–66 the overseas demand is more than one and a half times the UK demand.

While some of these overseas posts will be filled by ecologists trained in other countries, they should be more than adequate to absorb the slight over-production of ecologists in this country suggested by Tables 7 and 8. It is not clear whether this is in fact happening and the figures for the Nature Conservancy students (Table 3) show only 17 per cent emigration,

TABLE 10. Posts for ecologists advertised in Nature (1965–66) (data from twenty-six issues of *Nature*, chosen at random, between January 1965 and February 1966)

	UK		Africa		Australia and New Zealand		All other countries		Total overseas	Total UK and overseas
	s.s.	s.l.	s.s.	s.l.	s.s.	s.l.	s.s.	s.l.		
A. University lecturers, all grades										
1. Ecology	4	—	4	—		1.5	3	—	8.5	12.5
2. Freshwater, marine, entomology, agronomy, (assume 50 per cent ecologists)	—	6	—	3.5		1.5	—	1.5	6.5	12.5
3. General biology, botany, zoology, etc. (assume 25 per cent ecologists)	—	10	—	3.8		2	—	3.8	9.6	19.6
University research	7	3	—	—	—	—	—	—	—	10
B. Research, advisory, administration										
1. Ecology, conservation	2	—	6	5	4	—	1	3	19	21
2. Agriculture	3	28	—	13	1	15	1	4	34	65
3. Entomology	1	5	1	31	2	4	1	1	40	46
4. Forestry	—	—	—	5	—	—	—	6	11	11
5. Freshwater	4	6	—	3	—	1	—	1	5	15
6. Marine and fisheries	3	3	1	3	1	1	4	10	20	26
C. Teaching	2	10	—	1	—	—	—	—	4	13
Totals	26	71	12	68.3	9.5	24.5	10	30.3	154.6	251.6

and for the UCL Conservation Course (Table 4) only 8.6 per cent net emigration. A higher proportion of the overseas posts than of the UK ones are likely to represent new posts rather than a reshuffling of personnel within existing posts.

V. CONCLUSIONS

The figures presented are very tentative but certain conclusions may be drawn. The category 'ecologist' is not a very satisfactory one in the field of applied ecology. Almost any research scientist in agriculture, forestry, veterinary science, etc., must be at least one-tenth ecologist.

The fact that by far the largest proportion of ecologists are employed in universities suggests that ecology, unlike, say, chemistry, is a particularly academic and inward-looking discipline. This certainly used to be the case, but the situation is changing rapidly. It is to be hoped that more ecological employment will be forthcoming in the next few years outside the universities. The universities could assist in this process by making their ecology less academic and more applied. It would be valuable to find out what are the main ecological problems encountered by the land-linked professions, and how academic ecologists could help to solve them. If university ecologists carried out more consultancy work, as their enineering and architecture colleagues do, they might find that not only their income but also their teaching would profit from this.

The production of ecologists in the UK is running at approximately 150 per year, and the demand at 100 per year or rather more. The over-production could be fully absorbed by the overseas demand.

So far as I am aware this is the first attempt to assess the production of and demand for ecologists in the UK. Its shortcomings will be obvious. I suggest, however, that this is a subject in which the BES ought to be interested, and in which some continuous monitoring of the situation might be desirable. This could be done in conjunction with the Institute of Biology, who keep the situation in biology as a whole under review. The ecology of ecologists would be well worth careful study.

ACKNOWLEDGMENTS

I gratefully acknowledge the help of all the people who supplied the information on which Table 5 is based. I would also like to thank Miss D.M.Cant of the Nature Conservancy for providing the information on which Table 3 is based, and Mr R.A.French, the Treasurer of the BES, who allowed me to use his card index of members' addresses in preparing Table 1.

REFERENCES

MARSH R.W. (1962) Posts for biologists *J. Inst. Biol.* **9,** 61–62.
ASSOCIATION OF COMMONWEALTH UNIVERSITIES (1965) *Commonwealth Universities Yearbook,* 1965. London.

CAREER OPPORTUNITIES FOR ECOLOGISTS
IN THE DEVELOPING COUNTRIES

M.F.H.Selby

Ministry of Overseas Development

M.A.Brunt

Land Resources Division, Directorate of Overseas Survey

I. THE SCOPE OF ECOLOGICAL WORK OVERSEAS

The poverty of most of the world's inhabitants is a challenge to Britain and other industrialized countries. Most developing countries have a vital need to step up their agricultural production, so that they can get the best economic return from their land, and improve, from their own resources, the nutrition of their rapidly increasing populations. Most of them need also to increase their exports, particularly of agricultural products, in order to create balanced economies. Both ecological research, and the application of sound ecological principles, have a vital role to play in connection with this development. The British Government, in response to this challenge, is aiding the development of many of the poorer countries. The administration of this aid is the task of the Ministry of Overseas Development.

It is not possible in this brief review to cover all the aspects of ecological work overseas. The most important aspects in connection with the development of natural resources are in the field of applied ecology. This covers, *inter alia*, ecological survey leading to land resources appraisal, planning and development; forest ecology studies, in connection with the management of forest resources; range management studies, particularly in areas of low rainfall where cattle ranching, or game conservation and cropping, are being considered as alternative ways of using these areas; the ecological aspects of pest and disease control, for example tsetse-fly, mosquito and locust environmental studies; investigations into the biological control of pests in food stores; the study and management of catchment areas in relation to water and soil conservation; agronomic research, particularly in relation to the adaption of cropping systems and methods of production to environmental circumstances; climatology, notably studies of climate–soil–vegetation relationships, and microclimate in relation to crop growth, pests and diseases; certain aspects of soil investigations, particularly those relating to plant–water relationships and soil fauna; investigations into farming systems and their relation to

269

environmental conditions; and last, but by no means least, fisheries research, most of which is applied ecology.

The range management of semi-arid areas, and areas unsuited to arable farming or more profitable use, is a major problem in much of Africa, the Near East and Latin America. Mismanagement in such areas, either by attempting arable cropping where rainfall is too low or too sporadic, or by overstocking, has in many cases led to rapid deterioration of their productive capacity. In many areas this has resulted in destruction of the palatable grazing, encroachment of undesirable vegetation and erosion. The correct use and management of such areas calls for careful ecological studies, leading to a full understanding of the environment. In some areas decisions have to be taken whether the most efficient utilization will be through cattle or game ranching, and, if the latter, how the game is to be controlled and cropped. The land policy must be based on a close under-standing of all the factors involved, and of the long-term effects of their manipulation by man. A major range management study will shortly be started by FAO in Kenya, where such conditions exist over four-fifths of the country. It will be tackled by a team of specialists, including ecologists, range management experts and wild life biologists. Similar studies are being conducted in many other countries.

There are estimated to be some four and a half million square miles in East, West and Central Africa infested with tsetse-fly (*Glossina* spp.), the main vector of trypanosomiasis, which causes great damage to human and livestock populations not only in Africa but also in other parts of the world. Control and limitation of these parasites and their vectors would free enormous areas of productive land for human use and benefit. Early attempts for the most part consisted of indiscriminate bush-clearing to destroy the tsetse-fly habitat. They were inordinately expensive, but a good deal of basic work on tsetse-fly biology was also carried out from which all further work has devolved. They were followed by more refined methods of attack consisting of selective clearing of the undergrowth, the environment favoured by tsetse-flies for breeding or resting. With the development of modern synthetic insecticides, new weapons are now available. The most economical and effective use of these insecticides clearly depends on prior ecological study of the vector flies' relationship with the environment. Research into this problem is continuing in many countries. In Central Africa, for example, a group is carrying out a detailed biophysical study of the way in which the breeding performance of tsetse-flies is limited by site characteristics, temperature, season and by parasites. These studies are aimed to increase the efficiency of existing tsetse-fly control methods, in addition to being critically important to other members of the group who are investigating techniques to control tsetse-fly populations by the release of sterilized male flies.

It is probable that in the near future the sea, and the large inland lakes, will provide an increasing proportion of the protein requirements of the world's rapidly expanding population. Already over 50,000 metric tons of fish are caught annually, which is only slightly less than the total production of meat. However, it is not clear what the potential of the fisheries industry is, particularly in the tropics, and until considerable research has been carried out, much of it of an applied ecological nature, this problem will not be resolved. In East Africa, for example, the Ministry has recently been asked to supply a marine biologist to study the ecology of the bill fish, and to assess the full fisheries potential. Bill fish, a group of large predatory oceanic fish, include marlin, sailfish (Istiophoridae) and swordfish (Xiphiidae). They are not gregarious, and the only way to catch them in commercial numbers is to suspend numerous baited hooks in the sea at about the level at which they swim. This investigation will therefore try to determine the distribution of the bill fish; whether they migrate, and, if they do, why, and along what route; the level at which the fish swim and whether these habits vary seasonally or in relation to other factors. In addition, their feeding habits will be studied to determine preferences, and whether they change these habits with age or other events; the factors which influence the supply of their food will also be investigated.

Many aspects of the agronomic research carried out in the developing countries are forms of applied ecology. This is well illustrated by the rapid expansion of the Kenya coffee industry. Initially the most likely areas for coffee development were selected on the basis of ecological survey. This was followed by the establishment of variety trials in the different ecological areas, the varieties for each trial being selected again in relation to the dominant environmental factors of each area; cold hardiness at high altitudes, resistance to diseases prevalent in certain areas, and the ability to withstand water stress are all important factors in the selection. By these means it was possible to select varieties suitable to the various ecological zones prior to development.

II. THE WORK OF THE LAND RESOURCES DIVISION OF THE DIRECTORATE OF OVERSEAS SURVEYS

The following description of the work of the Land Resources Division of the Directorate of Overseas Surveys, Ministry of Overseas Development,

further illustrates the scope of ecological work overseas. The Directorate
was formed in 1946 in order to make topographic maps of the colonies.
using air photographs. Shortly after this, research into the use of air
photographs for both land-use and forestry investigation was started,
which, in 1959, led to the formation within the Directorate of the Forestry
and Land-Use Section. This Section has expanded, and the old Pool of
Colonial Soil Scientists has been incorporated within it. It is now a
Division of the Directorate, with an establishment of twenty-one scientific
graduate staff, all of whom are UK-based civil servants.

The main task of the Division, which works largely in Africa, the
Caribbean and the west Pacific, is to investigate land resources overseas,
and to make recommendations for their development. The work is
largely a form of applied ecology, the members of the Division working
within the following scientific disciplines: geology, geomorphology,
soil science, climatology, plant ecology, agriculture and forestry.

Joint enterprises with overseas governments, and sometimes with
international bodies, are usually undertaken. This co-operative approach
ensures that the technical resources of the Directorate are combined to
advantage with those of other organizations, and with local experience.

The following project descriptions illustrate three aspects of the Division's ecological work:
1. Regional land resources survey: the study, definition, and evaluation of
the environment for a large area of little-known country.
2. The investigation of specific resource development problems using the
ecological approach.
3. Forest inventory studies: an aspect of pure ecology.

1. *Regional land resources survey*
The development of air photography during the Second World War
led to a greater appreciation of its value, which resulted in the development
of survey techniques based on the use of the air photograph. In particular
the Division of Land Research and Regional Survey of the CSIRO in
Australia, faced with the problems of surveying and assessing the land
resources of large areas of little-known land, developed the land system
concept. The land system was defined by Christian & Stewart (1953) as
'an area, or group of areas, thoughout which there is a recurring pattern of
topography, soils and vegetation'. These land systems can effectively be
studied using air photographs. The early work on this subject has been
reviewed by Christian & Stewart (1964).

Land resources survey is thus a form of applied ecology, the environmental factors relating to the land resources of an area being investigated, and their interrelations studied. The results can then be used to assess the development potential of the area in question.

A land system is composed of a number of land-form units, each of which has a particular type of soil and vegetation cover. The land-form units and/or the physiognomically different vegetation types show on air photographs as distinctive patterns, whose limits can be marked, and thus maps made showing their distribution. These boundaries are subsequently

TABLE I. Relationships between land surfaces, land form, soil and vegetation in the Bamenda Highlands, West Cameroon, West Africa

Land surface or land-form unit	Climatic climax vegetation	Secondary vegetation	Soil
2400–3000 m mountain peaks	Alpine bamboo	—	Humic ferallitic lava-derived soils
1500–2100 m high lava plateau	Moist montane forest	*Hyparrhenia* and *Sporobolus* grassland	
1200 m surface	Moist evergreen forest (lowland rain forest)	Derived savanna	Coarse-grained sandy and deep fine-textured granite-derived soils
300 m surface	? Woodland	S. Guinea savanna	Granitic-derived soils with marked ironstone concretionary development

confirmed during field work, when the nature of each pattern is investigated. This involves the collection of data related to the soils, natural vegetation, and any other aspects of the environment pertinent to its use; for example, climatic, hydrological, land-use and forestry data.

The land system concept was employed during a recent investigation of the land resources of the Bamenda Highlands of West Cameroon, West Africa, where there is rivalry between local farmers and pasturalists for the use of the same land. The Cameroon Government therefore called for a survey, which would lead to the amelioration of this problem and the rational development of the area. These Highlands cover an area of some 1,813,000 hectares, and consist of a series of land surfaces separated from each other by steep escarpments, with an altitude range of approximately 300–3000 m. There is a close relationship between these land surfaces, the different land forms and their soil and vegetative cover as is shown in Table 1.

The project was handled in two stages, the first of which took 18 man-months and consisted of a preliminary study of the area by the Division, using air photographs and all the available relevant information. A synthesis was made (Bawden & Langdale-Brown, 1961) as a series of maps at a scale of 1/250,000 showing: the land-forms; the vegetation (as broad physiognomic classes) and present land-use; inferred land-use potential, together with a supporting memoir.

The second stage, carried out by the FAO of the UN, with the assistance of the Directorate, was a soil and land-use survey of 2 years' duration, leading to firm development proposals for the area. It was based on the above analysis of land-forms, which, together with the supporting data in the memoir, was in essence a division of the area into a series of land systems.

This second stage consisted of the following work:

(a) The mapped boundaries of the land-form units were checked and modi-fied where necessary.

(b) These units were subdivided on the basis of slope differences and degree of stoniness of the soil related to the possible development of mechanized agriculture in the area.

(c) The main soils of the region were described, and their distribution mapped at a scale of 1/200,000. Soil samples were collected from 361 pits and selected samples were analysed physically and chemically. This information was subsequently related to the performance of the main crops grown in the area.

(d) Leaf analyses of the main cash crop, *Arabica* coffee, were made and the nutrient deficiencies revealed related to the soil conditions; fertilizer applications to redress the deficiencies were proposed.

(e) The main climax vegetation communities were described and their inferred distribution mapped at a scale of 1/500,000. Community descrip-tions were made, based on visual estimation related to five abundance classes and on specimens identified at the Kew Herbarium.

(f) The extensive grasslands were studied in more detail, because the locally important cattle industry is based on them. Sites were selected whose history had been know for some years, and line intersects (Canfield, 1941) were measured to determine details of composition, percentage of ground cover, and height of the main communities.

(g) The available meteorological data were analysed and correlated with the distribution of climatic climax vegetation, which, together with topographic data and observation of weather movement, allowed a provisional elevenfold division of the area. Where the data allowed, evaporation values according to Penman (1948, 1963) were calculated.

This particular land resources survey provided the basis for recommendations covering the agricultural research and development programme for the area, and enabled the recommendations to be related to those ecological areas of greatest agricultural importance (Brunt, 1964; Brunt & Hawkins, 1965).

The Division now employs the land system concept widely for reconnaissance investigations, and has applied it in East Bechuanaland, where Bawden & Stobbs (1963) surveyed an area of approximately 18,650,000 hectares. It has more recently been used in Basutoland by Bawden & Carroll (1967) and in North Nigeria by Bawden & Tuley (1967).

2. *The investigation of specific resource development problems using the ecological approach: Christmas Island Coconut Survey*

Christmas Island, which is part of the Gilbert and Ellice Islands Colony, is an atoll in the central Pacific, with a land surface of approximately 360 sq. km. The colony has a rapidly increasing population, and their main source of income, the digging of high-grade phosphate, is declining; production will probably cease in about 10 years' time. In order to ameliorate this situation, the Government hopes to develop the coconut plantations on Christmas Island as an additional source of revenue and employment. The Land Resources Division was, therefore, asked to survey and report on the potential agricultural development of the island, particularly as a commercial coconut plantation. This has been done, the answer to this specific development problem being based on the following three-stage ecological investigation:

(a) All available information concerning Christmas Island, other similar islands, and the problems of growing coconuts on coral atolls was reviewed. A stereoscopic study was made of the 1/15,000-scale air photographs, both land-form and vegetation community patterns being recognized, and their boundaries were marked on the air photographs; these were then transferred to the air photomosaics of the island.

(b) The following field work was carried out during August and September 1965 by an officer of the Division, accompanied by a coconut agronomist of the Solomon Islands Department of Agriculture:

(i) Checks of the validity of the land-form and vegetation air photograph analysis.

(ii) Soil survey at series level within the land-form unit framework.

(iii) Study and description of the plant communities.

(iv) Ground water survey, to establish the extent and depth of the Ghyben–Herzberg freshwater lenses using resistivity techniques and tube wells, and to determine the chemical characteristics of the ground water at water-table level.

(v) Collection of rainwater samples for analysis.

(vi) Survey of the vigour of the existing coconut plantations, and the relationship between site and productivity; collection of leaf samples.

(vii) Investigation into the management of the plantations, as far as this affects the agronomic aspects of plantation development.

(viii) Establishment of experiments to test planting methods, germination, and the effect of applications of micro-nutrients on the nutrient deficiencies of the coconuts, as well as on possible leguminous cover crops.

(c) Various analyses were undertaken, including the analysis of soil, water and coconut leaf samples and the analysis of the meteorological data. The synthesis of the resultant information, and the production of the report (Jenken & Foale, 1966) were carried out in England. The physical and chemical analysis of soil samples was done at Rothamsted Experimental Station, and the chemical analysis of water samples by Unilever Plantations Group Laboratory.

The work described established the validity of the original land form and vegetation units, and demonstrated a significant relationship between these units and the varying performance of different parts of the coconut plantations. Moreover, a positive correlation between the chemical composition of the ground water, the soil and the palm leaves demonstrated that the serious micro-element deficiencies of manganese, iron and copper are true deficiencies and not simply a nutrient imbalance.

The results of the programme of experimental work, together with analysis of the plantation operations to be carried out, and the findings of the ecological survey, will thus ensure rational plantation development, confined to the most suitable sites on the island.

(3) *Forest inventory studies: an aspect of pure ecology*

The island of Erromango in the south Pacific is part of the Anglo-French condominium of the New Hebrides. It has forests of commercial value, containing amongst other species the Kauri pine (*Agathis obtusa*) and Tamanu (*Calophyllum neo-ebudicum*).

There is no reliable information on the growing stock in the forests and, as they are to be exploited, the administration requires information to control exploitation and provide for their proper management.

The Land Resources Division has, therefore, been asked to carry out forest inventory studies, aimed at providing the following information: estimates of the merchantable volume of mature timber by species and size-class, for mature and replacement stocking; site descriptions, as well as data on growth determined by growth studies on permanent sample plots.

These studies, in four stages, use techniques relevant to pure ecological investigation, as will be appreciated from the following description.

(a) *Selection of areas for detailed assessment*
This was accomplished by air photograph interpretation, supplemented by direct visual aerial reconnaissance, and resulted in three areas being chosen.

(b) *Detailed air photograph interpretation*
The areas chosen consist of homogeneous land-form units, whose limits were established by air photograph interpretation. The same technique was used to divide the forest up into forest types within each land-form unit, based on differences in the canopy pattern. In some cases these types are apparently single-dominant, climax, primary communities of Kauri pine, and in others they are variants of an extensive mixed community. A stratification of the forests by forest type and land form has thus been achieved. The boundaries of the units have been transferred to 1/50,000 maps.

(c) *Ground sampling*
The location of randomly selected base lines to be followed during the ground sampling of the strata will be planned using the above 1/50,000 forest type maps, the layout being determined by the land form. For example, in areas of deeply dissected land form the base lines will be run along the ridge tops, and offset lines, whose starting-points will be fixed at random, will be run at right-angles from the ridge base line to the valley bottom. Consecutive sample plots measuring 40 × 40 m (0.2 ha) will be set along the offset lines. The variation in the stocking of mature timber in a stratum (land-form or forest-type unit) will be used to determine the size of sample, i.e. number of sample plots per stratum, required to provide volume estimates of merchantable timber within acceptable error limits. Within the sample, growing stock data will be collected as follows:

T

All the trees of 50 cm d.b.h. and over (mature stocking) will be measured in all sample plots; the trees between 10 cm and 50 cm (intermediate stocking) will be measured in not less than one in every four of the sample plots, while the seedlings between 10 cm high and 10 cm diameter at breast height (d.b.h.) for regeneration stocking will be enumerated in one quadrat of, say, 10 m² randomly located in each offset line transect.

The following data will be collected for each sample:

1. Trees: (i) species; (ii) d.b.h.; (iii) merchantable height from felling base to first branch of all trees 50 cm d.b.h. and over; (iv) top diameter of merchantable length; (v) defect; (iv) crown diameters of selected Kauri and Tamanu trees.

2. Site factors: (i) situation; (ii) position on slope; (iii) aspect; (iv) drainage; (v) soil characteristics.

Herbarium material, timber specimens and soil samples will be collected for subsequent analysis in the UK. The data will be recorded on standard forms.

(d) *Data computation*

This is to be carried out at the British Forestry Commission's Research Headquarters, with the assistance of their statistician, using a Pegasus computer. A program has been written to allow stand tables, and the merchantable volume of the economic timber species, to be calculated (together with standard errors) from the data submitted. This information, related as it will be to specific sites, will allow rational planning of exploitation.

An analysis of species associations will also be carried out with the aid of the computer. Any significant correlations revealed between associations and site factors can then be used in making management decisions.

Thus data will be available which will provide the basis for the long-term management of the forests. They will also enable site assessments to be made in terms of agricultural development if required.

In addition to projects of the kind described, the Division helps particularly with the ecological aspects of the natural resources programme of the Ministry of Overseas Development, and where appropriate co-operates with other workers in the ecological field overseas.

III. QUALIFICATIONS AND OPPORTUNITIES

The basic qualifications required for most specialist ecologist posts in the developing countries is a good Honours degree in a natural science, usually in Botany or Zoology, but sometimes in Forestry, Agriculture or Geography, and appropriate postgraduate research training or experience.

The Ministry helps to fill posts and to supply staff for work of an ecological nature overseas at the request of overseas governments. Consequently it is not possible to gauge with any precise accuracy what the demand will be a number of years hence, although there is little doubt that the need will continue. As an indication of the present level of demand, the Ministry has been asked to fill posts for the following during the past 12 months: twenty-four agronomists (including pasture research officers), ten plant breeders and botanists, one ecologist, three soil surveyors, twenty-two foresters, six stored-products entomologists, nine tsetse entomologists, twelve fisheries research officers, one biologist, one micro-biologist, one soil physicist and one plant physiologist. In addition, vacancies have occurred for six plant pathologists and eleven entomologists, mainly, but not entirely, in connection with advisory duties. This is in addition to the work carried out overseas by the staff of the home-based organizations such as the Land Resources Division of the Directorate of Overseas Surveys.

The International Recruitment Unit of the Ministry has also been asked by United Nations organizations to help recruit the following personnel during the past 12 months to work in the ecological field: three range management ecologists, four wild-life biologists, one plant physiologist, one wild-life ecologist, one experimental ecologist, one bush control officer and two arid zone ecologists. In addition, of course, these organizations recruit direct on a world-wide basis.

There are also opportunities for ecologists in the teaching profession overseas, and the Inter-University Council have been asked to recruit twenty botanists, twelve agricultural botanists, twenty-two zoologists, four agricultural zoologists and three biologists for universities in developing countries overseas during the past 12 months. A limited number of vacancies also occur from time to time in commercial firms concerned particularly with land resources appraisal work overseas on a consultancy basis.

IV. TYPE OF APPOINTMENT

The Ministry may be able to provide specialists as part of the British aid effort in three ways:

First, they may be appointed under the Overseas Service Aid Scheme (OSAS), which covers many independent Commonwealth countries and dependent territories. Vacant posts in overseas government services are filled until the country concerned can provide enough of its own nationals, properly trained, to make this unnecessary. Newly qualified people from Britain are sometimes acceptable, but more often suitable postgraduate training and/or experience is also required. Under this scheme the overseas government pays the local salary for the job. The British Government adds an overseas allowance and provides passages and certain other allowances. The engagement is usually for one tour of 2–3 years. Salaries vary from place to place, the average being somewhere on a long scale from about £1250 per annum to about £2800, including overseas allowances. A gratuity is paid at the end of the contract, and in many countries this is now as high as 25 per cent of the salary earned during the contract. The majority of these posts are in Africa.

Secondly, requests are also received to provide experts under British Technical Assistance to help developing countries in any part of the world, normally in a senior and advisory capacity. These posts usually require people of exceptionally good experience in their particular field. Employment is directly under the Ministry of Overseas Development on contract, for the time required to do the job. Emoluments are broadly similar to those for OSAS appointments, depending on the exact nature of the post, and the qualifications and experience of the candidate. The engagement may be for any period from a few weeks to several years, the average being about 2 years.

Thirdly, through its International Recruitment Unit, the Ministry also helps international organizations, such as FAO and UNESCO, in finding suitable British candidates for their work in developing countries. These organizations normally need people with from 7 to 15 years' experience at responsible levels in the required specialized field.

In addition to filling posts overseas on contract, the Ministry also maintains certain home-based institutions to assist in overseas development work. These include the Land Resources Division of the Directorate of Overseas Surveys, whose work has been described, as well as the Tropical Stored Products Centre, and the Anti-Locust Research Centre, whose work is, in part, ecological. Furthermore, in order to provide opportunities of combining a home-based career with work overseas, arrangements have been made for the professional establishments of appropriate public organizations in this country to be increased, so that they can release an equivalent number of qualified staff at any time to go abroad under the sponsorship of the Ministry (Command 2736). Recruitment to the home-based posts is arranged by the organizations concerned, and not by the

Ministry. Some of these expanded home-based posts may be of interest to ecologists.

Any professionally qualified ecologist who is interested in obtaining a post overseas is invited to write to: The Appointments Officer, Room 301, Ministry of Overseas Development, Eland House, Stag Place, London, S.W.1, giving a brief description of his qualifications and experience.

It will thus be realized that opportunities for ecologists to work overseas are considerable. In comparison with the developed countries, much fundamental information about the environments of the developing countries is lacking, and ecological techniques can be employed with very great success to help with the development of the natural resources of these overseas countries.

REFERENCES

BAWDEN M.G. & LANGDALE-BROWN I. (1961) *An Aerial Photograph Reconnaissance of the Present and Possible Land Use in the Bamenda Area, South Cameroons*. Directorate of Overseas Surveys, Ministry of Overseas Development, London.

BAWDEN M.G. & STOBBS A.R. (1963) *The Land Resources of Eastern Bechuanaland*. Directorate of Overseas Surveys, Ministry of Overseas Development, London.

BAWDEN M.G. & CARROLL D.M. (1967) *The Land Resources of Lesotho (Basutoland)*. Directorate of Overseas Surveys, Ministry of Overseas Development, London.

BAWDEN M.G. & TULEY P. (1967) *The Land Resources of the Southern Sardauna and Southern Adamawa Provinces, Northern Nigeria*. Directorate of Overseas Surveys, Ministry of Overseas Development, London.

BRUNT M.A. (1964) The methods used during the FAO soil and land-use survey of the Bamenda Highlands, West Cameroon, West Africa. Paper to: *Natural Resources Conference, UNESCO, Toulouse*.

BRUNT M.A. & HAWKINS, P. (1965) *The Soils and Ecology of the West Cameroon*. ETAP Report 2083, 2 vols., FAO, Rome.

CANFIELD R.H. (1941) Application of the line interception method in sampling range vegetation. *J. For.* **39**, 388–394.

CHRISTIAN C.S. & STEWART C.A. (1953) *Survey of Catherine Darwin Region*, 1946. Land Res. Ser. No. 1, CSIRO, Australia.

CHRISTIAN C.S. & STEWART C.A. (1964). Methodology of integrated surveys. Paper to: *Natural Resources Conference, UNESCO, Toulouse*.

HMSO (1965) *Overseas Development: The Work of the New Ministry*. Cmnd. 2736, HMSO, London.

JENKIN R.N. & FOALE M.A. (1966) *An Investigation of the Coconut Growing Potential of Christmas Island*. Private communication.

PENMAN H.L. (1948) Natural evaporation from open water, bare soil and grass. *Proc. Roy. Soc. Lond.* (A) **193**, 120–145.

PENMAN H.L. (1963) *Vegetation and Hydrology*. Tech. Comm. 53, Comm. Bur. Soils, Farnham Royal.

INDEX

This Index supplements the Contents (see pp. v–viii) as a guide to the subjects discussed. An attempt has been made to cite all plants and animals suitable for use in teaching projects. Where definite locations of projects are given these are cited. References are also given to those institutions organizing courses and projects. In general, wild plants and animals are indexed both under their Latin and common names whereas commercial crops and domesticated animals are entered under their common names only.

The page numbers in **bold type** indicate citations in the references at the end of the contributions.